Everyman, I will go with thee, and be thy guide,
In thy most need to go by thy side.

This is No. 902 of Everyman's Library. A list of authors and their works in this series will be found at the end of this volume. The publishers will be pleased to send freely to all applicants a separate, annotated list of the Library.

J. M. DENT & SONS LIMITED
10–13 BEDFORD STREET LONDON W.C.2

E. P. DUTTON & CO. INC.
286–302 FOURTH AVENUE
NEW YORK

EVERYMAN'S LIBRARY
EDITED BY ERNEST RHYS

ESSAYS & BELLES-LETTRES

THE CITIZEN
OF THE WORLD *and* THE BEE
BY OLIVER GOLDSMITH · EDITED
BY AUSTIN DOBSON · INTRO-
DUCTION BY RICHARD CHURCH

OLIVER GOLDSMITH, born at Pallasmore, Co. Longford, Ireland. After a varied and unprofitable life in England and Ireland, tramped through Europe, 1754–6. Arriving penniless in London, he took to journalism. In spite of his success in literature, however, he died in poverty on 4th April 1774.

THE CITIZEN OF THE WORLD
THE BEE

OLIVER GOLDSMITH

LONDON: J. M. DENT & SONS LTD.
NEW YORK: E. P. DUTTON & CO. INC.

INTRODUCTION

It is nearly two hundred years since Samuel Johnson wrote the following words in a letter to a friend: 'Is there a man, sir, *now* who can pen an essay with such ease and elegance as Goldsmith?' I am disposed to re-orientate that challenging 'now' of Dr. Johnson's, and thus to bring his inquiry up to date, basing my assertion on the proof positive of the several hundred pages of golden and mellifluous prose that follow this Introduction.

Johnson's opinion was no casual remark. Of all Goldsmith's large circle of acquaintance, he knew him best, and appreciated him best, both as man and writer. On another occasion he described him as 'a man of such variety of power and such felicity of performance that he always seemed to do that best which he was doing; a man who had the art of being minute without tediousness, and general without confusion; whose language was copious without exuberance, exact without constraint, and easy without weakness.'

Macaulay, that magnificent prig-whig, was forced to corroborate Johnson's evidence, making certain qualifications in the matter of the vagabond's credentials. 'For accurate research,' he says, 'or grave disquisition, Goldsmith was not well qualified by nature or by education. He knew nothing accurately; his reading had been desultory; nor had he meditated deeply on what he had read.' And he is forced to conclude that while 'there have been many greater writers, perhaps no writer has been more uniformly agreeable'.

It would be amusing to collect further specimens of praise offered to this rather slovenly flautist. They would unite in emphasizing the ease, agreeableness, elegance, and all other generously emollient qualities of Goldsmith's prose. I should like to go farther, and point out how quickly these very elusive qualities appeared in full blandness in Goldsmith's work. They are not usually mastered until a man has been practising the craft of letters for a great many years. Youth is dogmatic and given to tragic contest; inexperience is laborious and tortuous.

But young, and inexperienced, Goldsmith wrote *The Bee*, and *The Citizen of the World*. One might almost say that he took up his pen for the first time to compose these essays, having despaired of becoming a lawyer, an apothecary, a bookseller's hack, and a schoolmaster. But these essays show no sign of the apprentice's hand. They never betray that formidable learnedness so dear to the undergraduate who is making his condescending bow in a provincial paper. They never force us to run to the dictionary, nor confuse us with dazzling quotations. They have that artful artlessness, that suave, happy simplicity, of the daily middle-leaders written by a jaded, disillusioned, heart-broken, leather-skinned journalist who has been at the trade for twelve hours a day during forty years.

How then, did Goldsmith acquire this quick professional excellence? After fooling around Europe with a flute and a complete set of irresponsibilities, he returned to England at the age of twenty-eight, three years after his Continental counterpart and exemplar, the Abbé Prévost, had become respectable and revised *Manon Lescaut*, the story of his own youthful vagabondage. In wandering from one university to another through Holland, Belgium, France, Switzerland, and Italy, Goldsmith had found his flute to be a means of livelihood, enabling him to travel between his debating matches, as free from economic cares as any wandering scholar during the Middle Ages. But returning to England, even to the civilized England of the eighteenth century, he found the air chilly with the initial frosts of a puritanical industrialism. His casual music found no patrons, and he had to try and work for his living.

It was then that he attempted his various expedients. Perhaps the most incongruous of them all was his effort to become a schoolmaster. Kindly, whimsical, vain, tactless, and inclined to a self-torturing buffoonery, he was the last person in the world to be given over to the merciless inquisition of school-boys. At the corner of Southampton Street, Peckham, where some sixty years later Robert Browning was born, Goldsmith must have given, and taken, incredibly clumsy knocks in the most difficult of all branches of the art of human contacts.

He emerged from his failures still irrepressible, and resolved as a last resort to try his hand at the trade of hack-writing. But here again he found that English customs had changed.

The patron of letters was no more. It remained for him to become a pioneer, along with his august monitor Dr. Johnson, in the effort to make literature exist—at least as a livelihood—without patrons. And for once he succeeded. Certainly he had the example of Addison and Steele before him; and we have his own acknowledgment of his indebtedness to the former. But where Addison gave gracefulness, Goldsmith added warmth and spontaneity; where Addison was urbane, Goldsmith was also cosmopolitan. That warmth, that spontaneity, that travelled and world-allusive friendliness, attracted a class of readers which was to develop into a public whose increasing mountain of pennies should fill the gap left by the defection of the cultured patrons, who had vanished before the advance of the newly-rich, barbarian Indian nabobs. Johnson and Goldsmith were practically the first journalists who lived by their pens without cadging in the anterooms of aristocrats. Johnson, as a gesture indicating the inauguration of the new régime, wrote his famous letter to Lord Chesterfield. Goldsmith did not even bother to disclaim the old procedure. With pent-roof upper-lip protruding (perhaps from an excess of flute-blowing) he ambled like a tragi-comic clown straight into the Grub Street ring, and made his début as a professional entertainer paid on the spot from the gate-money.

What enabled him to take this revolutionary step so easily and unconsciously? Obviously the first cause was his singular experience in acquiring a technique of vagabondage. For your perfect journalist is a complete vagabond. He must be inured to domestic discomfort, irregular hours, uncertain pay. He must, as Lord Northcliffe said, be ready to go at a moment's notice to Mexico, equipped with a handbag, a writing block, and a pen—or even without the handbag. He must wear family ties lightly or not at all. His vanity must be impervious to the irksomeness of anonymity. He must be able to say something about everything, and everything about something, and he must be acquiescent when his copy is cut by an editor who is ignorant of and uninterested in the subject concerned. Goldsmith was such a vagabond. His boyish fecklessness, together with poverty, dragged him early from the family roots. For the most formative years of his early manhood, he wandered over the more civilized parts of Europe, responsible only for himself,—and throwing even that responsibility over his shoulder every time he took the road.

A man of his disposition could afford this moral extravagance. He was one of those people who can blandly fall into sins that a greater man would have to commit deliberately, and in the commission break a rigid character. In this matter, Goldsmith again was like the Abbé Prévost, that angelic forger and fornicator. Miss Helen Waddell, who is so intimate with the eighteenth century, has already remarked the similarity. 'To understand Goldsmith,' she says, 'is to understand Prévost. There is the same extreme susceptibility to goodness, the same angelic simplicity, the same complete inconsequence.' The likeness between these two men is significant, as I shall show in a moment.

Fortified by these qualities, Goldsmith was able to tackle any subject with gaiety and lightheartedness, as every journalist should. He would write a history of the world, or of the fauna thereof. Or he would restrict himself to a history of Mecklenburg, or a poetical epistle about a haunch of venison. He would write a 'Series of Transactions and Authentic Testimonials respecting the supposed Cock-Lane Ghost,' or a 'Life of Richard Nash, of Bath, Esquire'. And we know what else he could write, when in poetic or dramatic mood.

Obviously so double-jointed a versatility must have been largely augmented by his adventures as a traveller. We have to consider also the style in which he clothed so various a content. During the period when that style was forming, he was in immediate contact with French authors and their work. He may have attended the later years of Crébillon, who died six years after Goldsmith returned to England. No doubt he was to be found in the opposite camp of Voltaire, picking up tricks of the controversial methods. And from Voltaire it was a stone's-throw to Diderot, who had much to impart in the art of occasional writing. It is all largely conjectural, but I find myself guided, by my ear for the cadence of a prose paragraph, to picture Goldsmith in association with many of the great figures who during the eighteenth century widened and deepened French prose, that superb vehicle of human reason and fantasy.

And most musically do I associate him with Prévost. We have already noted the similarity of character between the two men, For many years I have always—without knowledge; purely by ear—connected *Manon Lescaut* and *The Vicar of Wakefield*. The two books are the same *colour*. They

ring with the same *tone* (that very essential quality in literature, equivalent to *character* in life).   I was gratified, therefore,
when at the time Miss Waddell published her translation of the
1731 version of *Manon Lescaut*, the late Robert Garnett, a
fine French scholar, showed me an anonymous translation of
that same version published in England a few years before the
appearance of *The Vicar of Wakefield*.   The evidence of style
pointed with some emphasis to the probability that this
translation was by Goldsmith; one which had been forgotten,
so that until Miss Waddell's beautiful translation appeared,
this tale had been known in England only as the Abbé Prévost
revised it in 1753.   In this nice literary problem there is
certainly a field for exploration by some student seeking a
theme for a thesis for a doctorate.

What I now want to emphasize, however, is the importation
of French cadence and fluidity of prose formation which Goldsmith brought into English.   Compare one of his essays with
those of Johnson in *The Rambler*, or even in *The Idler*, and
see the difference in ease and familiarity.   Compare it with
Addison, and still you will be impressed with the increase
of flexibility, the colloquiality.   Those qualities Goldsmith
brought from France, as a bee brings pollen from a flower;
and he added them permanently to English prose.

The essays in this volume are a fair specimen of Goldsmith's
early prose.   *The Citizen of the World*, in taking the form of a
series of letters by 'a Chinese Philosopher, Residing in London,
to his Friends in the East', is an obvious imitation of Montesquieu, who began his literary career similarly with *Les
Lettres Persanes*, a device for commenting with requisite
detachment about morals and customs in Europe.   The
temper of *The Citizen of the World*, as also that of *The Bee*,
which makes up the rest of this volume, is best portrayed by
a quotation which reveals both Goldsmith's conscious aim
and unconscious achievement:

'Homer finely imagines his deity turning away with horror
from the prospect of a field of battle, and seeking tranquillity
among a nation noted for peace and simplicity.   Happy, could
any effort of mine, but for a moment, repress that savage
pleasure some men find in the daily accounts of human misery!
How gladly would I lead them from scenes of blood and
altercation, to prospects of innocence and ease, where every
breeze breathes health, and every sound is but the echo of
tranquillity.'

And like Prévost, he proceeds to exude this spirit of benevolence and true love, true charity, as it manifests itself in the slums and brothels, the prisons and taverns, amongst the most degraded and disreputable members of human society. It is a noble, a Christ-like achievement; utterly unrespectable (as that word has been mostly misused). No wonder that Johnson should have said of this gentle creature: 'Let not his frailties be remembered. *He was a very great man*'. So I conclude, as I began, this introduction, with words by the man who knew Goldsmith most intimately, and loved him most shrewdly.

1934.   RICHARD CHURCH.

The following is a list of Oliver Goldsmith's works (1728–1774):

Memoirs of a Protestant condemned to the Galleys of France for his Religion (translation), 2 vols., 1758; Enquiry into the Present State of Polite Learning in Europe, 1759; The Bee, being Essays on the Most Interesting Subjects (eight numbers of a weekly periodical), 1759; History of Mecklenburgh, 1762; The Mystery Revealed, containing a Series of Transactions and Authentic Testimonials respecting the supposed Cock-Lane Ghost, 1762; The Citizen of the World, or Letters from a Chinese Philosopher Residing in London to his Friends in the East (from the *Public Ledger*, 1760, 1761), 2 vols., 1762; Life of Richard Nash, of Bath, Esquire, 1762; A History of England in a Series of Letters from a Nobleman to his Son, 2 vols., 1764; The Traveller, 1765; Essays, 1765; The Vicar of Wakefield, a tale supposed to be written by himself, 2 vols., 1766; The Good-Natur'd Man, a Comedy, 1768; The Roman History, from the foundation of the City of Rome to the destruction of the Western Empire, 2 vols., 1769; Abridgment by the Author, 1772; The Deserted Village, 1770; The Life of Thomas Parnell, compiled from original papers and memoirs, 1770; Life of Henry St. John, Lord Viscount Bolingbroke, 1770; The History of England, from the Earliest Times to the Death of George II, 4 vols., 1771; Abridged Edition, 1774; Threnodia Augustalis, sacred to the memory of Her Royal Highness the Princess Dowager of Wales, 1772; She Stoops to Conquer, or the Mistakes of a Night, 1773; Retaliation, a Poem, including Epitaphs on the most distinguished Wits of this Metropolis, 1774 (five editions were published this year; the fifth edition contains the postscript and epitaph on Caleb Whitefoord); The Grecian History, from the Earliest State to the Death of Alexander the Great, 2 vols., 1774; An History of the Earth and Animated Nature, 8 vols., 1774; The Haunch of Venison, a Poetical Epistle to Lord Clare, 1776; another edition, with additions and corrections, appeared this same year; A Survey of Experimental Philosophy considered in its Present State of Improvement, 2 vols., 1776; The Captivity, an Oratorio, 1836 (first printed in the Trade edition of Goldsmith's Works, 1820).

Goldsmith contributed to the *Monthly Review, Critical Review, Literary Magazine, Busy Body, Public Ledger, British Magazine, Lady's Magazine, Westminster Magazine*, and *Universal Magazine*; he edited Poems for Young Ladies, 1766; Beauties of English Poesy, 1767; to him is attributed The History of Little Goody Two-Shoes, published by Newbery, 3rd ed., 1766; and also A Pretty Book of Pictures for Little Masters and Misses, etc., 9th ed., 1767; and his trans. include Formey's Concise History of Philosophy, 1766; Scarron's Comic Romance, 1775. An abridged edition of Plutarch's Lives was undertaken by him in collaboration with Joseph Collyer, 1762; The Grumbler, an adaption of Brueys and Palaprat's Le Grondeur, was performed once at Covent Garden in 1773, but not printed by the author. Some New Essays were issued in 1927, edited by R. S. Crane.

The miscellaneous works of Goldsmith (containing his Essays and Poems) were published in 1775, 1792, and in 1801 with the Percy Memoir; Poems and Plays, 1777; Poetical and Dramatic Works, 1780.

Among later editions are those by Prior, 4 vols., 1837; Cunningham, 4 vols., 1854; J. F. Waller, 1864, etc.; J. W. M. Gibbs, 1884–6; the Globe Edition, 1869. Many smaller collections have been published.

The complete Poetical Works were edited by Austin Dobson (Oxford Edition), 1906.

The Vicar of Wakefield has appeared in innumerable editions, has been frequently illustrated, and translated into nearly every European language.

A bibliography of Goldsmith's works appears in Seven XVIII Century Bibliographies, by I. A. Williams, 1924.

Life: The life known as the 'Percy Memoir' (see above), 1801, and later editions; by James Prior, 1837; John Forster, Life and Adventures of Oliver Goldsmith, 1848, 1854, 1855, 1903; Washington Irving (founded on two previous biographies), with selections, 1844, 1849, 1850; W. Black (English Men of Letters), 1878; Austin Dobson (Great Writers), 1888, 1899; Macaulay (Encyclopædia Britannica), ed. H. B. Cotterill, 1904, and published in Blackie's English Classics, 1901; Oliver Goldsmith (Cameo Classics, No. 4), 1905. See also The History and Sources of Percy's Memoir of Goldsmith, by K. C. Balderston, 1926.

CONTENTS

THE CITIZEN OF THE WORLD

THE BEE

THE CITIZEN OF THE WORLD

THE EDITOR'S PREFACE [1]

THE schoolmen had formerly a very exact way of computing the abilities of their Saints or authors. Escobar, for instance, was said to have learning as five, genius as four, and gravity as seven. Caramuel was greater than he. His learning was as eight, his genius as six, and his gravity as thirteen. Were I to estimate the merits of our Chinese Philosopher by the same scale, I would not hesitate to state his genius still higher; but as to his learning and gravity, these I think might safely be marked as nine hundred and ninety-nine, within one degree of absolute frigidity.

Yet upon his first appearance here, many were angry not to find him as ignorant as a Tripoline ambassador, or an Envoy from Mujac. They were surprised to find a man born so far from London, that school of prudence and wisdom, endued even with a moderate capacity. They expressed the same surprise at his knowledge that the Chinese do at ours. *How comes it*, said they, *that the Europeans, so remote from China, think with so much justice and precision? They have never read our books, they scarcely know even our letters, and yet they talk and reason just as we do.* [2] The truth is, the Chinese and we are pretty much alike. Different degrees of refinement, and not of distance, mark the distinctions among mankind. Savages of the most opposite climates, have all but one character of improvidence and rapacity; and tutored nations, however separate, make use of the very same methods to procure refined enjoyment.

The distinctions of polite nations are few; but such as are peculiar to the Chinese, appear in every page of the following correspondence. The metaphors and allusions are all drawn from the East. Their formality our author carefully preserves. Many of their favourite tenets in morals are illustrated. The Chinese are always concise, so is he. Simple, so is he. The Chinese are grave and sententious, so is he. But in one particular, the resemblance is peculiarly striking: the Chinese are often dull; and so is he. Nor has my assistance been wanting.

[1] [i.e. Goldsmith's Preface.]   [2] Le Comte, Vol. I, p. 210.

We are told in an old romance of a certain knight errant and his horse who contracted an intimate friendship. The horse most usually bore the knight, but, in cases of extraordinary dispatch, the knight returned the favour, and carried his horse. Thus in the intimacy between my author and me, he has usually given me a lift of his Eastern sublimity, and I have sometimes given him a return of my colloquial ease.

Yet it appears strange in this season of panegyric, when scarce an author passes unpraised either by his friends or himself, that such merit as our Philosopher's should be forgotten. While the epithets of ingenious, copious, elaborate, and refined, are lavished among the mob, like medals at a coronation, the lucky prizes fall on every side, but not one on him. I could on this occasion make myself melancholy, by considering the capriciousness of public taste, or the mutability of fortune; but during this fit of morality, lest my reader should sleep, I'll take a nap myself, and when I awake tell him my dream.

I imagined the Thames was frozen over, and I stood by its side. Several booths were erected upon the ice, and I was told by one of the spectators, that FASHION FAIR was going to begin, He added, that every author who would carry his works there, might probably find a very good reception. I was resolved however to observe the humours of the place in safety from the shore, sensible that ice was at best precarious, and having been always a little cowardly in my sleep.

Several of my acquaintance seemed much more hardy than I, and went over the ice with intrepidity. Some carried their works to the fair on sledges, some on carts, and those which were more voluminous, were conveyed in waggons. Their temerity astonished me. I knew their cargoes were heavy, and expected every moment they would have gone to the bottom. They all entered the fair, however, in safety, and each soon after returned to my great surprise, highly satisfied with his entertainment, and the bargains he had brought away.

The success of such numbers at last began to operate upon me. If these, cried I, meet with favour and safety, some luck may, perhaps, for once attend the unfortunate. I am resolved to make a new adventure. The furniture, frippery, and fireworks of China, have long been fashionably bought up. I'll try the fair with a small cargo of Chinese morality. If the Chinese have contributed to vitiate our taste, I'll try how far they can help to improve our understanding. But as others have driven into the market in waggons, I'll cautiously begin by venturing with a wheel-barrow. Thus resolved, I baled up my goods and fairly ventured; when, upon just entering the fair, I fancied the ice that had supported an hundred waggons before, cracked under me, and wheel-barrow and all went to the bottom.

Upon awaking from my reverie, with the fright, I cannot help wishing that the pains taken in giving this correspondence an English dress, had been employed in contriving new political systems, or new plots for farces. I might then have taken my station in the world, either as a poet or a philosopher, and made one in those little societies where men club to raise each other's reputation. But at present I belong to no particular class. I resemble one of those solitary animals, that has been forced from its forest to gratify human curiosity. My earliest wish was to escape unheeded through life; but I have been set up for half-pence, to fret and scamper at the end of my chain. Tho' none are injured by my rage, I am naturally too savage to court any friends by fawning; too obstinate to be taught new tricks; and too improvident to mind what may happen: I am appeased, though not contented. Too indolent for intrigue, and too timid to push for favour, I am—But what signifies what am I.

’Ελπὶς καὶ σὺ τύχη, μέγα χαίρετε· τὸν λιμέν’ εὗρον.
    Οὐδὲν ἐμοὶ χ’ ὑμῖν· παίζετε τοὺς μετ’ ἐμέ.

LETTERS FROM A CITIZEN OF THE WORLD
TO HIS FRIENDS IN THE EAST

LETTER I.—*To Mr. * * * *, Merchant in London.*

Amsterdam.

SIR,

YOURS of the 13th instant, covering two bills, one on Messrs. R. and D., value £478, 10s., and the other on Mr. * * * *, value £285, duly came to hand, the former of which met with honour, but the other has been trifled with, and I am afraid will be returned protested.

The bearer of this is my friend, therefore let him be yours. He is a native of Honan in China, and one who did me signal services when he was a mandarine, and I a factor at Canton. By frequently conversing with the English there, he has learned the language, though he is entirely a stranger to their manners and customs. I am told he is a philosopher, I am sure he is an honest man; that to you will be his best recommendation, next to the consideration of his being the friend of, Sir,

Yours, &c.

LETTER II.—*Lond. From Lien Chi Altangi to * * * *, Merchant in Amsterdam.*

FRIEND OF MY HEART,

May the wings of peace rest upon thy dwelling, and the shield of conscience preserve thee from vice and misery: for all thy favours accept my gratitude and esteem, the only tributes a poor philosophic wanderer can return; sure fortune is resolved to make me unhappy, when she gives others a power of testifying their friendship by actions, and leaves me only words to express the sincerity of mine.

I am perfectly sensible of the delicacy with which you endeavour to lessen your own merit and my obligations. By calling your late instances of friendship only a return for former favours, you would induce me to impute to your justice what I owe to your generosity.

The services I did you at Canton, justice, humanity, and my

7

office bade me perform; those you have done me since my arrival at Amsterdam, no laws obliged you to, no justice required, even half your favours would have been greater than my most sanguine expectations.

The sum of money therefore which you privately conveyed into my baggage, when I was leaving Holland, and which I was ignorant of till my arrival in London, I must beg leave to return. You have been bred a merchant, and I a scholar; you consequently love money better than I. You can find pleasure in superfluity, I am perfectly content with what is sufficient; take therefore what is yours, it may give you some pleasure, even though you have no occasion to use it; my happiness it cannot improve, for I have already all that I want.

My passage by sea from Rotterdam to England, was more painful to me than all the journies I ever made on land. I have traversed the immeasurable wilds of Mogul Tartary; felt all the rigours of Siberian skies; I have had my repose an hundred times disturbed by invading savages, and have seen without shrinking the desert sands rise like a troubled ocean all around me; against these calamities I was armed with resolution; but in my passage to England, though nothing occurred that gave the mariners any uneasiness, to one who was never at sea before, all was a subject of astonishment and terror. To find the land disappear, to see our ship mount the waves swift as an arrow from the Tartar bow, to hear the wind howling through the cordage, to feel a sickness which depresses even the spirits of the brave; these were unexpected distresses, and consequently assaulted me unprepared to receive them.

You men of Europe think nothing of a voyage by sea. With us of China, a man who has been from sight of land is regarded upon his return with admiration. I have known some provinces where there is not even a name for the ocean. What a strange people therefore am I got amongst, who have founded an empire on this unstable element, who build cities upon billows that rise higher than the mountains of Tipartala, and make the deep more formidable than the wildest tempest.

Such accounts as these, I must confess, were my first motives for seeing England. These induced me to undertake a journey of seven hundred painful days, in order to examine its opulence, buildings, arts, sciences, and manufactures on the spot. Judge then my disappointment on entering London, to see no signs of that opulence so much talked of abroad; wherever I turn, I am presented with a gloomy solemnity in the houses, the streets, and the inhabitants; none of that beautiful gilding which makes a principal ornament in Chinese architecture. The streets of Nankin are sometimes strewed with gold leaf; very different are those of London: in the midst of their pavements, a great lazy puddle moves muddily along; heavy laden machines with wheels of unwieldy thickness crowd up every passage; so that a stranger, instead of finding time for observation, is often happy if he has time to escape from being crushed to pieces.

The houses borrow very few ornaments from architecture; their chief decoration seems to be a paltry piece of painting, hung out at their doors or windows, at once a proof of their indigence and vanity. Their vanity, in each having one of those pictures exposed to public view; and their indigence, in being unable to get them better painted. In this respect, the fancy of their painters is also deplorable. Could you believe it? I have seen five black lions and three blue boars in less than the circuit of half a mile; and yet you know that animals of these colours are no where to be found except in the wild imaginations of Europe.

From these circumstances in their buildings, and from the dismal looks of the inhabitants, I am induced to conclude that the nation is actually poor; and that like the Persians, they make a splendid figure every where but at home. The proverb of Xixofou, is that a man's riches may be seen in his eyes; if we judge of the English by this rule, there is not a poorer nation under the sun.

I have been here but two days, so will not be hasty in my decisions; such letters as I shall write to Fipsihi in Moscow, I beg you 'll endeavour to forward with all diligence; I shall send them open, in order that you may take copies or translations, as you are equally versed in the Dutch and Chinese languages. Dear friend, think of my absence with regret, as I sincerely regret yours; even while I write, I lament our separation. Farewell.

LETTER III.—*From Lien Chi Altangi, to the care of Fipsihi, resident in Moscow; to be forwarded by the Russian caravan to Fum Hoam, first President of the Ceremonial Academy at Pekin in China.*

THINK not, O thou guide of my youth, that absence can impair my respect, or interposing trackless deserts blot your reverend figure from my memory. The farther I travel I feel the pain of separation with stronger force; those ties that bind me to my native country, and you, are still unbroken. By every remove, I only drag a greater length of chain.

Could I find ought worth transmitting from so remote a region as this to which I have wandered, I should gladly send it; but instead of this, you must be contented with a renewal of my former professions, and an imperfect account of a people with whom I am as yet but superficially acquainted. The remarks of a man who has been but three days in the country can only be those obvious circumstances which force themselves upon the imagination: I consider myself here as a newly created Being introduced into a new world; every object strikes with wonder and surprise. The imagination still unsated, seems the only active principle of the mind. The most trifling occurrences give pleasure, till the gloss of novelty is worn away. When I have ceased to wonder, I may possibly grow wise; I may then call the reasoning principle to my aid, and compare those objects with each other, which were before examined without reflection.

Behold me then in London, gazing at the strangers, and they at me; it seems they find somewhat absurd in my figure; and had I been never from home it is possible I might find an infinite fund of ridicule in theirs; but by long travelling I am taught to laugh at folly alone, and to find nothing truly ridiculous but villainy and vice.

When I had just quitted my native country, and crossed the Chinese wall, I fancied every deviation from the customs and manners of China was a departing from nature: I smiled at the blue lips and red foreheads of the Tonguese; and could hardly contain when I saw the Daures dress with their heads with horns. The Ostiacs powdered with red earth; and the Calmuck beauties tricked out in all the finery of sheep skin appeared highly ridiculous; but I soon perceived that the ridicule lay not in them but in me; that I falsely condemned others of absurdity, because they happened to differ from a standard originally founded in prejudice and partiality.

I find no pleasure therefore in taxing the English with departing from nature in their external appearance, which is all I yet know of their character; it is possible they only endeavour to improve her simple plan, since every extravagance in dress proceeds from a desire of becoming more beautiful than nature made us; and this is so harmless a vanity that I not only pardon but approve it: A desire to be more excellent than others is what actually makes us so, and as thousands find a livelihood in society by such appetites, none but the ignorant inveigh against them.

You are not insensible, most reverend Fum Hoam, what numberless trades, even among the Chinese, subsist by the harmless pride of each other. Your nose-borers, feet-swathers, tooth-stainers, eye-brow pluckers, would all want bread, should their neighbours want vanity. These vanities, however, employ much fewer hands in China than in England; and a fine gentleman, or a fine lady, here dressed up to the fashion, seems scarcely to have a single limb that does not suffer some distortions from art.

To make a fine gentleman, several trades are required, but chiefly a barber: you have undoubtedly heard of the Jewish champion, whose strength lay in his hair: one would think that the English were for placing all wisdom there: To appear wise, nothing more is requisite here than for a man to borrow hair from the heads of all his neighbours, and clap it like a bush on his own: the distributors of law and physic stick on such quantities, that it is almost impossible, even in idea to distinguish between the head and the hair.

Those whom I have been now describing, affect the gravity of the lion: those I am going to describe more resemble the pert vivacity of smaller animals. The barber, who is still master of the ceremonies, cuts their hair close to the crown; and then with a composition of meal and hog's lard, plasters the whole in such a manner, as to make it impossible to distinguish whether the patient wears a cap or a plaster; but to make the picture more perfectly striking, conceive the tail of some beast, a greyhound's tail, or a pig's tail for instance, appended to the back of the head, and reaching down to that place where tails in other animals are generally seen to begin; thus betailed and bepowdered, the man of taste fancies he improves in beauty, dresses up his hard-featured face in smiles, and attempts to look hideously tender. Thus equipped, he is qualified to make love, and hopes for success more from the powder on the outside of his head, than the sentiments within.

Yet when I consider what sort of a creature the fine lady is, to whom he is supposed to pay his addresses, it is not strange to find him thus equipped in order to please. She is herself every whit as fond of powder, and tails, and hog's lard as he: to speak my secret sentiments, most reverend Fum, the ladies here are horridly ugly; I can hardly endure the sight of them;

they no way resemble the beauties of China: the Europeans have a quite different idea of beauty from us; when I reflect on the small footed perfections of an Eastern beauty, how is it possible I should have eyes for a woman whose feet are ten inches long. I shall never forget the beauties of my native city of Nanfew. How very broad their faces; how very short their noses; how very little their eyes; how very thin their lips; how very black their teeth; the snow on the tops of Bao is not fairer than their cheeks; and their eye-brows are small as the line by the pencil of Quamsi. Here a lady with such perfections would be frightful; Dutch and Chinese beauties indeed have some resemblance, but English women are entirely different; red cheeks, big eyes, and teeth of a most odious whiteness, are not only seen here, but wished for; and then they have such masculine feet, as actually serve *some* for walking!

Yet uncivil as nature has been, they seem resolved to outdo her in unkindness; they use white powder, blue powder, and black powder for their hair, and a red powder for the face on some particular occasions.

They like to have the face of various colours, as among the Tartars of Koreki, frequently sticking on, with spittle, little black patches on every part of it, except on the tip of the nose, which I have never seen with a patch. You'll have a better idea of their manner of placing these spots, when I have finished a map of an English face patched up to the fashion, which shall shortly be sent to increase your curious collection of paintings, medals, and monsters.

But what surprises more than all the rest, is, what I have just now been credibly informed by one of this country; 'Most ladies here, says he, have two faces; one face to sleep in, and another to show in company: the first is generally reserved for the husband and family at home, the other put on to please strangers abroad; the family face is often indifferent enough, but the out-door one looks something better; this is always made at the toilet, where the looking-glass and toad-eater sit in council, and settle the complexion of the day.'

I can't ascertain the truth of this remark; however, it is actually certain, that they wear more clothes within doors than without; and I have seen a lady who seemed to shudder at a breeze in her own apartment, appear half naked in the streets. Farewell.

LETTER IV.—*To the same.*

THE English seem as silent as the Japanese, yet vainer than the inhabitants of Siam. Upon my arrival I attributed that reserve to modesty, which I now find has its origin in pride. Condescend to address them first, and you are sure of their acquaintance; stoop to flattery, and you conciliate their friendship and esteem. They bear hunger, cold, fatigue, and all the miseries of life without shrinking; danger only calls forth their fortitude; they even exult in calamity; but contempt is what they cannot bear. An Englishman fears contempt more than death; he often flies to death as a refuge from its pressure; and dies when he fancies the world has ceased to esteem him.

Pride seems the source not only of their national vices, but of their national virtues also. An Englishman is taught to love his king as his friend, but to acknowledge no other master than the laws which himself has contributed to enact. He despises those nations, who, that one may be free, are all content to be slaves; who first lift a tyrant into terror, and then shrink under his power as if delegated from heaven. Liberty is echoed in all their assemblies, and thousands might be found ready to offer up their lives for the sound, though perhaps not one of all the number understands its meaning. The lowest mechanic however looks upon it as his duty to be a watchful guardian of his country's freedom, and often uses a language that might seem haughty, even in the mouth of the great emperor who traces his ancestry to the moon.

A few days ago, passing by one of their prisons, I could not avoid stopping, in order to listen to a dialogue which I thought might afford me some entertainment. The conversation was carried on between a debtor through the grate of his prison, a porter, who has stopped to rest his burden, and a soldier at the window. The subject was upon a threatened invasion from France, and each seemed extremely anxious to rescue his country from the impending danger. '*For my part*, cries the prisoner, *the greatest of my apprehensions is for our freedom; if the French should conquer, what would become of English liberty. My dear Friends, liberty is the Englishman's prerogative; we must preserve that at the expense of our lives, of that the French shall never deprive us; it is not to be expected that men who are slaves themselves would preserve our freedom should they happen to conquer:* Ay, slaves, cries the porter, they are all slaves, fit only to carry burdens every one of them. Before I would stoop to slavery, may this be my poison (and he held the goblet in his hand) may this be my poison—but I would sooner list for a soldier.'

The soldier taking the goblet from his friend, with much awe fervently cried out, *It is not so much our liberties as our religion that would suffer by such a change. Ay, our religion, my lads. May the Devil sink me into flames,* (such was the solemnity of his adjuration) *if the French should come over, but our religion would be utterly undone.* So saying, instead of a libation, he applied the goblet to his lips, and confirmed his sentiments with a ceremony of the most persevering devotion.

In short, every man here pretends to be a politician; even the fair sex are sometimes found to mix the severity of national altercation, with the blandishments of love, and often become conquerors by more weapons of destruction than their eyes.

This universal passion for politics is gratified by Daily Gazettes, as with us at China. But as in ours, the emperor endeavours to instruct his people, in theirs the people endeavour to instruct the administration. You must not, however, imagine, that they who compile these papers have any actual knowledge of the politics, or the government of a state; they only collect their materials from the oracle of some coffee-house, which oracle has himself gathered them the night before from a beau at a gaming-table, who has pillaged his knowledge from a great man's porter, who had had his information from the great man's gentleman, who has invented the whole story for his own amusement the night preceding.

The English in general seem fonder of gaining the esteem than the love of those they converse with: this gives a formality to their amusements; their gayest conversations have something too wise for innocent relaxation; though in company you are seldom disgusted with the absurdity of a fool, you are seldom lifted into rapture by those strokes of vivacity, which give instant, though not permanent pleasure.

What they want, however, in gaiety, they make up in politeness. You smile at hearing me praise the English for their politeness: you who have heard very different accounts from the missionaries at Pekin, who have seen such a different behaviour in their merchants and seamen at home. But I must still repeat it, the English seem more polite than any of their neighbours; their great art in this respect lies in endeavouring, while they oblige, to lessen the force of the favour. Other countries are fond of obliging a stranger; but seem desirous that he should be sensible of the obligation. The English confer their kindness with an appearance of indifference, and give away benefits with an air as if they despised them.

Walking a few days ago between an English and Frenchman into the suburbs of the city, we were overtaken by a heavy shower of rain. I was unprepared; but they had each large coats, which defended them from what seemed to me a perfect inundation. The Englishman seeing me shrink from the weather accosted me thus: '*Psha, man, what dost shrink at? here, take this coat; I don't want it; I find it no way useful to me; I had as lief be without it.*' The Frenchman began to shew his politeness in turn. '*My dear friend,*' cries he, '*why won't you oblige me by making use of my coat; you see how well it defends me from the rain; I should not choose to part with it to others, but to such a friend as you, I could even part with my skin to do him service.*'

From such minute instances as these, most reverend Fum Hoam, I am sensible your sagacity will collect instruction. The volume of nature is the book of knowledge; and he becomes most wise who makes the most judicious selection. Farewell.

LETTER V.—*To the same.*

I HAVE already informed you of the singular passion of this nation for politics. An Englishman not satisfied with finding by his own prosperity the contending powers of Europe properly balanced, desires also to know the precise value of every weight in either scale. To gratify this curiosity, a leaf of political instruction is served up every morning with tea. When our politician has feasted upon this, he repairs to a coffee-house, in order to ruminate upon what he has read, and increase his collection; from thence he proceeds to the ordinary, enquires what news, and treasuring up every acquisition there, hunts about all the evening in quest of more, and carefully adds it to the rest. Thus at night he retires home, full of the important advices of the day. When lo! awaking next morning he finds the instructions of yesterday a collection of absurdity or palpable falsehood. This, one would think, a mortifying repulse in the pursuit of wisdom; yet our politician, no way discouraged, hunts on, in order to collect fresh materials, and in order to be again disappointed.

I have often admired the commercial spirit which prevails over Europe; have been surprised to see them carry on a traffic with productions, that an Asiatic stranger would deem entirely useless. It is a proverb in China, that an European suffers not even his spittle to be lost; the maxim, however, is not sufficiently strong; since they sell even their Lies to great advantage. Every nation drives a considerable trade in this commodity with their neighbours.

An English dealer in this way, for instance, has only to ascend to his work-house, and manufacture a turbulent speech averred to be spoken in the senate; or a report supposed to be dropt at court; a piece of scandal that strikes at a popular mandarine; or a secret treaty between two neighbouring powers. When finished, these goods are baled up, and consigned to a factor abroad, who sends in return two battles, three sieges, and a shrewd letter filled with dashes ———, blanks   and * * * * of great importance.

Thus you perceive that a single gazette is the joint manufacture of Europe: and he who would peruse it with a philosophical eye might perceive in every paragraph something characteristic of the nation to which it belongs. A map does not exhibit a more distinct view of the boundaries and situation of every country, than its news does a picture of the genius, and the morals of its inhabitants. The superstition and erroneous delicacy of Italy, the formality of Spain, the cruelty of Portugal, the fears of Austria, the confidence of Prussia, the levity of France, the avarice of Holland, the pride of England, the absurdity of Ireland, and the national partiality of Scotland, are all conspicuous in every page.

But, perhaps, you may find more satisfaction in a real news paper, than in my description of one; I therefore send a specimen, which may serve to exhibit the manner of their being written, and distinguish the characters of the various nations which are united in its composition.

NAPLES. We have lately dug up here a curious Etruscan monument, broke in two in the raising. The characters are scarce visible; but Nugosi, the learned antiquary, supposes it to have been erected in honour of Picus, a Latin King, as one of the lines may be plainly distinguished to begin with a P. It is hoped this discovery will produce something valuable, as the literati of our twelve academies are deeply engaged in the disquisition.

PISA. Since father Fudgi, prior of St. Gilbert's, has gone to reside at Rome, no miracles have been performed at the shrine of St. Gilbert; the devout begin to grow uneasy, and some begin actually to fear that St. Gilbert has forsaken them with the reverend father.

LUCCA. The administrators of our serene republic, have frequent conferences upon the part they shall take in the present commotions of Europe. Some are for sending a body of their troops, consisting of one company of foot, and six horsemen, to make a diversion in favour of the empress queen; others are as strenuous asserters of the Prussian interest; what turn these debates may take, time only can discover. However, certain it is, we shall be able to bring into the field at the opening of the next campaign, seventy-five armed men, a commander in chief, and two drummers of great experience.

SPAIN. Yesterday the new king shewed himself to his subjects, and after having staid half an hour in his balcony, retired to the royal apartment. The night concluded on this extraordinary occasion with illuminations, and other demonstrations of joy.

The queen is more beautiful than the rising sun, and reckoned one of the first wits in Europe: she had a glorious opportunity of displaying the readiness of her invention, and her skill in repartee lately at court. The duke of Lerma, coming up to her with a low bow and a smile, and presenting a nosegay set with diamonds, *Madam*, cries he, *I am your most obedient humble servant.* *Oh, Sir*, replies the queen, without any prompter, or the least hesitation, *I'm very proud of the very great honour you do me.* Upon which she made a low curtsy, and all the courtiers fell a laughing at the readiness and the smartness of her reply.

LISBON. Yesterday we had an *auto de fe*, at which were burned three young women accused of heresy, one of them of exquisite beauty; two Jews, and an old woman, convicted of being a witch: One of the friars, who attended this last, reports, that he saw the devil fly out of her at the stake in the shape of a flame of fire. The populace behaved on this occasion with great good humour, joy, and sincere devotion.

Our *merciful Sovereign* has been for some time past recovered of his fright: though so atrocious an attempt deserved to exterminate half the nation, yet he has been graciously pleased to spare the lives of his subjects, and not above five hundred have been broke upon the wheel, or otherwise executed upon this horrid occasion.

VIENNA. We have received certain advices that a party of twenty thousand Austrians, having attacked a much superior body of Prussians, put them all to flight, and took the rest prisoners of war.

BERLIN. We have received certain advices that a party of twenty thousand Prussians, having attacked a much superior body of Austrians, put them to flight, and took a great number of prisoners, with their military chest, cannon, and baggage.

Though we have not succeeded this campaign to our wishes; yet, when we think of him who commands us, we rest in security: while we sleep, our king is watchful for our safety.

PARIS. We shall soon strike a signal blow. We have seventeen flat-bottomed boats at Havre, The people are in excellent spirits, and our ministers make no difficulty in raising the supplies.

We are all undone; the people are discontented to the last degree; the ministers are obliged to have recourse to the most rigorous methods to raise the expense of the war.

Our distresses are great; but madam Pompadour continues to supply our king, who is now growing old, with a fresh lady every night. His health, thank heaven, is still pretty well; nor is he in the least unfit, as was reported, for any kind of royal exercitation. He was so frighted at the affair of Damien, that his physicians were apprehensive lest his reason should suffer, but that wretch's tortures soon composed the kingly terrors of his breast.

ENGLAND. Wanted an usher to an academy. *N.B.* He must be able to read, dress hair, and must have had the small pox.

DUBLIN. We hear that there is a benevolent subscription on foot among the nobility and gentry of this kingdom, who are great patrons of merit, in order to assist Black and All Black, in his contest with the Padereen mare.

We hear from Germany that prince Ferdinand has gained a complete victory, and taken twelve kettle drums, five standards, and four waggons of ammunition prisoners of war.

EDINBURGH. We are positive when we say that Saunders M'Gregor, who was lately executed for horse-stealing, is not a Scotchman, but born in Carrickfergus. Farewell.

LETTER VI.—*Fum Hoam, first President of the Ceremonial Academy at Pekin, to Lien Chi Altangi, the discontented wanderer; by the way of Moscow.*

WHETHER sporting on the flowery banks of the river Irtis, or scaling the steepy mountains of Douchenour: whether traversing the black deserts of Kobi, or giving lessons of politeness to the savage inhabitants of Europe;—in whatever country, whatever climate, and whatever circumstances, all hail! May Tien, the universal soul, take you under his protection, and inspire you with a superior portion of himself.

How long, my friend, shall an enthusiasm for knowledge continue to obstruct your happiness, and tear you from all the connexions that make life pleasing? How long will you continue to rove from climate to climate, circled by thousands, and yet without a friend, feeling all the inconveniences of a crowd, and all the anxiety of being alone.

I know you will reply, that the refined pleasure of growing every day wiser, is a sufficient recompence for every inconvenience. I know you will talk of the vulgar satisfaction of soliciting happiness from sensual enjoyment only, and probably enlarge upon the exquisite raptures of sentimental bliss. Yet, believe me, friend, you are deceived; all our pleasures, though seemingly never so remote from sense, derive their origin from some one of the senses. The most exquisite demonstration in mathematics, or the most pleasing disquisition in metaphysics, if it does not ultimately tend to increase some sensual satisfaction is delightful only to fools, or to men who have by long habit contracted a false idea of pleasure; and he who separates sensual and sentimental enjoyments, seeking happiness from mind alone, is in fact as wretched as the naked inhabitant of the forest, who places all happiness in the first, regardless of the latter. There are two extremes in this respect; the savage who swallows down the draught of pleasure without staying to reflect on his happiness, and the sage who passeth the cup while he reflects on the conveniences of drinking.

It is with a heart full of sorrow, my dear Altangi, that I must inform you that what the world calls happiness must now be yours no longer. Our great emperor's displeasure at your leaving China, contrary to the rules of our government, and the immemorial custom of the empire, has produced the most terrible effects. Your wife, daughter, and the rest of your family have been seized by his order, and appropriated to his use; all except your son are now the peculiar property of him who possesses all; him I have hidden from the officers employed for this purpose; and even at the hazard of my life I have concealed him. The youth seems obstinately bent on finding you out, wherever you are; he is determined to face every danger that opposes his pursuit. Though yet but fifteen, all his father's virtues and obstinacy sparkle in his eyes, and mark him as one destined to no mediocrity of fortune.

You see, my dearest friend, what imprudence has brought thee to; from opulence, a tender family, surrounding friends, and your master's esteem, it has reduced thee to want, persecution; and still worse, to our mighty monarch's displeasure. Want of prudence is too frequently the want of virtue; nor is there on earth a more powerful advocate for vice than poverty. As I shall endeavour to guard thee from the one, so guard thyself from the other; and still think of me with affection and esteem.   Farewell.

LETTER VII.—*From Lien Chi Altangi, to Fum Hoam, first President of the Ceremonial Academy at Pekin, in China.*

The Editor thinks proper to acquaint the reader that the greatest part of the following letter seems to him to be little more than a rhapsody of sentences borrowed from Confucius, the Chinese philosopher.

A WIFE, a daughter carried into captivity to expiate my offence, a son scarce yet arrived at maturity, resolving to encounter every danger in the pious pursuit of one who has undone him, these indeed are circumstances of distress; tho' my tears were more precious than the gems of Golconda, yet would they fall upon such an occasion.

But I submit to the stroke of heaven, I hold the volume of Confucius in my hand, and as I read grow humble, and patient, and wise. We should feel sorrow, says he, but not sink under its oppression; the heart of a wise man should resemble a mirror, which reflects every object without being sullied by any. The wheel of fortune turns incessantly round, and who can say within himself I shall to-day be uppermost. We should hold the immutable mean that lies between insensibility and anguish; our attempts should be not to extinguish nature, but to repress it; not to stand unmoved at distress, but endeavour to turn every disaster to our own advantage. Our greatest glory is, not in never falling, but in rising every time we fall.

I fancy myself at present, O thou reverend disciple of Tao, more than a match for all that can happen; the chief business of my life has been to procure wisdom, and the chief object of that wisdom was to be happy. My attendance on your lectures, my conferences with the missionaries of Europe, and all my subsequent adventures upon quitting China, were calculated to increase the sphere of my happiness, not my curiosity. Let

European travellers cross seas and deserts merely to measure the height of a mountain, to describe the cataract of a river, or tell the commodities which every country may produce; merchants or geographers, perhaps, may find profit by such discoveries, but what advantage can accrue to a philosopher from such accounts, who is desirous of understanding the human heart, who seeks to know the *men* of every country, who desires to discover those differences which result from climate, religion, education, prejudice, and partiality.

I should think my time very ill bestowed, were the only fruits of my adventures to consist in being able to tell, that a tradesman of London lives in a house three times as high as that of our great Emperor; that the ladies wear longer clothes than the men, that the priests are dressed in colours which we are taught to detest, and that their soldiers wear scarlet, which is with us the symbol of peace and innocence. How many travellers are there, who confine their relations to such minute and useless particulars! For one who enters into the genius of those nations with whom he has conversed, who discloses their morals, their opinions, the ideas which they entertain of religious worship, the intrigues of their ministers, and their skill in sciences, there are twenty, who only mention some idle particulars, which can be of no real use to a true philosopher. All their remarks tend, neither to make themselves nor others more happy; they no way contribute to control their passions, to bear adversity, to inspire true virtue, or raise a detestation of vice.

Men may be very learned, and yet very miserable; it is easy to be a deep geometrician, or a sublime astronomer, but very difficult to be a good man; I esteem, therefore, the traveller who instructs the heart, but despise him who only indulges the imagination; a man who leaves home to mend himself and others is a philosopher; but he who goes from country to country, guided by the blind impulse of curiosity, is only a vagabond. From Zerdusht down to him of Tyanea, I honour all those great names who endeavoured to unite the world by their travels; such men grew wiser as well as better, the farther they departed from home, and seemed like rivers, whose streams are not only increased, but refined, as they travel from their source.

For my own part, my greatest glory is, that travelling has not more steeled my constitution against all the vicissitudes of climate, and all the depressions of fatigue, than it has my mind against the accidents of fortune, or the accesses of despair. Farewell.

LETTER VIII.—*From Lien Chi Altangi, to Fum Hoam, first President of the Ceremonial Academy at Pekin, in China.*

How insupportable! oh thou possessor of heavenly wisdom, would be this separation, this immeasurable distance from my friend, were I not able thus to delineate my heart upon paper, and to send thee daily a map of my mind.

I am every day better reconciled to the people among whom I reside, and begin to fancy that in time I shall find them more opulent, more charitable, and more hospitable than I at first imagined. I begin to learn somewhat of their manners and customs, and to see reasons for several deviations which they make from us, from whom all other nations derive their politeness as well as their original.

In spite of taste, in spite of prejudice, I now begin to think their women tolerable; I can now look on a languishing blue eye without disgust, and pardon a set of teeth, even though whiter than ivory. I now begin to fancy there is no universal standard for beauty. The truth is, the manners of the ladies in this city are so very open, and so vastly engaging, that I am inclined to pass over the more glaring defects of their persons, since compensated by the more solid, yet latent beauties of the mind; what though they want black teeth, or are deprived of the allurements of feet no bigger than their thumbs, yet still they have souls, my friend, such souls, so free, so pressing, so hospitable, and so engaging——I have received more invitations in the streets of London from the sex in one night, than I have met with at Pekin in twelve revolutions of the moon.

Every evening as I return home from my usual solitary excursions, I am met by several of those well disposed daughters of hospitality, at different times and in different streets, richly dressed, and with minds not less noble than their appearance. You know that nature has indulged me with a person by no means agreeable; yet are they too generous to object to my homely appearance; they feel no repugnance at my broad face and flat nose; they perceive me to be a stranger, and that alone is a sufficient recommendation. They even seem to think it their duty to do the honours of the country by every act of complaisance in their power. One takes me under the arm, and in a manner forces me along; another catches me round the neck, and desires to partake in this office of hospitality; while a third, kinder still, invites me to refresh my spirits with wine.

Wine is in England reserved only for the rich, yet here even wine is given away to the stranger!

A few nights ago, one of these generous creatures, dressed all in white, and flaunting like a meteor by my side, forcibly attended me home to my own apartment. She seemed charmed with the elegance of the furniture, and the convenience of my situation. And well indeed she might, for I have hired an apartment for not less than two shillings of their money every week. But her civility did not rest here; for at parting, being desirous to know the hour, and perceiving my watch out of order, she kindly took it to be repaired by a relation of her own, which you may imagine will save some expense, and she assures me that it will cost her nothing. I shall have it back in a few days when mended, and am preparing a proper speech expressive of my gratitude on the occasion: *Celestial excellence*, I intend to say, *happy am I in having found out, after many painful adventures, a land of innocence, and a people of humanity: I may rove into other climes, and converse with nations yet unknown, but where shall I meet a soul of such purity as that which resides in thy breast! Sure thou hast been nurtured by the bill of the Shin Shin, or sucked the breasts of the provident Gin Hiung. The melody of thy voice could rob the Chong Fou of her whelps, or inveigle the Boh that lives in the midst of the waters. Thy servant shall ever retain a sense of thy favour; and one day boast of thy virtue, sincerity, and truth, among the daughters of China.* Adieu.

LETTER IX.—*To the same.*

I HAVE been deceived! she whom I fancied a daughter of Paradise has proved to be one of the infamous disciples of Han! I have lost a trifle, I have gained the consolation of having discovered a deceiver. I once more, therefore, relax into my former indifference with regard to the English ladies, they once more begin to appear disagreeable in my eyes: Thus is my whole time passed in forming conclusions which the next minute's experience may probably destroy; the present moment becomes a comment on the past, and I improve rather in humility than wisdom.

Their laws and religion forbid the English to keep more than one woman, I therefore concluded that prostitutes were banished from society; I was deceived; every man here keeps as many wives as he can maintain; the laws are cemented with blood, praised and disregarded. The very Chinese, whose religion allows him two wives, takes not half the liberties of the English in this particular. Their laws may be compared to the books of the Sybils, they are held in great veneration, but seldom read, or seldomer understood; even those who pretend to be their guardians dispute about the meaning of many of them, and confess their ignorance of others. The law therefore which commands them to have but one wife, is strictly observed only by those for whom one is more than sufficient, or by such as have not money to buy two. As for the rest, they violate it publicly, and some glory in its violation. They seem to think like the Persians, that they give evident marks of manhood by increasing their seraglio. A mandarine therefore here generally keeps four wives, a gentleman three, and a stage-player two. As for the magistrates, the country justices and squires, they are employed first in debauching young virgins, and then punishing the transgression.

From such a picture you will be apt to conclude, that he who employs four ladies for his amusement, has four times as much constitution to spare as he who is contented with one; that a Mandarine is much cleverer than a gentleman, and a gentleman than a player, and yet it is quite the reverse; a Mandarine is frequently supported on spindle shanks, appears emaciated by luxury, and is obliged to have recourse to variety, merely from the weakness, not the vigour of his constitution, the number of his wives being the most equivocal symptom of his virility.

Besides the country squire, there is also another set of men, whose whole employment consists in corrupting beauty; these the silly part of the fair sex call amiable; the more sensible part of them, however, give them the title of abominable. You will probably demand what are the talents of a man thus caressed by the majority of the opposite sex; what talents, or what beauty is he possessed of superior to the rest of his fellows. To answer you directly, he has neither talents nor beauty, but then he is possessed of impudence and assiduity. With assiduity and impudence, men of all ages, and all figures, may commence admirers. I have even been told of some who made professions of expiring for love, when all the world could perceive they were going to die of old age: and what is more surprising still, such battered beaus are generally most infamously successful.

A fellow of this kind employs three hours every morning in dressing his head, by which is understood only his hair.

He is a professed admirer, not of any particular lady, but of the whole sex.

He is to suppose every lady has caught cold every night, which gives him an opportunity of calling to see how she does the next morning.

He is upon all occasions to show himself in very great pain for the ladies; if a lady drops even a pin, he is to fly in order to present it.

He never speaks to a lady without advancing his mouth to her ear, by which he frequently addresses more senses than one.

Upon proper occasions he looks excessively tender. This is performed by laying his hand upon his heart, shutting his eyes, and showing his teeth.

He is excessively fond of dancing a minuet with the ladies, by which is only meant walking round the floor eight or ten times with his hat on, affecting great gravity, and sometimes looking tenderly on his partner.

He never affronts any man himself, and never resents an affront from another.

He has an infinite variety of small talk upon all occasions, and laughs when he has nothing more to say.

Such is the killing creature who prostrates himself to the sex till he has undone them; all whose submissions are the effects of design, and who to please the ladies almost becomes himself a lady.

LETTER X.—*To the same.*

I HAVE hitherto given you no account of my journey from China to Europe, of my travels through countries, where Nature sports in primeval rudeness, where she pours forth her wonders in solitude; countries, from whence the rigorous climate, the sweeping inundation, the drifted desert, the howling forest, and mountains of immeasurable height banish the husbandman, and spread extensive desolation; countries where the brown Tartar wanders for a precarious subsistence, with an heart that never felt pity, himself more hideous than the wilderness he makes.

You will easily conceive the fatigue of crossing vast tracts of land, either desolate, or still more dangerous by its inhabitants. The retreat of men, who seem driven from society, in order to make war upon all the human race; nominally professing a subjection to Moscovy or China, but without any resemblance to the countries on which they depend.

After I had crossed the great wall, the first objects that presented themselves were the remains of desolated cities, and all the magnificence of venerable ruin. There were to be seen temples of beautiful structure, statues wrought by the hand of a master, and around a country of luxuriant plenty; but not one single inhabitant to reap the bounties of nature. These were prospects that might humble the pride of kings, and repress human vanity. I asked my guide the cause of such desolation. These countries, says he, were once the dominions of a Tartar prince; and these ruins the seat of arts, elegance, and ease. This prince waged an unsuccessful war with one of the emperors of China; he was conquered, his cities plundered, and all his subjects carried into captivity. Such are the effects of the ambition of Kings! Ten Dervises, says the Indian proverb, shall sleep in peace upon a single carpet, while two kings shall quarrel though they have kingdoms to divide them. Sure, my friend, the cruelty and the pride of man have made more deserts than Nature ever made! she is kind, but man is ungrateful!

Proceeding in my journey through this pensive scene of desolated beauty, in a few days I arrived among the Daures, a nation still dependent on China. Xaizigar is their principal city, which, compared with those of Europe, scarcely deserves the name. The governors and other officers, who are sent yearly from Pekin, abuse their authority, and often take the wives and daughters of the inhabitants to themselves. The Daures, accustomed to base submission, feel no resentment at those injuries, or stifle what they feel. Custom and necessity teach even barbarians the same art of dissimulation that ambition and intrigue inspire in the breasts of the polite. Upon beholding such unlicensed stretches of power, alas, thought I, how little does our wise and good emperor know of these intolerable exactions! these provinces are too distant for complaint, and too insignificant to express redress. The more distant the government, the honester should be the governor to whom it is entrusted; for hope of impunity is a strong inducement to violation.

The religion of the Daures is more absurd than even that of the sectaries of Fohi. How would you be surprised, O sage disciple and follower of Confucius! you who believe one eternal intelligent cause of all, should you be present at the barbarous ceremonies of this infatuated people. How would you deplore the blindness and folly of mankind. His boasted reason seems only to light him astray, and brutal instinct more regularly points out the path to happiness. Could you think it? they adore a wicked divinity; they fear him and they worship him; they imagine him a malicious Being, ready to injure and ready to be appeased. The men and women assemble at midnight in a hut, which serves for a temple. A priest stretches himself on the ground, and all the people pour forth the most horrid cries, while drums and timbrels swell the infernal concert. After this dissonance, miscalled music, has continued about two hours, the priest rises from the ground, assumes an air of inspiration, grows big with the inspiring dæmon, and pretends to a skill in futurity.

In every country, my friend, the bonzes, the brachmans, and the priests deceive the people; all reformations begin from the laity; the priests point us out the way to heaven with their fingers, but stand still themselves, nor seem to travel towards the country in view.

The customs of this people correspond to their religion; they keep their dead for three days on the same bed where the person died; after which they bury him in a grave moderately deep, but with the head still uncovered. Here for several days they present him different sorts of meats; which, when they perceive he does not consume, they fill up the grave, and desist from desiring him to eat for the future. How, how can mankind be guilty of such strange absurdity; to entreat a dead body already putrid to partake of the banquet? Where, I again repeat it, is human reason! not only some men, but whole nations, seem divested of its illumination. Here we observe a whole country adoring a divinity through fear, and attempting to feed the dead. These are their most serious and most religious occupations: are these men rational, or are not the apes of Borneo more wise?

Certain I am, O thou instructor of my youth! that without philosophers, without some few virtuous men, who seem to be of a different nature from the rest of mankind, without such as these the worship of a wicked divinity would surely be established over every part of the earth. Fear guides more to their duty than gratitude: for one man who is virtuous from the love of virtue; from the obligation which he thinks he lies under to the giver of all; there are ten thousand who are good only from their apprehensions of punishment. Could these last be persuaded, as the Epicureans were, that heaven had no thunders in store for the villain, they would no longer continue to acknowledge subordination, or thank that Being who gave them existence.   Adieu.

LETTER XI.—*To the same.*

From such a picture of Nature in primeval simplicity, tell me, my much respected friend, are you in love with fatigue and solitude? Do you sigh for the severe frugality of the wandering Tartar, or regret being born amidst the luxury and dissimulation of the polite? Rather tell me, has not every kind of life vices peculiarly its own? Is it not a truth, that refined countries have more vices, but those not so terrible, barbarous nations few, and they of the most hideous complexion? Perfidy and fraud are the vices of civilized nations, credulity and violence those of the inhabitants of the desert. Does the luxury of the one produce half the evils of the inhumanity of the other? Certainly those philosophers, who declaim against luxury, have but little understood its benefits; they seem insensible, that to luxury we owe not only the greatest part of our knowledge, but even of our virtues.

It may sound fine in the mouth of a declaimer when he talks of subduing our appetites, of teaching every sense to be content with a bare sufficiency, and of supplying only the wants of Nature; but is there not more satisfaction in indulging those appetites, if with innocence and safety, than in restraining them? Am not I better pleased in enjoyment than in the sullen satisfaction of thinking that I can live without enjoyment? The more various our artificial necessities, the wider is our circle of pleasure; for all pleasure consists in obviating necessities as they rise; luxury, therefore, as it encreases our wants, encreases our capacity for happiness.

Examine the history of any country remarkable for opulence and wisdom, you will find they would never have been wise had they not been first luxurious; you will find poets, philosophers, and even patriots, marching in Luxury's train. The reason is obvious; we then only are curious after knowledge when we find it connected with sensual happiness. The senses ever point out the way, and reflection comments upon the discovery. Inform a native of the desert of Kobi, of the exact measure of the parallax of the moon, he finds no satisfaction at all in the information; he wonders how any could take such pains, and lay out such treasures in order to solve so useless a difficulty; but connect it with his happiness, by showing that it improves navigation, that by such an investigation he may have a warmer coat, a better gun, or a finer knife, and he is instantly in raptures at so great an improvement. In short, we only desire to know what we desire to possess; and whatever we may talk against it, luxury adds the spur to curiosity, and gives us a desire of becoming more wise.

But not our knowledge only, but our virtues are improved by luxury. Observe the brown savage of Thibet, to whom the fruits of the spreading promegranate supply food, and its branches an habitation. Such a character has few vices I grant, but those he has are of the most hideous nature, rapine and cruelty are scarce crimes in his eye, neither pity nor tenderness, which ennoble every virtue, has any place in his heart; he hates his enemies, and kills those he subdues. On the other hand, the polite Chinese and civilized European seem even to love their enemies. I have just now seen an instance where the English have succoured those enemies whom their own countrymen actually refused to relieve.

The greater the luxuries of every country, the more closely, politically speaking, is that country united. Luxury is the child of society alone, the luxurious man stands in need of a thousand different artists to furnish out his happiness; it is more likely, therefore, that he should be a good citizen who is connected by motives of self-interest with so many, than the abstemious man who is united to none.

In whatsoever light therefore we consider luxury, whether as employing a number of hands naturally too feeble for more laborious employment, as finding a variety of occupation for others who might be totally idle, or as furnishing out new inlets to happiness, without encroaching on mutual property, in whatever light we regard it, we shall have reason to stand up in its defence, and the sentiment of Confucius still remains unshaken; *that we should enjoy as many of the luxuries of life as are consistent with our own safety, and the prosperity of others, and that he who finds out a new pleasure is one of the most useful members of society.*

LETTER XII.—*To the same.*

FROM the funeral solemnities of the Daures, who think themselves the politest people in the world, I must make a transition to the funeral solemnities of the English, who think themselves as polite as they. The numberless ceremonies which are used here when a person is sick, appear to me so many evident marks of fear and apprehension. Ask an Englishman, however, whether he is afraid of death, and he boldly answers in the negative; but observe his behaviour in circumstances of approaching sickness, and you will find his actions give his assertions the lie.

The Chinese are very sincere in this respect; they hate to die, and they confess their terrors: a great part of their life is spent in preparing things proper for their funeral; a poor artizan shall spend half his income in providing himself a tomb twenty years before he wants it; and denies himself the necessaries of life, that he may be amply provided for when he shall want them no more.

But people of distinction in England really deserve pity, for they die in circumstances of the most extreme distress. It is an established rule, never to let a man know that he is dying; physicians are sent for, the clergy are called, and every thing passes in silent solemnity round the sick bed; the patient is in agonies, looks round for pity, yet not a single creature will say that he is dying. If he is possessed of fortune, his relations entreat him to make his will, as it may restore the tranquillity of his mind. He is desired to undergo the rites of the church, for decency requires it. His friends take their leave only because they don't care to see him in pain. In short, an hundred stratagems are used to make him do what he might have been induced to perform only by being told; *Sir, you are past all hopes, and had as good think decently of dying*.

Besides all this, the chamber is darkened, the whole house echoes to the cries of the wife, the lamentations of the children, the grief of the servants, and the sighs of friends. The bed is surrounded with priests and doctors in black, and only flambeaux emit a yellow gloom. Where is the man, how intrepid soever, that would not shrink at such a hideous solemnity? For fear of affrighting their expiring friends, the English practise all that can fill them with terror. Strange effect of human prejudice thus to torture merely from mistaken tenderness!

You see, my friend, what contradictions there are in the tempers of those islanders; when prompted by ambition, revenge, or disappointment, they meet death with the utmost resolution; the very man who in his bed would have trembled at the aspect of a doctor, shall go with intrepidity to attack a bastion, or deliberately noose himself up in his garters.

The passion of the Europeans for magnificent interments, is equally strong with that of the Chinese. When a tradesman dies, his frightful face is painted up by an undertaker, and placed in a proper situation to receive company: this is called lying in state. To this disagreeable spectacle all the idlers in town flock, and learn to loathe the wretch dead, whom they despised when living. In this manner you see some who would have refused a shilling to save the life of their dearest friend, bestow thousands on adorning their putrid corpse. I have been told of a fellow, who grown rich by the price of blood, left it in his will that he should lie in state, and thus unknowingly gibbeted himself into infamy, when he might have otherwise quietly retired into oblivion.

When the person is buried, the next care is to make his epitaph; they are generally reckoned best which flatter most; such relations therefore as have received most benefits from the defunct, discharge this friendly office; and generally flatter in proportion to their joy. When we read those monumental histories of the dead, it may be justly said, that *all men are equal in the dust*; for they all appear equally remarkable for being the most sincere Christians, the most benevolent neighbours, and the honestest men of their time. To go through an European cemetery, one would be apt to wonder how mankind could have so basely degenerated from such excellent ancestors; every tomb pretends to claim your reverence and regret; some are praised for piety in those inscriptions who never entered the temple until they were dead; some are praised for being excellent poets, who were never mentioned, except for their dulness, when living: others for sublime orators, who were never noted except for their impudence; and others still for military achievements, who were never in any other skirmishes but with the watch. Some even make epitaphs for themselves, and bespeak the reader's good-will. It were indeed to be wished that every man would early learn in this manner to make his own; that he would draw it up in terms as flattering as possible; and that he would make it the employment of his whole life to deserve it!

I have not yet been in a place called Westminster Abbey, but soon intend to visit it. There I am told I shall see justice done to deceased merit; none, I am told, are permitted to be buried there but such as have adorned as well as improved mankind. There no intruders by the influence of friends or fortune, presume to mix their unhallowed ashes with philosophers, heroes, and poets. Nothing but true merit has a place in that awful sanctuary: the guardianship of the tombs is committed to several reverend priests, who are never guilty for a superior reward of taking down the names of good men, to make room for others of equivocal character, nor ever profaned the sacred walls with pageants, that posterity cannot know, or shall blush to own.

I always was of opinion, that sepulchral honours of this kind should be considered as a national concern, and not trusted to the care of the priests of any country, how respectable soever; but from the conduct of the reverend personages, whose disinterested patriotism I shall shortly be able to discover, I am taught to retract my former sentiments. It is true, the Spartans and the Persians made a fine political use of sepulchral vanity; they permitted none to be thus interred, who had not fallen in the vindication of their country; a monument thus became a real mark of distinction, it nerved the hero's arm with tenfold vigour; and he fought without fear, who only fought for a grave.   Farewell.

LETTER XIII—*From the same.*

I AM just returned from Westminster-abbey, the place of sepulture for the philosophers, heroes, and kings of England. What a gloom do monumental inscriptions and all the venerable remains of deceased merit inspire! Imagine a temple marked with the hand of antiquity, solemn as religious awe, adorned with all the magnificence of barbarous profusion, dim windows, fretted pillars, long colonnades, and dark ceilings. Think then, what were my sensations at being introduced to such a scene. I stood in the midst of the temple, and threw my eyes round on the walls filled with the statues, the inscriptions, and the monuments of the dead.

Alas, I said to myself, how does pride attend the puny child of dust even to the grave! Even humble as I am, I possess more consequence in the present scene than the greatest hero of them all; they have toiled for an hour to gain a transient immortality, and are at length retired to the grave, where they have no attendant but the worm, none to flatter but the epitaph.

As I was indulging such reflections, a gentleman dressed in black, perceiving me to be a stranger, came up, entered into conversation, and politely offered to be my instructor and guide through the temple. If any monument, said he, should particularly excite your curiosity, I shall endeavour to satisfy your demands. I accepted with thanks the gentleman's offer, adding, that 'I was come to observe the policy, the wisdom, and the justice of the English, in conferring rewards upon deceased merit. If adulation like this, continued I, be properly conducted, as it can no ways injure those who are flattered, so it may be a glorious incentive to those who are now capable of enjoying it. It is the duty of every good government to turn this monumental pride to its own advantage, to become strong in the aggregate from the weakness of the individual. If none but the truly great have a place in this awful repository, a temple like this will give the finest lessons of morality, and be a strong incentive to true ambition. I am told, that none have a place here but characters of the most distinguished merit.' The man in black seemed impatient at my observations, so I discontinued my remarks, and we walked on together to take a view of every particular monument in order as it lay.

As the eye is naturally caught by the finest objects, I could not avoid being particularly curious about one monument which appeared more beautiful than the rest; that, said I to my guide, I take to be the tomb of some very great man. By the peculiar excellence of the workmanship, and the magnificence of the design, this must be a trophy raised to the memory of some king who has saved his country from ruin, or law-giver, who has reduced his fellow-citizens from anarchy into just subjection. ——It is not requisite, replied my companion smiling, to have such qualifications in order to have a very fine monument here. More humble abilities will suffice. *What! I suppose then, the gaining two or three battles, or the taking half a score towns, is thought a sufficient qualification?* Gaining battles, or taking towns, replied the man in black, may be of service; but a gentleman may have a very fine monument here without ever seeing a battle or a siege. *This then is the monument of some poet, I presume, of one whose wit has gained him immortality?* No, sir, replied my guide, the gentleman who lies here never made verses; and as for wit, he despised it in others, because he had none himself. *Pray tell me then in a word*, said I peevishly, *what is the great man who lies here particularly remarkable for?* Remarkable, Sir! said my companion; why, Sir, the gentleman that lies here is remarkable, very remarkable——for a tomb in Westminster-abbey. *But, head of my Ancestors! how has he got here? I fancy he could never bribe the guardians of the temple to give him a place: Should he not be ashamed to be seen among company, where even moderate merit would look like infamy?* I suppose, replied the man in black, the gentleman was rich, and his friends, as is usual in such a case, told him he was great.

He readily believed them; the guardians of the temple, as they got by the self-delusion, were ready to believe him too; so he paid his money for a fine monument; and the workman, as you see, has made him one the most beautiful. Think not, however, that this gentleman is singular in his desire of being buried among the great, there are several others in the temple, who, hated and shunned by the great while alive, have come here, fully resolved to keep them company now they are dead.

As we walked along to a particular part of the temple, There, says the gentleman, pointing with his finger, that is the poets' corner; there you see the monuments of Shakespear, and Milton, and Prior, and Drayton. Drayton, I replied, I never heard of him before, but I have been told of one Pope, is he there? It is time enough, replied my guide, these hundred years, he is not long dead, people have not done hating him yet. Strange, cried I, can any be found to hate a man, whose life was wholly spent in entertaining and instructing his fellow creatures! Yes, says my guide, they hate him for that very reason. There are a set of men called answerers of books, who take upon them to watch the republic of letters, and distribute reputation by the sheet; they somewhat resemble the eunuchs in a seraglio, who are incapable of giving pleasure themselves, and hinder those that would. These answerers have no other employment but to cry out Dunce, and Scribbler, to praise the dead, and revile the living, to grant a man of confessed abilities some small share of merit, to applaud twenty blockheads in order to gain the reputation of candour, and to revile the moral character of the man whose writings they cannot injure. Such wretches are kept in pay by some mercenary bookseller, or more frequently, the bookseller himself takes this dirty work off their hands, as all that is required is to be very abusive and very dull; every Poet of any genius is sure to find such enemies, he feels, though he seems to despise their malice, they make him miserable here, and in the pursuit of empty fame, at last he gains solid anxiety.

Has this been the case with every poet I see here? cried I—Yes, with every mother's son of them, replied he, except he happened to be born a mandarine. If he has much money, he may buy reputation from your book answerers, as well as a monument from the guardians of the temple.

But are there not some men of distinguished taste, as in China, who are willing to patronise men of merit and soften the rancour of malevolent dulness?

I own there are many, replied the man in black, but, alas!

Sir, the book answerers crowd about them, and call themselves the writers of books; and the patron is too indolent to distinguish; thus poets are kept at a distance, while their enemies eat up all their rewards at the mandarine's table.

Leaving this part of the temple, we made up to an iron gate, through which my companion told me we were to pass in order to see the monuments of the kings. Accordingly I marched up without further ceremony, and was going to enter, when a person who held the gate in his hand, told me I must pay first. I was surprised at such a demand; and asked the man whether the people of England kept a *show*? Whether the paltry sum he demanded was not a national reproach? Whether it was not more to the honour of the country to let their magnificence or their antiquities be openly seen, than thus meanly to tax a curiosity which tended to their own honour? As for your questions, replied the gate-keeper, to be sure they may be very right, because I don't understand them, but as for that there three-pence, I farm it from one, who rents it from another, who hires it from a third, who leases it from the guardians of the temple, and we all must live. I expected upon paying here to see something extraordinary, since what I had seen for nothing filled me with so much surprise; but in this I was disappointed; there was little more within than black coffins, rusty armour, tattered standards, and some few slovenly figures in wax. I was sorry I had paid, but I comforted myself by considering it would be my last payment. A person attended us, who, without once blushing, told a hundred lies; he talked of a lady who died by pricking her finger, of a king with a golden head, and twenty such pieces of absurdity; Look ye there, gentlemen, says he, pointing to an old oak chair, there's a curiosity for ye; in that chair the kings of England were crowned, you see also a stone underneath, and that stone is Jacob's pillow. I could see no curiosity either in the oak chair or the stone; could I, indeed, behold one of the old kings of England seated in this, or Jacob's head laid upon the other, there might be something curious in the sight; but in the present case, there was no more reason for my surprise than if I should pick a stone from their streets, and call it a curiosity, merely because one of the kings happened to tread upon it as he passed in a procession.

From hence our conductor led us through several dark walks and winding ways, uttering lies, talking to himself, and flourishing a wand which he held in his hand. He reminded me of the black magicians of Kobi. After we had been almost fatigued with a variety of objects, he, at last, desired me to consider attentively a certain suit of armour, which seemed to shew nothing remarkable. This armour, said he, belonged to general Monk. *Very surprising, that a general should wear armour.* And pray, added he, observe this cap, this is general Monk's cap. *Very strange indeed, very strange, that a general should have a cap also! Pray friend, what might this cap have cost originally?* That, Sir, says he, I don't know, but this cap is all the wages I have for my trouble. *A very small recompence, truly,* said I. Not so very small, replied he, for every gentleman puts some money into it, and I spend the money. *What, more money! still more money!* Every gentleman gives something, Sir. I'll give thee nothing, returned I; the guardians of the temple should pay you your wages, friend, and not permit you to squeeze thus from every spectator. When we pay our money at the door to see a show, we never give more as we are going out. Sure the guardians of the temple can never think they get enough. Shew me the gate; if I stay longer, I may probably meet with more of those ecclesiastical beggars.

Thus leaving the temple precipitately, I returned to my lodgings, in order to ruminate over what was great, and to despise what was mean in the occurrences of the day.

LETTER XIV.—*From the same.*

I WAS some days ago agreeably surprised by a message from a lady of distinction, who sent me word, that she most passionately desired the pleasure of my acquaintance; and, with the utmost impatience, expected an interview. I will not deny, my dear Fum Hoam, but that my vanity was raised at such an invitation. I flattered myself that she had seen me in some public place, and had conceived an affection for my person, which thus induced her to deviate from the usual decorums of the sex. My imagination painted her in all the bloom of youth and beauty. I fancied her attended by the Loves and Graces, and I set out with the most pleasing expectations of seeing the conquest I had made.

When I was introduced into her apartment, my expectations were quickly at an end; I perceived a little shrivelled figure indolently reclined on a sofa, who nodded by way of approbation at my approach. This, as I was afterwards informed, was the lady herself, a woman equally distinguished for rank, politeness,

taste, and understanding. As I was dressed after the fashion
of Europe, she had taken me for an Englishman, and consequently saluted me in her ordinary manner; but when the
footman informed her grace that I was the gentleman from
China, she instantly lifted herself from the couch, while her eyes
sparkled with unusual vivacity. 'Bless me! can this be the
gentleman that was born so far from home? What an unusual
share of *somethingness* in his whole appearance. Lord, how I
am charmed with the outlandish cut of his face; how bewitching
the exotic breadth of his forehead. I would give the world to
see him in his own country dress. Pray turn about, Sir, and
let me see you behind. There! there's a travell'd air for you.
You that attend there, bring up a plate of beef cut into small
pieces; I have a violent passion to see him eat. Pray, Sir, have
you got your chop sticks about you? It will be so pretty to see
the meat carried to the mouth with a jerk. Pray speak a little
Chinese: I have learned some of the language myself. Lord,
have you nothing pretty from China about you; something that
one does not know what to do with? I have got twenty things
from China that are of no use in the world. Look at those
jars, they are of the right pea-green: these are the furniture.'
Dear madam, said I, *these, though they may appear fine in your
eyes, are but paltry to a Chinese; but, as they are useful utensils, it
is proper they should have a place in every apartment.* Useful!
Sir, replied the lady; sure you mistake, they are of no use in the
world. *What! are they not filled with an infusion of tea as in
China?* replied I. Quite empty and useless upon my honour,
Sir. *Then they are most cumbrous and clumsy furniture in the
world, as nothing is truly elegant but what unites use with beauty.*
I protest, says the lady, I shall begin to suspect thee of being an
actual barbarian. I suppose you hold my two beautiful pagods
in contempt. *What!* cried I, *has Fohi spread his gross supersti-
tions here also? Pagods of all kinds are my aversion.* A Chinese,
a traveller, and want taste! it surprises me. Pray, Sir, examine
the beauties of that Chinese temple which you see at the end of
the garden. Is there anything in China more beautiful? *Where
I stand I see nothing, madam, at the end of the garden that may not
as well be called an Egyptian pyramid as a Chinese temple; for that
little building in view is as like the one as t'other.* What! Sir, is
not that a Chinese temple? you must surely be mistaken. Mr
Freeze, who designed it, called it one, and nobody disputes his
pretensions to taste. I now found it vain to contradict the lady
in any thing she thought fit to advance; so was resolved rather

to act the disciple than the instructor. She took me through several rooms all furnished, as she told me, in the Chinese manner; sprawling dragons, squatting pagods, and clumsy mandarines, were stuck upon every shelf: In turning round one must have used caution not to demolish a part of the precarious furniture.

In a house like this, thought I, one must live continually upon the watch; the inhabitant must resemble a knight in an enchanted castle, who expects to meet an adventure at every turning. *But, madam,* said I, *do not accidents ever happen to all this finery?* Man, Sir, replied the lady, is born to misfortunes, and it is but fit I should have a share. Three weeks ago, a careless servant snapped off the head of a favourite mandarine: I had scarce done grieving for that, when a monkey broke a beautiful jar; this I took the more to heart, as the injury was done me by a friend: however, I survived the calamity; when yesterday crash went half a dozen dragons upon the marble hearth stone; and yet I live; I survive it all: you can't conceive what comfort I find under afflictions from philosophy. There is Seneca, and Bolingbroke, and some others, who guide me through life, and teach me to support its calamities.—I could not but smile at a woman who makes her own misfortunes, and then deplores the miseries of her situation. Wherefore, tired of acting with dissimulation, and willing to indulge my meditations in solitude, I took leave just as the servant was bringing in a plate of beef, pursuant to the directions of his mistress. Adieu.

LETTER XV.—*From the same.*

THE better sort here pretend to the utmost compassion for animals of every kind; to hear them speak, a stranger would be apt to imagine they could hardly hurt the gnat that stung them; they seem so tender, and so full of pity, that one would take them for the harmless friends of the whole creation; the protectors of the meanest insect or reptile that was privileged with existence. And yet would you believe it, I have seen the very men who have thus boasted of their tenderness at the same time devouring the flesh of six different animals tossed up in a fricassee. Strange contrariety of conduct; they pity and they eat the objects of their compassion. The lion roars with terror over its captive; the tiger sends forth its hideous shriek to intimidate its prey; no creature shows any fondness for its short-lived prisoner, except a man and a cat.

Man was born to live with innocence and simplicity, but he has deviated from nature; he was born to share the bounties of heaven, but he has monopolised them; he was born to govern the brute creation, but he is become their tyrant. If an epicure now shall happen to surfeit on his last night's feast, twenty animals the next day are to undergo the most exquisite tortures in order to provoke his appetite to another guilty meal. Hail, O ye simple, honest bramins of the east, ye inoffensive friends of all that was born to happiness as well as you: you never sought a short-lived pleasure from the miseries of other creatures. You never studied the tormenting arts of ingenious refinement; you never surfeited upon a guilty meal. How much more purified and refined are all your sensations than ours: you distinguish every element with the utmost precision; a stream untasted before is new luxury, a change of air is a new banquet, too refined for western imaginations to conceive.

Though the Europeans do not hold the transmigration of souls, yet one of their doctors has, with great force of argument, and great plausibility of reasoning, endeavoured to prove that the bodies of animals are the habitations of dæmons and wicked spirits, which are obliged to reside in these prisons till the resurrection pronounces their everlasting punishment; but are previously condemned to suffer all the pains and hardships inflicted upon them by man, or by each other here. If this be the case, it may frequently happen, that while we whip pigs to death, or boil live lobsters, we are putting some old acquaintance, some near relation, to excruciating tortures, and are serving him up to the very same table where he was once the most welcome companion.

'Kabul,' says the Zendavesta, 'was born on the rushy banks of the river Mawra; his possessions were great, and his luxuries kept pace with the affluence of his fortune; he hated the harmless bramins, and despised their holy religion; every day his table was decked out wth the flesh of an hundred different animals, and his cooks had an hundred different ways of dressing it, to solicit even satiety.

'Notwithstanding all his eating, he did not arrive at old age, he died of a surfeit, caused by intemperance: upon this, his soul was carried off, in order to take its trial before a select assembly of the souls of those animals which his gluttony had caused to be slain, and who were now appointed his judges.

'He trembled before a tribunal, to every member of which, he had formerly acted as an unmerciful tyrant: he sought for

pity, but found none disposed to grant it. Does he not remember, cries the angry boar, to what agonies I was put, not
to satisfy his hunger, but his vanity? I was first hunted to
death, and my flesh scarce thought worthy of coming once to
his table. Were my advice followed, he should do penance in
the shape of an hog, which in life he most resembled.

'I am rather, cries a sheep upon the bench, for having him
suffer under the appearance of a lamb, we may then send him
through four or five transmigrations in the space of a month.
Were my voice of any weight in the assembly, cries a calf, he
should rather assume such a form as mine: I was bled every day,
in order to make my flesh white, and at last killed without mercy.
Would it not be wiser, cries a hen, to cram him in the shape of
a fowl, and then smother him in his own blood as I was served?
The majority of the assembly were pleased with this punishment, and were going to condemn him without further delay,
when the ox rose up to give his opinion: I am informed, says this
councillor, that the prisoner at the bar has left a wife with child
behind him. By my knowledge in divination I foresee that this
child will be a son, decrepit, feeble, sickly, a plague to himself
and all about him. What say you then, my companions, if
we condemn the father to animate the body of his own son;
and by this means make him feel in himself those miseries his
intemperance must otherwise have entailed upon his posterity.
The whole court applauded the ingenuity of his torture, they
thanked him for his advice. Kabul was driven once more to
revisit the earth; and his soul in the body of his own son, passed
a period of thirty years, loaded with misery, anxiety, and
disease.'

LETTER XVI.—*From the same.*

I KNOW not whether I am more obliged to the Chinese missionaries for the instruction I have received from them, or
prejudiced by the falsehoods they have made me believe. By
them I was told that the Pope was universally allowed to be
a man, and placed at the head of the church; in England, however, they plainly prove him to be an whore in man's clothes,
and often burn him in effigy as an impostor. A thousand books
have been written on either side of the question; priests are
eternally disputing against each other; and those mouths that
want argument are filled with abuse. Which party must I
believe, or shall I give credit to neither? When I survey the

absurdities and falsehoods with which the books of the Europeans are filled, I thank heaven for having been born in China, and that I have sagacity enough to detect imposture.

The Europeans reproach us with false history and fabulous chronology; how should they blush to see their own books, many of which are written by the doctors of their religion, filled with the most monstrous fables, and attested with the utmost solemnity. The bounds of a letter do not permit me to mention all the absurdities of this kind, which in my reading I have met with. I shall confine myself to the accounts which some of their lettered men give of the persons of some of the inhabitants on our globe. And not satisfied with the most solemn asseverations, they sometimes pretend to have been eye-witnesses of what they describe.

A Christian doctor in one of his principal performances [1] says, that it was not impossible for a whole nation to have but one eye in the middle of the forehead. He is not satisfied with leaving it in doubt; but in another work [2] assures us, that the fact was certain, and that he himself was an eye-witness of it. *When*, says he, *I took a journey into Ethiopia in company with several other servants of Christ, in order to preach the gospel there; I beheld in the southern provinces of that country a nation which had only one eye in the midst of their foreheads.*

You will, no doubt, be surprised, reverend Fum, with this author's effrontery; but alas he is not alone in this story; he has only borrowed it from several others who wrote before him. Solinus creates another nation of Cyclops,—the Arimaspians who inhabit those countries that border on the Caspian sea. This author goes on to tell us of a people of India, who have but one leg and one eye, and yet are extremely active, run with great swiftness, and live by hunting. These people we scarce know how to pity or admire; but the men whom Pliny calls Cynamolci, who have got the heads of dogs, really deserve our compassion. Instead of languages they express their sentiments by barking. Solinus confirms what Pliny mentions; and Simon Mayole, a French bishop, talks of them as of particular and familiar acquaintances. *After passing the deserts of Egypt*, says he, *we meet with the Kunokephaloi, who inhabit those regions that border on Ethiopia; they live by hunting; they cannot speak, but whistle; their chins resemble a serpent's head; their hands are armed with long sharp claws; their breast resembles that of a greyhound; and*

<hr>

[1] Augustin, de Civit. Dei, lib. xvi, p. 422.
[2] Id. ad fratres in Eremo, Serm. xxxvii.

they excel in swiftness and agility. Would you think it, my friend, that these odd kind of people are, notwithstanding their figure, excessively delicate; not even an alderman's wife, or Chinese mandarine, can excel them in this particular. *These People*, continues our faithful bishop, *never refuse wine; love roast and boiled meat; they are particularly curious in having their meat well dressed, and spurn at it if in the least tainted. When the Ptolemies reigned in Egypt* (says he a little further on) *those men with dogs' heads taught Grammar and Music.* For men who had no voices to teach music, and who could not speak to teach grammar, is, I confess a little extraordinary. Did ever the disciples of Fohi broach any thing more ridiculous?

Hitherto we have seen men with heads strangely deformed, and with dogs' heads; but what would you say if you heard of men without any heads at all? Pomponius Mela, Solinus, and Aulus Gellius, describe them to our hand: 'The Blemiæ have a nose, eyes, and mouth on their breasts; or, as others will have it, placed on their shoulders.'

One would think that these authors had an antipathy to the human form, and were resolved to make a new figure of their own: but let us do them justice; though they sometimes deprive us of a leg, an arm, an head, or some such trifling part of the body, they often as liberally bestow upon us something that we wanted before. Simon Mayole seems our particular friend in this respect: if he has denied heads to one part of mankind, he has given tails to another. He describes many of the English of his time, which is not more than an hundred years ago, as having tails. His own words are as follow: *In England there are some families which have tails, as a punishment for deriding an Augustin Friar sent by St. Gregory, and who preached in Dorsetshire. They sewed the tails of different animals to his clothes; but soon they found those tails entailed on them and their posterity for ever.* It is certain that the author had some ground for this description; many of the English wear tails to their wigs to this very day, as a mark, I suppose, of the antiquity of their families, and perhaps as a symbol of those tails with which they were formerly distinguished by Nature.

You see, my friend, there is nothing so ridiculous that has not at some time been said by some philosopher. The writers of books in Europe seem to think themselves authorised to say what they please; and an ingenious philosopher among them [1] has openly asserted, that he would undertake to persuade the

[1] Fontenelle.

whole republic of readers to believe that the sun was neither the cause of light nor heat; if he could only get six philosophers on his side. Farewell.

LETTER XVII.—*From the same.*

WERE an Asiatic politician to read the treaties of peace and friendship that have been annually making for more than an hundred years among the inhabitants of Europe, he would probably be surprised how it should ever happen that Christian princes could quarrel among each other. Their compacts for peace are drawn up with the utmost precision, and ratified with the greatest solemnity; to these each party promises a sincere and inviolable obedience, and all wears the appearance of open friendship and unreserved reconciliation.

Yet, notwithstanding those treaties, the people of Europe are almost continually at war. There is nothing more easy than to break a treaty ratified in all the usual forms, and yet neither party be the aggressor. One side, for instance, breaks a trifling article by mistake; the opposite party upon this makes a small but premeditated reprisal; this brings on a return of greater from the other; both sides complain of injuries and infractions; war is declared; they beat, are beaten; some two or three hundred thousand men are killed, they grow tired, leave off just where they began; and so sit coolly down to make new treaties.

The English and French seem to place themselves foremost among the champion states of Europe. Though parted by a narrow sea, yet are they entirely of opposite characters; and from their vicinity are taught to fear and admire each other. They are at present engaged in a very destructive war, have already spilled much blood, are excessively irritated; and all upon account of one side's desiring to wear greater quantities of *furs* than the other.

The pretext of the war is about some lands a thousand leagues off; a country cold, desolate, and hideous; a country belonging to a people who were in possession for time immemorial. The savages of Canada claim a property in the country in dispute; they have all the pretensions which long possession can confer. Here they had reigned for ages without rivals in dominion; and knew no enemies but the prowling bear or insidious tyger; their native forests produced all the necessaries of life, and they found ample luxury in the enjoyment. In this manner they might have continued to live to eternity, had not the English been informed that those countries produced furs in great abundance. From that moment the country became an object of desire; it was found that furs were things very much wanted in England; the ladies edged some of their clothes with furs, and muffs were worn both by gentlemen and ladies. In short, furs were found indispensably necessary for the happiness of the state: and the king was consequently petitioned to grant not only the country of Canada, but all the savages belonging to it, to the subjects of England, in order to have the people supplied with proper quantities of this necessary commodity.

So very reasonable a request was immediately complied with, and large colonies were sent abroad to procure furs, and take possession. The French, who were equally in want of furs (for they were as fond of muffs and tippets as the English), made the very same request to their monarch, and met with the same gracious reception from their king, who generously granted what was not his to give. Wherever the French landed, they called the country their own; and the English took possession wherever they came upon the same equitable pretensions. The harmless savages made no opposition; and could the intruders have agreed together, they might peaceably have shared this desolate country between them. But they quarrelled about the boundaries of their settlements, about grounds and rivers to which neither side could shew any other right than that of power, and which neither could occupy but by usurpation. Such is the contest, that no honest man can heartily wish success to either party.

The war has continued for some time with various success. At first the French seemed victorious; but the English have of late dispossessed them of the whole country in dispute. Think not, however, that success on one side is the harbinger of peace: on the contrary, both parties must be heartily tired to effect even a temporary reconciliation. It should seem the business of the victorious party to offer terms of peace; but there are many in England, who, encouraged by success, are for still protracting the war.

The best English politicians, however, are sensible, that to keep their present conquests, would be rather a burthen than an advantage to them, rather a diminution of their strength than an encrease of power. It is in the politic as in the human constitution; if the limbs grow too large for the body, their size, instead of improving, will diminish the vigour of the whole. The colonies should always bear an exact proportion to the mother country; when they grow populous, they grow powerful, and by becoming powerful, they become independent also; thus subordination is destroyed, and a country swallowed up in the extent of its own dominions. The Turkish empire would be more formidable, were it less extensive—were it not for those countries, which it can neither command, nor give entirely away, which it is obliged to protect, but from which it has no power to exact obedience.

Yet, obvious as these truths are, there are many Englishmen who are for transplanting new colonies into this late acquisition, for peopling the deserts of America with the refuse of their countrymen, and (as they express it) with the waste of an exuberant nation. But who are those unhappy creatures who are to be thus drained away? Not the sickly, for they are unwelcome guests abroad as well as at home; nor the idle, for they would starve as well behind the Apalachian mountains as in the streets of London. This refuse is composed of the laborious and enterprising, of such men as can be serviceable to their country at home, of men who ought to be regarded as the sinews of the people, and cherished with every degree of political indulgence. And what are the commodities which this colony, when established, is to produce in return? Why raw silk, hemp, and tobacco. England, therefore, must make an exchange of her best and bravest subjects for raw silk, hemp, and tobacco; her hardy veterans and honest tradesmen, must be trucked for a box of snuff or a silk petticoat. Strange absurdity! Sure the politics of the Daures are not more strange, who sell their religion, their wives, and their liberty for a glass bead, or a paltry penknife. Farewell.

LETTER XVIII.—*From the same.*

THE English love their wives with much passion, the Hollanders with much prudence. The English when they give their hands, frequently give their hearts; the Dutch give the hand, but keep the heart wisely in their own possession. The English love with violence, and expect violent love in return; the Dutch are satisfied with the slightest acknowledgments, for they give little away. The English expend many of the matrimonial comforts in the first year; the Dutch frugally husband out their pleasures, and are always constant because they are always indifferent.

C 9⁰²

There seems very little difference between a Dutch bridegroom and a Dutch husband. Both are equally possessed of the same cool unexpecting serenity; they can see neither Elysium nor Paradise behind the curtain; and *Yiffrow* is not more a goddess on the wedding night, than after twenty years' matrimonial acquaintance. On the other hand, many of the English marry, in order to have one happy month in their lives; they seem incapable of looking beyond that period; they unite in hopes of finding rapture, and disappointed in that, disdain ever to accept of happiness. From hence we see open hatred ensue; or what is worse, concealed disgust under the appearance of fulsome endearment. Much formality, great civility, and studied compliments are exhibited in public; cross looks, sulky silence, or open recrimination, fill up their hours of private entertainment.

Hence I am taught, whenever I see a new married couple more than ordinarily fond before faces, to consider them as attempting to impose upon the company or themselves, either hating each other heartily, or consuming that stock of love in the beginning of their course, which should serve them through their whole journey. Neither side should expect those instances of kindness which are inconsistent with true freedom or happiness to bestow. Love, when founded in the heart, will shew itself in a thousand unpremeditated sallies of fondness; but every cool deliberate exhibition of the passion, only argues little understanding, or great insincerity.

Choang was the fondest husband, and Hansi the most endearing wife in all the kingdom of Korea: they were a pattern of conjugal bliss; the inhabitants of the country around saw, and envied their felicity; wherever Choang came, Hansi was sure to follow; and in all the pleasures of Hansi, Choang was admitted a partner. They walked hand in hand wherever they appeared, shewing every mark of mutual satisfaction, embracing, kissing, their mouths were for ever joined, and to speak in the language of anatomy, it was with them one perpetual anastomosis.

Their love was so great, that it was thought nothing could interrupt their mutual peace; when an accident happened, which, in some measure, diminished the husband's assurance of his wife's fidelity; for love so refined as his was subject to a thousand little disquietudes.

Happening to go one day alone among the tombs that lay at some distance from his house, he there perceived a lady dressed in the deepest mourning, (being clothed all over in white) fanning the wet clay that was raised over one of the graves with a large fan, which she held in her hand. Choang, who had early been taught wisdom in the school of Lao, was unable to assign a cause for her present employment; and coming up, civilly demanded the reason. Alas, replied the lady, her eyes bathed in tears; how is it possible to survive the loss of my husband, who lies buried in this grave; he was the best of men, the tenderest of husbands; with his dying breath he bid me never marry again till the earth over his grave should be dry; and here you see me steadily resolving to obey his will, and endeavouring to dry it with my fan. I have employed two whole days in fulfilling his commands, and am determined not to marry till they are punctually obeyed, even though his grave should take up four days in drying.

Choang, who was struck with the widow's beauty, could not, however, avoid smiling at her haste to be married; but, concealing the cause of his mirth, civilly invited her home; adding, that he had a wife who might be capable of giving her some consolation. As soon as he and his guest were returned, he imparted to Hansi in private what he had seen, and could not avoid expressing his uneasiness, that such might be his own case if his dearest wife should one day happen to survive him.

It is impossible to describe Hansi's resentment at so unkind a suspicion. As her passion for him was not only great, but extremely delicate, she employed tears, anger, frowns, and exclamations, to chide his suspicions; the widow herself was inveighed against; and Hansi declared she was resolved never to sleep under the same roof with a wretch, who, like her, could be guilty of such barefaced inconstancy. The night was cold and stormy; however, the stranger was obliged to seek another lodging, for Choang was not disposed to resist, and Hansi would have her way.

The widow had scarce been gone an hour, when an old disciple of Choang's, whom he had not seen for many years, came to pay him a visit. He was received with the utmost ceremony, placed in the most honourable seat at supper, and the wine began to circulate with great freedom. Choang and Hansi exhibited open marks of mutual tenderness, and unfeigned reconciliation: nothing could equal their apparent happiness; so fond an husband, so obedient a wife, few could behold without regretting their own infelicity. When, lo! their happiness was at once disturbed by a most fatal accident. Choang fell lifeless in an apoplectic fit upon the floor. Every method was used, but in vain, for his recovery. Hansi was at first inconsolable for his death; after some hours, however, she found spirit to read his last will. The ensuing day she began to moralise and talk wisdom; the next day she was able to comfort the young disciple; and, on the third, to shorten a long story, they both agreed to be married.

There was now no longer mourning in the apartments; the body of Choang was now thrust into an old coffin, and placed in one of the meanest rooms, there to lie unattended until the time prescribed by law for his interment. In the mean time Hansi, and the young disciple, were arrayed in the most magnificent habits; the bride wore in her nose a jewel of immense price, and her lover was dressed in all the finery of his former master, together with a pair of artificial whiskers that reached down to his toes. The hour of their nuptials was arrived; the whole family sympathised with their approaching happiness; the apartments were brightened up with lights that diffused the most exquisite perfume, and a lustre more bright than noon-day. The lady expected her youthful lover in an inner apartment with impatience; when his servant approaching with terror in his countenance, informed her, that his master was fallen into a fit, which would certainly be mortal, unless the heart of a man lately dead could be obtained, and applied to his breast. She scarce waited to hear the end of his story, when, tucking up her clothes, she ran with a mattock in her hand to the coffin, where Choang lay, resolving to apply the heart of her dead husband as a cure for the living. She therefore struck the lid with the utmost violence. In a few blows the coffin flew open, when the body, which, to all appearance had been dead, began to move. Terrified at the sight, Hansi dropped the mattock, and Choang walked out, astonished at his own situation, his wife's unusual magnificence, and her more amazing surprise. He went among the apartments, unable to conceive the cause of so much splendour. He was not long in suspense before his domestics informed him of every transaction since he first became insensible. He could scarce believe what they told him, and went in pursuit of Hansi herself, in order to receive more certain information, or to reproach her infidelity. But she prevented his reproaches: he found her weltering in blood; for she had stabbed herself to the heart, being unable to survive her shame and disappointment.

Choang, being a philosopher, was too wise to make any loud lamentations; he thought it best to bear his loss with serenity; so, mending up the old coffin where he had lain himself, he placed his faithless spouse in his room; and, unwilling that so many nuptial preparations should be expended in vain, he the same night married the widow with the large fan.

As they both were apprised of the foibles of each other before hand, they knew how to excuse them after marriage. They lived together for many years in great tranquillity, and not expecting rapture, made a shift to find contentment. Farewell.

LETTER XIX.—*To the same*.

THE gentleman dressed in black, who was my companion through Westminster Abbey, came yesterday to pay me a visit; and after drinking tea, we both resolved to take a walk together, in order to enjoy the freshness of the country, which now begins to resume its verdure. Before we got out of the suburbs, however, we were stopped in one of the streets by a crowd of people, gathered in a circle round a man and his wife, who seemed too loud and too angry to be understood. The people were highly pleased with the dispute, which upon inquiry we found to be between Dr. Cacafogo, an apothecary, and his wife. The doctor, it seems, coming unexpectedly into his wife's apartment, found a gentleman there in circumstances not in the least equivocal.

The doctor, who was a person of nice honour, resolving to revenge the flagrant insult, immediately flew to the chimney-piece, and taking down a rusty blunderbuss, drew the trigger upon the defiler of his bed; the delinquent would certainly have been shot through the head, but that the piece had not been charged for many years. The gallant made a shift to escape through the window, but the lady still remained; and as she well knew her husband's temper, undertook to manage the quarrel without a second. He was furious, and she loud; their noise had gathered all the mob who charitably assembled on the occasion, not to prevent, but to enjoy the quarrel.

Alas, said I to my companion, what will become of this unhappy creature thus caught in adultery! Believe me, I pity her from my heart; her husband, I suppose will shew her no mercy. Will they burn her as in India, or behead her as in Persia; will they load her with stripes as in Turkey, or keep her in perpetual imprisonment, as with us in China? Prythee, what is the wife's punishment in England for such offences? When a lady is thus caught tripping, replied my companion, they never punish her, but the husband. You surely jest, interrupted I; I am a foreigner, and you would abuse my ignorance! I am really serious, returned he; Dr. Cacafogo has caught his wife in the act; but as he had no witnesses, his small testimony goes for nothing; the consequence therefore of his discovery will be, that she may be packed off to live among her relations, and the doctor must be obliged to allow her a separate maintenance. Amazing! cried I; is it not enough that she is permitted to live separate from the object she detests, but must he give her money to keep her in spirits too? That he must, says my guide; and be called a cuckold by all his neighbours into the bargain. The men will laugh at him, the ladies will pity him; and all that his warmest friends can say in his favour, will be, that the *poor good soul has never had any harm in him.* I want patience, interrupted I; what! are there no private chastisements for the wife; no schools of penitence to shew her her folly; no rods for such delinquents? Psha, man, replied he smiling; if every delinquent among us were to be treated in your manner, one half of the kingdom would flog the other.

I must confess, my dear Fum, that if I were an English husband, of all things I would take care not to be jealous, nor busily pry into those secrets my wife was pleased to keep from me. Should I detect her infidelity, what is the consequence? If I calmly pocket the abuse, I am laughed at by her and her gallant; if I talk my griefs aloud like a tragedy hero, I am laughed at by the whole world. The course then I would take would be, whenever I went out, to tell my wife where I was going, lest I should unexpectedly meet her abroad in company with some dear deceiver. Whenever I returned, I would use a peculiar rap at the door, and give four loud hems as I walked deliberately up the stair-case. I would never inquisitively peep under her bed, or look behind the curtains. And even though I knew the captain was there, I would calmly take a dish of my wife's cool tea, and talk of the army with reverence.

Of all nations, the Russians seem to me to behave most wisely in such circumstances. The wife promises her husband never to let him see her transgressions of this nature; and he as punctually promises, whenever she is so detected, without the least anger, to beat her without mercy: so they both know what each has to expect; the lady transgresses, is beaten, taken again into favour, and all goes on as before.

When a Russian young lady, therefore, is to be married, her father, with a cudgel in his hand, asks the bridegroom, whether he chooses this virgin for his bride? to which the other replies in the affirmative. Upon this, the father turning the lady three times round, and giving her three strokes with his cudgel on the back; *My dear*, cries he, *these are the last blows you are ever to receive from your tender father, I resign my authority, and my cudgel to your husband; he knows better than me the use of either.* The bridegroom knows decorums too well to accept of the cudgel abruptly; he assures the father that the lady will never want it, and that he would not for the world make any use of it. But the father, who knows what the lady may want better than he, insists upon his acceptance. Upon this, there follows a scene of Russian politeness, while one refuses, and the other offers the cudgel. The whole, however, ends with the bridegroom's taking it, upon which the lady drops a curtsy in token of obedience, and the ceremony proceeds as usual.

There is something excessively fair and open in this method of courtship. By this, both sides are prepared for all the matrimonial adventures that are to follow. Marriage has been compared to a game of skill for life; it is generous thus in both parties to declare they are sharpers in the beginning. In England, I am told both sides use every art to conceal their defects from each other before marriage, and the rest of their lives may be regarded as doing penance for their former dissimulation. Farewell.

LETTER XX.—*From the same.*

The republic of letters is a very common expression among the Europeans; and yet when applied to the learned of Europe, is the most absurd that can be imagined, since nothing is more unlike a republic than the society which goes by that name. From this expression one would be apt to imagine, that the learned were united into a single body, joining their interests, and concurring in the same design. From this one might be apt to compare them to our literary societies in China, where each acknowledges a just subordination; and all contribute to build the temple of science, without attempting from ignorance or envy to obstruct each other.

But very different is the state of learning here; every member of this fancied republic is desirous of governing, and none willing to obey; each looks upon his fellow as a rival, not an assistant in the same pursuit. They calumniate, they injure, they despise, they ridicule each other: if one man writes a book that pleases, others shall write books to show that he might have given still greater pleasure, or should not have pleased. If one happens to hit upon something new, there are numbers ready to assure the public that all this was no novelty to them or the learned; that Cardanus or Brunus, or some other author too dull to be generally read, had anticipated the discovery. Thus, instead of uniting like the members of a commonwealth, they are divided into almost as many factions as there are men; and their jarring constitution, instead of being styled a republic of letters, should be entitled, an anarchy of literature.

It is true, there are some of superior abilities who reverence and esteem each other; but their mutual admiration is not sufficient to shield off the contempt of the crowd. The wise are but few, and they praise with a feeble voice; the vulgar are many, and roar in reproaches. The truly great seldom unite in societies, have few meetings, no cabals; the dunces hunt in full cry till they have run down a reputation, and then snarl and fight with each other about dividing the spoil. Here you may see the compilers, and the book-answerers of every month, when they have cut up some respectable name, most frequently reproaching each other with stupidity and dulness: resembling the wolves of the Russian forest, who prey upon venison, or horse flesh when they can get it; but in cases of necessity, lying in wait to devour each other. While they have new books to cut up, they make a hearty meal; but if this resource should unhappily fail, then it is that critics eat up critics, and compilers rob from compilations.

Confucius observes that it is the duty of the learned to unite society more closely, and to persuade men to become citizens of the world; but the authors I refer to, are not only for dis-uniting society, but kingdoms also; if the English are at war with France, the dunces of France think it their duty to be at war with those of England. Thus Freron, one of their first rate scribblers, thinks proper to characterise all the English writers in the gross. 'Their whole merit,' says he, 'consists in exaggeration, and often in extravagance; correct their pieces as you please, there still remains a leaven which *corrupts* the whole. They sometimes discover genius, but not the smallest share of taste: England is not a soil for the plants of genius to thrive in.' This is open enough, with not the least adulation in the picture; but hear what a Frenchman of acknowledged abilities says upon the same subject. 'I am at a loss to determine in what we excel the English, or where they excel us; when I compare the merits of both in any one species of literary composition, so many reputable and pleasing writers present themselves from either country, that my judgment rests in suspense: I am pleased with the disquisition, without finding the object of my inquiry.' But lest you should think the French alone are faulty in this respect, hear how an English journalist delivers his sentiments of them. 'We are amazed, says he, to find so many works translated from the French, while we have such numbers neglected of our own. In our opinion, notwithstanding their fame throughout the rest of Europe, the French are the most contemptible reasoners (we had almost said writers) that can be imagined. However, nevertheless, excepting, etc.' Another English writer, Shaftesbury, if I remember, on the contrary, says, that the French authors are pleasing and judicious, more clear, more methodical, and entertaining than those of his own country.

From these opposite pictures, you perceive that the good authors of either country praise, and the bad revile each other; and yet, perhaps, you will be surprised that indifferent writers should thus be the most apt to censure, as they have the most to apprehend from recrimination; you may, perhaps, imagine that such as are possessed of fame themselves should be most ready to declare their opinions, since what they say, might pass for decision. But the truth happens to be, that the great are solicitous only of raising their own reputations, while the opposite class, alas! are solicitous of bringing every reputation down to a level with their own.

But let us acquit them of malice and envy; a critic is often guided by the same motives that direct his author. The author endeavours to persuade us, that he has written a good book: the critic is equally solicitous to show that he could write a better, had he thought proper. A critic is a being possessed of all the vanity, but not the genius, of a scholar, incapable, from his native weakness, of lifting himself from the ground, he applies to contiguous merit for support, makes the sportive sallies of another's imagination his serious employment, pretends to take our feelings under his care, teaches where to condemn, where to lay the emphasis of praise, and may with as much justice be called a man of taste, as the Chinese who measures his wisdom by the length of his nails.

If then a book, spirited or humorous, happens to appear in the republic of letters, several critics are in waiting to bid the public not to laugh at a single line of it, for themselves had read it; and they know what is most proper to excite laughter. Other critics contradict the fulminations of this tribunal, call them all spiders, and assure the public, that they ought to laugh without restraint. Another set are in the mean time quietly employed in writing notes to the book, intended to show the particular passages to be laughed at; when these are out, others still there are who write notes upon notes. Thus a single new book employs not only the paper-makers, the printers, the press-men, the bookbinders, the hawkers, but twenty critics, and as many compilers. In short, the body of the learned may be compared to a Persian army, where there are many pioneers, several sutlers, numberless servants, women and children in abundance, and but few soldiers.   Adieu.

LETTER XXI.—*To the same.*

THE English are as fond of seeing plays acted as the Chinese; but there is a vast difference in the manner of conducting them. We play our pieces in the open air, the English theirs under cover; we act by day-light, they by the blaze of torches. One of our plays continues eight or ten days successively; an English piece seldom takes up above four hours in the representation.

My companion in black, with whom I am now beginning to contract an intimacy, introduced me a few nights ago to the play-house, where we placed ourselves conveniently at the foot of the stage. As the curtain was not drawn before my arrival, I had an opportunity of observing the behaviour of the spectators, and indulging those reflections which novelty generally inspires.

The rich in general were placed in the lowest seats, and the poor rose above them in degrees proportioned to their poverty. The order of precedence seemed here inverted; those who were undermost all the day, now enjoyed a temporary eminence, and became masters of the ceremonies. It was they who called for the music, indulging every noisy freedom, and testifying all the insolence of beggary in exaltation.

They who held the middle region seemed not so riotous as those above them, nor yet so tame as those below; to judge by their looks, many of them seemed strangers there as well as myself. They were chiefly employed during this period of expectation in eating oranges, reading the story of the play, or making assignations.

Those who sat in the lowest rows, which are called the pit, seemed to consider themselves as judges of the merit of the poet and the performers; they were assembled partly to be amused, and partly to show their taste; appearing to labour under that restraint which an affection of superior discernment generally produces. My companion, however, informed me, that not one in an hundred of them knew even the first principles of criticism; that they assumed the right of being censors because there was none to contradict their pretensions; and that every man who now called himself a connoisseur, became such to all intents and purposes.

Those who sat in the boxes appeared in the most unhappy situation of all. The rest of the audience came merely for their own amusement; these rather to furnish out a part of the entertainment themselves. I could not avoid considering them as acting parts in dumb show, not a curtsy or nod, that was not the result of art; not a look nor a smile that was not designed for murder. Gentlemen and ladies ogled each other through spectacles; for my companion observed, that blindness was of late become fashionable; all affected indifference and ease, while their hearts at the same time burned for conquest. Upon the whole, the lights, the music, the ladies in their gayest dresses, the men with cheerfulness and expectation in their looks, all conspired to make a most agreeable picture, and to fill an heart that sympathises at human happiness with an inexpressible serenity.

The expected time for the play to begin at last arrived, the curtain was drawn, and the actors came on. A woman, who personated a queen, came in curtsying to the audience, who clapped their hands upon her appearance. Clapping of hands is, it seems, the manner of applauding in England: the manner is absurd; but every country, you know, has its peculiar absurdities. I was equally surprised, however, at the submission of the actress, who should have considered herself as a queen, as at the little discernment of the audience who gave her such marks of applause before she attempted to deserve them. Preliminaries between her and the audience being thus adjusted, the dialogue was supported between her and a most hopeful youth, who acted the part of her confidant. They both appeared in extreme distress, for it seems the queen had lost a child some fifteen years before, and still keeps its dear resemblance next her heart, while her kind companion bore a part in her sorrows.

Her lamentations grew loud. Comfort is offered, but she

detests the very sound. She bids them preach comfort to the winds. Upon this her husband comes in, who seeing the queen so much afflicted, can himself hardly refrain from tears or avoid partaking in the soft distress. After thus grieving through three scenes, the curtain dropped for the first act.

Truly, said I to my companion, these kings and queens are very much disturbed at no very great misfortune; certain I am were people of humbler stations to act in this manner, they would be thought divested of common sense. I had scarce finished this observation, when the curtain rose, and the king came on in a violent passion. His wife had, it seems, refused his proffered tenderness, had spurned his royal embrace; and he seemed resolved not to survive her fierce disdain. After he had thus fretted, and the queen had fretted through the second act, the curtain was let down once more.

Now, says my companion, you perceive the king to be a man of spirit, he feels at every pore; one of your phlegmatic sons of clay would have given the queen her own way, and let her come to herself by degrees; but the king is for immediate tenderness, or instant death: death and tenderness are leading passions of every modern buskined hero; this moment they embrace, and the next stab, mixing daggers and kisses in every period.

I was going to second his remarks, when my attention was engrossed by a new object; a man came in balancing a straw upon his nose, and the audience were clapping their hands in all the raptures of applause. To what purpose, cried I, does this unmeaning figure make his appearance; is he a part of the plot? Unmeaning do you call him, replied my friend in black; this is one of the most important characters of the whole play; nothing pleases the people more than the seeing a straw balanced; there is a great deal of meaning in the straw; there is something suited to every apprehension in the sight; and a fellow possessed of talents like these is sure of making his fortune.

The third act now began with an actor, who came to inform us that he was the villain of the play, and intended to shew strange things before all was over. He was joined by another, who seemed as much disposed for mischief as he; their intrigues continued through this whole division. If that be a villain, said I, he must be a very stupid one, to tell his secrets without being asked; such soliloquies of late are never admitted in China.

The noise of clapping interrupted me once more; a child of six years old was learning to dance on the stage, which gave the ladies and mandarines infinite satisfaction. I am sorry, said I, to see the pretty creature so early learning so very bad a trade; dancing being, I presume, as contemptible here as in China. Quite the reverse, interrupted my companion; dancing is a very reputable and genteel employment here; men have a greater chance for encouragement from the merit of their heels than their heads. One who jumps up and flourishes his toes three times before he comes to the ground, may have three hundred a year; he who flourishes them four times, gets four hundred; but he who arrives at five is inestimable, and may demand what salary he thinks proper. The female dancers too are valued for this sort of jumping and crossing; and 'tis a cant word among them, that she deserves most who shews highest. But the fourth act is begun, let us be attentive.

In the fourth act the queen finds her long lost child, now grown up into a youth of smart parts, and great qualifications; wherefore she wisely considers that the crown will fit his head better than that of her husband, whom she knows to be a driveller. The king discovers her design, and here comes on the deep distress; he loves the queen, and he loves the kingdom; he resolves therefore, in order to possess both, that her son must die. The queen exclaims at his barbarity; is frantic with rage, and at length overcome with sorrow, falls into a fit; upon which the curtain drops, and the act is concluded.

Observe the art of the poet, cries my companion; when the queen can say no more, she falls into a fit. While thus her eyes are shut, while she is supported in the arms of Abigail, what horrors do we not fancy. We feel it in every nerve; take my word for it, that fits are the true aposiopesis of modern tragedy.

The fifth act began, and a busy piece it was. Scenes shifting, trumpets sounding, mobs hallooing, carpets spreading, guards bustling from one door to another; gods, dæmons, daggers, racks and ratsbane. But whether the king was killed, or the queen was drowned, or the son was poisoned, I have absolutely forgotten.

When the play was over, I could not avoid observing, that the persons of the drama appeared in as much distress in the first act as the last: How is it possible, said I, to sympathise with them through five long acts! Pity is but a short-lived passion; I hate to hear an actor mouthing trifles, neither startings, strainings, nor attitudes affect me unless there be cause: after I have been once or twice deceived by those unmeaning alarms, my heart sleeps in peace, probably unaffected by the principal distress. There should be one great passion aimed at by the actor as well as the poet, all the rest should be subordinate, and only contribute to make that the greater; if the actor therefore exclaims upon every occasion in the tones of despair, he attempts to move us too soon; he anticipates the blow, he ceases to affect though he gains our applause.

I scarce perceived that the audience were almost all departed; wherefore mixing with the crowd, my companion and I got into the street; where essaying an hundred obstacles from coach wheels and palanquin poles, like birds in their flight through the branches of a forest, after various turnings, we both at length got home in safety. Adieu.

LETTER XXII.—*From the same.*

THE letter which came by the way of Smyrna, and which you sent me unopened, was from my son. As I have permitted you to take copies of all those I send to China, you might have made no ceremony in opening those directed to me. Either in joy or sorrow, my friend should participate in my feelings. *It would give pleasure to see a good man pleased at my success; it would give almost equal pleasure to see him sympathise at my disappointment.*

Every account I receive from the East seems to come loaded with some new affliction. My wife and daughter were taken from me, and yet I sustained the loss with intrepidity; my son is made a slave among the barbarians, which was the only blow that could have reached my heart: yes, I will indulge the transports of Nature for a little, in order to shew I can overcome them in the end. *True magnanimity consists not in* NEVER *falling, but in* RISING *every time we fall.*

When our mighty emperor had published his displeasure at my departure, and seized upon all that was mine, my son was privately secreted from his resentment. Under the protection and guardianship of Fum Hoam, the best and the wisest of all the inhabitants of China; he was for some time instructed in the learning of the missionaries, and the wisdom of the East. But hearing of my adventures, and incited by filial piety, he was resolved to follow my fortunes, and share my distress.

He passed the confines of China in disguise; hired himself as a camel-driver to a caravan that was crossing the desarts of

Thibet, and was within one day's journey of the river Laur, which divides that country from India, when a body of wandering Tartars falling unexpectedly upon the caravan, plundered it, and made those who escaped their first fury slaves. By those he was led into the extensive and desolate regions that border on the shores of the Aral lake.

Here he lived by hunting; and was obliged to supply every day a certain proportion of the spoil to regale his savage masters; his learning, his virtues, and even his beauty were qualifications that no way served to recommend him; they knew no merit but that of providing large quantities of milk and raw flesh; and were sensible of no happiness but that of rioting on the undressed meal.

Some merchants from Mesched, however, coming to trade with the Tartars for slaves, he was sold among the number, and led into the kingdom of Persia, where he is now detained. He is there obliged to watch the looks of a voluptuous and cruel master, a man fond of pleasure yet incapable of refinement, whom many years service in war has taught pride, but not bravery.

That treasure which I still keep within my bosom, my child, my all that was left to me, is now a slave.[1] Good heavens, why was this? why have I been introduced into this mortal apartment, to be a spectator of my own misfortunes, and the misfortunes of my fellow creatures? wherever I turn, what a labyrinth of doubt, error, and disappointment appears: why was I brought into being; for what purposes made; from whence have I come; whither strayed; or to what regions am I hastening? Reason cannot resolve. It lends a ray to shew the horrors of my prison, but not a light to guide me to escape them. Ye boasted revelations of the earth, how little do you aid the inquiry.

How am I surprised at the inconsistency of the magi; their two principles of good and evil affright me. The Indian who bathes his visage in urine, and calls it piety, strikes me with astonishment. The Christian who believes in three gods, is highly absurd. The Jews who pretend that deity is pleased with the effusion of blood, are not less displeasing. I am equally surprised that rational beings can come from the extremities of the earth, in order to kiss a stone, or scatter pebbles. How contrary to reason are those; and yet all pretend to teach me to be happy.

[1] This whole apostrophe seems most literally translated from Ambulaaohamed, the Arabian poet. [Goldsmith's note.]

Surely all men are blind and ignorant of truth. Mankind wanders, unknowing his way from morning till the evening. Where shall we turn after happiness; or is it wisest to desist from the pursuit? Like reptiles in a corner of some stupendous palace, we peep from our holes; look about us, wonder at all we see, but are ignorant of the great architect's design: O for a revelation of himself, for a plan of his universal system: O for the reasons of our creation; or why were we created to be thus unhappy! If we are to experience no other felicity but what this life affords, then are we miserable indeed. If we are born only to look about us, repine and die; then has heaven been guilty of injustice. If this life terminates my existence, I despise the blessings of providence, and the wisdom of the giver. If this life be my all, let the following epitaph be written on the tomb of Altangi. *By my father's crimes I received this. By my own crimes I bequeath it to posterity!*

LETTER XXIII.—*To the same.*

YET while I sometimes lament the case of humanity, and the depravity of human nature, there now and then appear gleams of greatness that serve to relieve the eye oppressed with the hideous prospect, and resemble those cultivated spots that are sometimes found in the midst of an Asiatic wilderness. I see many superior excellences among the English, which it is not in the power of all their follies to hide: I see virtues, which in other countries are known only to a few, practised here by every rank of people.

I know not whether it proceeds from their superior opulence that the English are more charitable than the rest of mankind; whether by being possessed of all the conveniences of life themselves, they have more leisure to perceive the uneasy situation of the distressed; whatever be the motive, they are not only the most charitable of any other nation, but most judicious in distinguishing the properest objects of compassion.

In other countries the giver is generally influenced by the immediate impulse of pity; his generosity is exerted as much to relieve his own uneasy sensations, as to comfort the object in distress: in England benefactions are of a more general nature; some men of fortune and universal benevolence propose the proper objects; the wants and the merits of the petitioners are canvassed by the people; neither passion nor pity find a place in the cool discussion; and charity is then only exerted when it has received the approbation of reason.

A late instance of this finely directed benevolence forces itself strongly on my imagination, that it in a manner reconciles me to pleasure, and once more makes me the universal friend of man.

The English and French have not only political reasons to induce them to mutual hatred, but often the more prevailing motive of private interest to widen the breach; a war between other countries is carried on collectively, army fights against army, and a man's own private resentment is lost in that of the community; but in England and France the individuals of each country plunder each other at sea without redress, and consequently feel that animosity against each other which passengers do at a robber. They have for some time carried on an expensive war; and several captives have been taken on both sides. Those made prisoners by the French have been used with cruelty, and guarded with unnecessary caution. Those taken by the English, being much more numerous, were confined in the ordinary manner: and, not being released by their countrymen, began to feel all those inconveniences which arise from want of covering and long confinement.

Their countrymen were informed of their deplorable situation; but they, more intent on annoying their enemies than relieving their friends, refused the least assistance. The English now saw thousands of their fellow creatures starving in every prison, forsaken by those whose duty it was to protect them, labouring with disease, and without clothes to keep off the severity of the season. National benevolence prevailed over national animosity: their prisoners were indeed enemies, but they were enemies in distress; they ceased to be hateful, when they no longer continued to be formidable: forgetting therefore their national hatred, the men who were brave enough to conquer, were generous enough to forgive: and they, whom all the world seemed to have disclaimed, at last found pity and redress from those they attempted to subdue. A subscription was opened, ample charities collected, proper necessaries procured, and the poor gay sons of a merry nation were once more taught to resume their former gaiety.

When I cast my eye over the list of those who contributed on this occasion, I find the names almost entirely English, scarce one foreigner appears among the number. It was for Englishmen alone to be capable of such exalted virtue. I own, I cannot look over this catalogue of good men and philosophers without thinking better of myself, because it makes me entertain a more favourable opinion of mankind: I am particularly struck with one who writes these words upon the paper that enclosed his benefaction. *The mite of an Englishman, a citizen of the world, to Frenchmen, prisoners of war, and naked.* I only wish that he may find as much pleasure from his virtues, as I have done in reflecting upon them, that alone will amply reward him. Such a one, my friend, is an honour to human nature; he makes no private distinctions of party; all that are stamped with the divine image of their Creator are friends to him; he is a *native of the world*; and the emperor of China may be proud that he has such a countryman.

To rejoice at the destruction of our enemies, is a foible grafted upon human nature, and we must be permitted to indulge it: the true way of atoning for such an ill-founded pleasure, is thus to turn our triumph into an act of benevolence, and to testify our own joy by endeavouring to banish anxiety from others.

Hamti, the best and wisest emperor that ever filled the throne, after having gained three signal victories over the Tartars, who had invaded his dominions, returned to Nankin in order to enjoy the glory of his conquest. After he had rested for some days, the people, who are naturally fond of processions, impatiently expected the triumphant entry, which emperors upon such occasions were accustomed to make. Their murmurs came to the emperor's ear. He loved his people, and was willing to do all in his power to satisfy their just desires. He therefore assured them, that he intended, upon the next feast of the Lanthorns, to exhibit one of the most glorious triumphs that had ever been seen in China.

The people were in raptures at his condescension; and, on the appointed day, assembled at the gates of the palace with the most eager expectations. Here they waited for some time without seeing any of those preparations which usually precede a pageant. The lanthorn, with ten thousand tapers, was not yet brought forth; the fire-works, which usually covered the city walls, were not yet lighted; the people once more began to murmur at this delay; when in the midst of their impatience, the palace gates flew open, and the emperor himself appeared, not in splendour or magnificence, but in an ordinary habit, followed by the blind, the maimed, and the strangers of the city, all in new clothes, and each carrying in his hand money enough to supply his necessities for the year. The people were at first amazed, but soon perceived the wisdom of their king, who taught them that to make one man happy was more truly great than having ten thousand captives groaning at the wheels of his chariot.   Adieu.

LETTER XXIV.—*To the same*.

WHATEVER may be the merits of the English in other sciences, they seem peculiarly excellent in the art of healing. There is scarcely a disorder incident to humanity, against which they are not possessed with a most infallible antidote. The professors of other arts confess the inevitable intricacy of things; talk with doubt, and decide with hesitation; but doubting is entirely unknown in medicine; the advertising professors here delight in cases of difficulty; be the disorder never so desperate or radical, you will find numbers in every street, who, by levelling a pill at the part affected, promise a certain cure without loss of time, knowledge of a bedfellow, or hindrance of business.

When I consider the assiduity of this profession, their benevolence amazes me. They not only in general give their medicines for half value, but use the most persuasive remonstrances to induce the sick to come and be cured. Sure there must be something strangely obstinate in an English patient, who refuses so much health upon such easy terms; does he take a pride in being bloated with a dropsy? Does he find pleasure in the alternations of an intermittent fever? Or feel as much satisfaction in nursing up his gout, as he found pleasure in acquiring it? He must, otherwise he would never reject such repeated assurances of instant relief. What can be more convincing than the manner in which the sick are invited to be well? The doctor first begs the most earnest attention of the public to what he is going to propose; he solemnly affirms the pill was never found to want success; he produces a list of those who have been rescued from the grave by taking it. Yet, notwithstanding all this, there are many here who now and then think proper to be sick; only sick did I say? There are some who even think proper to die! Yes, by the head of Confucius they die; though they might have purchased the health-restoring specific for half a crown at every corner.

I am amazed, my dear Fum Hoam, that these doctors who know what an obstinate set of people they have to deal with, have never thought of attempting to revive the dead. When the living are found to reject their prescriptions, they ought in conscience to apply to the dead, from whom they can expect no such mortifying repulses; they would find in the dead the most complying patients imaginable; and what gratitude might they not expect from the patient's son, now no longer an heir, and his wife, now no longer a widow.

Think not, my friend, that there is any thing chimerical in such an attempt; they already perform cures equally strange: What can be more truly astonishing than to see old age restored to youth, and vigour to the most feeble constitutions; yet this is performed here every day; a simple electuary effects these wonders, even without the bungling ceremonies of having the patient boiled up in a kettle, or ground down in a mill.

Few physicians here go through the ordinary courses of education, but receive all their knowledge of medicine by immediate inspiration from heaven. Some are thus inspired even in the womb; and what is very remarkable, understand their profession as well at three years old as at threescore. Others have spent a great part of their lives unconscious of any latent excellence, till a bankruptcy, or a residence in gaol, have called their miraculous powers into exertion. And others still there are indebted to their superlative ignorance alone for success. The more ignorant the practitioner, the less capable is he thought of deceiving. The people here judge, as they do in the East; where it is thought absolutely requisite that a man should be an idiot before he pretend to be either a conjuror or a doctor.

When a physician by inspiration is sent for, he never perplexes the patient by previous examination; he asks very few questions, and those only for form sake. He knows every disorder by intuition. He administers the pill or drop for every distemper; nor is more inquisitive than the farrier while he drenches an horse. If the patient lives, then has he one more to add to the surviving list; if he dies, then it may be justly said of the patient's disorder, *that as it was not cured, the disorder was incurable.*

LETTER XXV.—*From the same.*

I was some days ago in company with a politician, who very pathetically declaimed upon the miserable situation of his country: he assured me, that the whole political machine was moving in a wrong track, and that scarce even abilities like his own could ever set it right again. 'What have we, said he, to do with the wars on the continent; we are a commercial nation; we have only to cultivate commerce like our neighbours the Dutch; it is our business to encrease trade by settling new colonies: riches are the strength of a nation; and for the rest, our ships, our ships alone will protect us.' I found it vain to oppose my feeble arguments to those of a man who thought himself wise enough to direct even the ministry; I fancied, however, that I saw with more certainty, because I reasoned without prejudice: I therefore begged leave instead of argument, to relate a short history. He gave me a smile at once of condescension and contempt, and I proceeded as follows to describe, THE RISE AND DECLENSION OF THE KINGDOM OF LAO.

Northward of China, and in one of the doublings of the great wall, the fruitful province of Lao enjoyed its liberty and a peculiar government of its own. As the inhabitants were on all sides surrounded by the wall, they feared no sudden invasion from the Tartars; and being each possessed of property, they were zealous in its defence.

The natural consequences of security and affluence in any country is a love of pleasure; when the wants of nature are supplied, we see after the conveniences; when possessed of these, we desire the luxuries of life; and when every luxury is provided, it is then ambition takes up the man, and leaves him still something to wish for: the inhabitants of the country from primitive simplicity soon began to aim at elegance, and from elegance, proceeded to refinement. It was now found absolutely requisite for the good of the state, that the people should be divided: formerly the same hand that was employed in tilling the ground, or in dressing up the manufactures, was also in time of need a soldier; but the custom was now changed; for it was perceived, that a man bred up from childhood to the arts either of peace or war, became more eminent by this means in his respective profession. The inhabitants were therefore now distinguished into artisans and soldiers; and while those improved the luxuries of life, these watched for the security of the people.

A country possessed of freedom has always two sorts of enemies to fear: foreign foes who attack its existence from without, and internal miscreants who betray its liberties within. The inhabitants of Lao were to guard against both. A country of artisans were most likely to preserve internal liberty; and a nations of soldiers were fittest to repel a foreign invasion. Hence naturally arose a division of opinion between the artizans and soldiers of the kingdom. The artizans ever complaining, that freedom was threatened by an armed internal force, were for disbanding the soldiers, and insisted that their walls, their walls alone were sufficient to repel the most formidable invasion: the warriors, on the contrary, represented the power of the neighbouring kings, the combinations formed against their state, and the weakness of the wall which every earthquake might overturn. While this altercation continued, the kingdom might be justly said to enjoy its greatest share of vigour: every order in the state, by being watchful over each other, contributed to diffuse happiness equally and balanced the state. The arts of peace flourished, nor were those of war neglected; the neighbouring powers, who had nothing to apprehend from the ambition of men whom they only saw solicitous not for riches but freedom, were contented to traffic with them: they sent their goods to be manufactured in Lao, and paid a large price for them upon their return.

By these means this people at length became moderately rich, and their opulence naturally invited the invader; a Tartar prince led an immense army against them, and they as bravely stood up in their own defence; they were still inspired with a love of their country; they fought the barbarous enemy with fortitude, and gained a complete victory.

From this moment, which they regarded as the completion of their glory, historians date their downfall. They had risen in strength by a love of their country, and fell by indulging ambition. The country possessed by the invading Tartars, seemed to them a prize that would not only render them more formidable for the future, but which would encrease their opulence for the present; it was unanimously resolved, therefore, both by soldiers and artizans, that those desolate regions should be peopled by colonies from Lao. When a trading nation begins to act the conqueror, it is then perfectly undone: it subsists in some measure by the support of its neighbours; while they continue to regard it without envy or apprehension, trade may flourish; but when once it presumes to assert as its right what is only enjoyed as a favour, each country reclaims that part of commerce which it has power to take back, and turns it into some other channel more honourable, though perhaps less convenient.

Every neighbour now began to regard with jealous eyes this ambitious common-wealth, and forbade their subjects any future intercourse with them. The inhabitants of Lao, however, still pursued the same ambitious maxims; it was from their colonies alone they expected riches; and riches, said they, are strength, and strength is security. Numberless were the migrations of the desperate and enterprising of this country to people the desolate dominions lately possessed by the Tartar; between these colonies and the mother country, a very advantageous trafic was at first carried on, the republic sent their colonies large quantities of the manufactures of the country, and they in return provided the republic with an equivalent in ivory and ginseng. By this means the inhabitants became immensely rich, and this produced an equal degree of voluptuousness; for men who have much money will always find some fantastical modes of enjoyment. How shall I mark the steps by which they declined! Every colony in process of time spreads over the whole country where it first was planted. As it grows more populous, it becomes more polite; and those manufactures for which it was in the beginning obliged to others, it learns to dress up itself: such was the case with the colonies of Lao; they in less than a century became a powerful and a polite people, and the more polite they grew, the less advantageous was the commerce which still subsisted between them and others. By this means the mother country being abridged in its commerce grew poorer but not less luxurious. Their former wealth had introduced luxury; and wherever luxury once fixes, no art can either lessen or remove it. Their commerce with their neighbours was totally destroyed; and that with their colonies was every day naturally and necessarily declining; they still, however, preserved the insolence of wealth, without a power to support it, and persevered in being luxurious while contemptible from poverty. In short, the state resembled one of those bodies bloated with disease, whose bulk is only a symptom of its wretchedness.

Their former opulence only rendered them more impotent, as those individuals who are reduced from riches to poverty, are of all men the most unfortunate and helpless. They had imagined, because their colonies tended to make them rich upon the first acquisition, they would still continue to do so; they now found however, that on themselves alone they should have depended for support; that colonies ever afforded but temporary affluence, and when cultivated and polite are no longer useful. From such a concurrence of circumstances they soon became contemptible. The emperor Honti invaded them with a powerful army. Historians do not say whether their colonies were too remote to lend assistance, or else were desirous of shaking off their dependence: But certain it is, they scarce made any resistance; their walls were now found but a weak defence; and they at length were obliged to acknowledge subjection to the empire of China.

Happy, very happy might they have been, had they known when to bound their riches and their glory; had they known that extending empire is often diminishing power, that countries are ever strongest which are internally powerful; that colonies by draining away the brave and enterprising, leave the country in the hands of the timid, and the avaricious; that walls give little protection, unless manned with resolution; that too much commerce may injure a nation as well as too little; and that there is a wide difference between a conquering and a flourishing empire. Adieu.

LETTER XXVI.—*To the same.*

THOUGH fond of many acquaintances, I desire an intimacy only with a few. The man in black whom I have often mentioned, is one whose friendship I could wish to acquire, because he possesses my esteem. His manners, it is true, are tinctured with some strange inconsistencies; and he may be justly termed an humourist in a nation of humourists. Though he is generous even to profusion, he affects to be thought a prodigy of parsimony and prudence; though his conversation be replete with the most sordid and selfish maxims, his heart is dilated with the most unbounded love. I have known him profess himself a man-hater, while his cheek was glowing with compassion; and while his looks were softened into pity, I have heard him use the language of the most unbounded ill-nature. Some affect humanity and tenderness, others boast of having such dispositions from Nature; but he is the only man I ever knew who seemed ashamed of his natural benevolence. He takes as much pains to hide his feelings as any hypocrite would to conceal his indifference; but on every unguarded moment the mask drops off, and reveals him to the most superficial observer.

In one of our late excursions into the country, happening to discourse upon the provision that was made for the poor in England, he seemed amazed how any of his countrymen could be so foolishly weak as to relieve occasional objects of charity, when the laws had made such ample provision for their support. In every parish house, says he, the poor are supplied with food, clothes, fire, and a bed to lie on; they want no more, I desire no more myself; yet still they seem discontented. I'm surprised at the inactivity of our magistrates, in not taking up such vagrants who are only a weight upon the industrious; I'm surprised that the people are found to relieve them, when they must be at the same time sensible that it, in some measure, encourages idleness, extravagance, and imposture. Were I to advise any man for whom I had the least regard, I would caution him by all means not to be imposed upon by their false pretences: let me assure you, Sir, they are impostors, every one of them; and rather merit a prison than relief.

He was proceeding in this strain earnestly, to dissuade me from an imprudence of which I am seldom guilty: when an old man who still had about him the remnants of tattered finery, implored our compassion. He assured us that he was no common beggar, but forced into the shameful profession, to support a dying wife and five hungry children. Being pre-possessed against such falsehoods, his story had not the least influence upon me; but it was quite otherwise with the man in black; I could see it visibly operate upon his countenance, and effectually interrupt his harangue. I could easily perceive that his heart burned to relieve the five starving children, but he seemed ashamed to discover his weakness to me. While he thus hesitated between compassion and pride, I pretended to look another way, and he seized this opportunity of giving the poor petitioner a piece of silver, bidding him at the same time, in order that I should not hear, go work for his bread, and not tease passengers with such impertinent falsehoods for the future.

As he had fancied himself quite unperceived, he continued, as we proceeded, to rail against beggars with as much animosity as before; he threw in some episodes on his own amazing pru-dence and economy, with his profound skill in discovering im-postors; he explained the manner in which he would deal with beggars were he a magistrate, hinted at enlarging some of the prisons for their reception, and told two stories of ladies that were robbed by beggarmen. He was beginning a third to the same purpose, when a sailor with a wooden leg once more crossed our walks, desiring our pity, and blessing our limbs. I was for going on without taking any notice, but my friend looking wishfully upon the poor petitioner, bid me stop, and he would shew me with how much ease he could at any time detect an impostor.

He now therefore assumed a look of importance, and in an

angry tone began to examine the sailor, demanding in what engagement he was thus disabled and rendered unfit for service. The sailor replied in a tone as angrily as he, that he had been an officer on board a private ship of war, and that he had lost his leg abroad in defence of those who did nothing at home. At this reply, all my friend's importance vanished in a moment; he had not a single question more to ask; he now only studied what method he should take to relieve him unobserved. He had however no easy part to act, as he was obliged to preserve the appearance of ill-nature before me, and yet relieve himself by relieving the sailor. Casting therefore a furious look upon some bundles of chips which the fellow carried in a string at his back, my friend demanded how he sold his matches; but not waiting for a reply, desired, in a surly tone, to have a shilling's worth. The sailor seemed at first surprised at his demand, but soon recollected himself, and presenting his whole bundle, Here, master, says he, take all my cargo, and a blessing into the bargain.

It is impossible to describe with what an air of triumph my friend marched off with his new purchase, he assured me that he was firmly of opinion that those fellows must have stolen their goods, who could thus afford to sell them for half value; he informed me of several different uses to which those chips might be applied; he expatiated largely upon the savings that would result from lighting candles with a match instead of thrusting them into the fire. He averred, that he would as soon have parted with a tooth as his money to those vagabonds, unless for some valuable consideration. I cannot tell how long this panegyric upon frugality and matches might have continued, had not his attention been called off by another object more distressful than either of the former. A woman in rags, with one child in her arms, and another on her back, was attempting to sing ballads, but with such a mournful voice that it was difficult to determine whether she was singing or crying. A wretch, who, in the deepest distress still aimed at good humour, was an object my friend was by no means capable of withstanding: his vivacity, and his discourse were instantly interrupted; upon this occasion his very dissimulation had forsaken him. Even, in my presence, he immediately applied his hands to his pockets, in order to relieve her; but guess his confusion, when he found he had already given away all the money he carried about him to former objects. The misery painted in the woman's visage, was not half so strongly expressed as the agony in his. He continued to search for some time, but to no purpose, till, at length, recollecting himself, with a face of ineffable good-nature, as he had no money, he put into her hands his shilling's worth of matches.

LETTER XXVII.—*To the same.*

As there appeared something reluctantly good in the character of my companion, I must own it surprised me what could be his motives for thus concealing virtues which others take such pains to display. I was unable to repress my desire of knowing the history of a man who thus seemed to act under continual restraint, and whose benevolence was rather the effect of appetite than reason.

It was not however till after repeated solicitations he thought proper to gratify my curiosity. 'If you are fond, says he, of hearing *hair breadth 'scapes*, my history must certainly please; for I have been for twenty years upon the very verge of starving, without ever being starved.

'My father, the younger son of a good family, was possessed of a small living in the church. His education was above his fortune, and his generosity greater than his education. Poor as he was, he had his flatterers still poorer than himself; for every dinner he gave them, they returned him an equivalent in praise; and this was all he wanted; the same ambition that actuates a monarch at the head of an army, influenced my father at the head of his table; he told the story of the ivy tree, and that was laughed at; he repeated the jest of the two scholars and one pair of breeches, and the company laughed at that; but the story of Taffy in the sedan chair was sure to set the table in a roar; thus his pleasure encreased in proportion to the pleasure he gave; he loved all the world, and he fancied all the world loved him.

'As his fortune was but small, he lived up to the very extent of it; he had no intentions of leaving his children money, for that was dross; he was resolved they should have learning; for learning, he used to observe, was better than silver or gold. For this purpose he undertook to instruct us himself; and took as much pains to form our morals, as to improve our understanding. We were told that universal benevolence was what first cemented society; we were taught to consider all the wants of mankind as our own; to regard the *human divine* with affection and esteem; he wound us up to be mere machines of pity, and rendered us incapable of withstanding the slightest impulse made either by real or fictitious distress; in a word, we were perfectly instructed in the art of *giving away* thousands before we were taught the more necessary qualifications of *getting* a farthing.

'I cannot avoid imagining, that thus refined by his lessons out of all my suspicion, and divested of even all the little cunning which Nature had given me, I resembled, upon my first entrance into the busy and insidious world, one of those gladiators who were exposed without armour in the amphitheatre at Rome. My father, however, who had only seen the world on one side, seemed to triumph in my superior discernment; though my whole stock of wisdom consisted in being able to talk like himself upon subjects that once were useful, because they were then topics of the busy world; but that now were utterly useless, because connected with the busy world no longer.

'The first opportunity he had of finding his expectations disappointed, was at the very middling figure I made in the university; he had flattered himself that he would soon see me rising into the foremost rank in literary reputation, but was mortified to find me utterly unnoticed and unknown. His disappointment might have been partly ascribed to his having over-rated my talents, and partly to my dislike of mathematical reasoning at a time, when my imagination and memory yet unsatisfied, were more eager after new objects, than desirous of reasoning upon those I knew. This did not, however, please my tutors, who observed indeed, that I was a little dull; but at the same time allowed, that I seemed to be very *good-natured*, and had no harm in me.

'After I had resided at college seven years, my father died, and left me—his blessing. Thus shoved from shore without ill-nature to protect, or cunning to guide, or proper stores to subsist me in so dangerous a voyage, I was obliged to embark in the wide world at twenty-two. But, in order to settle in life, my friends *advised* (for they always advise when they begin to despise us) they advised me, I say, to go into orders.

'To be obliged to wear a long wig, when I liked a short one, or a black coat, when I generally dressed in brown, I thought was such a restraint upon my liberty, that I absolutely rejected the proposal. A priest in England, is not the same mortified creature with a bonze in China; with us, not he that fasts best, but eats best, is reckoned the best liver; yet I rejected a life of luxury, indolence, and ease, from no other consideration but that boyish one of dress. So that my friends were now perfectly

satisfied I was undone; and yet they thought it a pity for one who
had not the least harm in him, and was so very good-natured.

'Poverty naturally begets dependence, and I was admitted
as flatterer to a great man. At first I was surprised, that the
situation of a flatterer at a great man's table could be thought
disagreeable; there was no great trouble in listening attentively
when his lordship spoke, and laughing when he looked round for
applause. This even good-manners might have obliged me to
perform. I found, however, too soon that his lordship was a
greater dunce than myself; and from that very moment flattery
was at an end. I now rather aimed at setting him right, than
at receiving his absurdities with submission: to flatter those we
do not know is an easy task; but to flatter our intimate acquaintances, all whose foibles are strongly in our eye, is drudgery
insupportable. Every time I now opened my lips in praise, my
falsehood went to my conscience; his lordship soon perceived
me to be very unfit for service; I was therefore discharged: my
patron at the same time being graciously pleased to observe,
that he believed I was tolerably good-natured, and had not the
least harm in me.

'Disappointed in ambition I had recourse to love. A young
lady, who lived with her aunt, and was possessed of a pretty
fortune in her own disposal, had given me, as I fancied, some
reason to expect success. The symptoms by which I was guided
were striking; she had always laughed with me at her awkward
acquaintance, and at her aunt among the number; she always
observed, that a man of sense would make a better husband
than a fool, and I as constantly applied the observation in my
own favour. She continually talked in my company of friendship and the beauties of the mind, and spoke of Mr. Shrimp,
my rival's high-heel'd shoes with detestation. These were
circumstances which I thought strongly in my favour; so after
resolving, and re-resolving, I had courage enough to tell her my
mind. Miss heard my proposal with serenity, seeming at the
same time to study the figures of her fan. Out at last it came.
There was but one small objection to complete our happiness,
which was no more than—that she was married three months
before to Mr. Shrimp, with high-heel'd shoes! By way of consolation however she observed, that tho' I was disappointed in
her, my addresses to her aunt would probably kindle her into
sensibility; as the old lady always allowed me to be very good-
natured, and not to have the least share of harm in me.

'Yet still I had friends, numerous friends, and to them I was resolved to apply. O friendship! thou fond soother of the human breast, to thee we fly in every calamity; to thee the wretched seek for succour; on thee the care-tired son of misery fondly relies; from thy kind assistance the unfortunate always hopes relief, and may be ever sure of—disappointment! My first application was to a city scrivener, who had frequently offered to lend me money when he knew I did not want it. I informed him, that now was the time to put his friendship to the test; that I wanted to borrow a couple of hundreds for a certain occasion, and was resolved to take it up from him. And pray, Sir, cried my friend, do you want all this money? Indeed I never wanted it more, returned I. I am sorry for that, cries the scrivener, with all my heart; for they who want money when they come to borrow, will always want money when they should come to pay.

'From him I flew with indignation to one of the best friends I had in the world, and made the same request. Indeed, Mr. Dry-bone, cries my friend, I always thought it would come to this. You know, Sir, I would not advise you but for your own good; but your conduct has hitherto been ridiculous in the highest degree, and some of your acquaintance always thought you a very silly fellow; let me see, you want two hundred pounds; do you only want two hundred, Sir, exactly? To confess a truth, returned I, I shall want three hundred; but then I have another friend from whom I can borrow the rest. Why then, replied my friend, if you would take my advice; and you know I should not presume to advise you but for your own good; I would recommend it to you to borrow the whole sum from that other friend; and then one note will serve for all, you know.

'Poverty now began to come fast upon me, yet instead of growing more provident or cautious as I grew poor, I became every day more indolent and simple. A friend was arrested for fifty pounds, I was unable to extricate him except by becoming his bail. When at liberty he fled from his creditors, and left me to take his place. In prison I expected greater satisfactions than I had enjoyed at large. I hoped to converse with men in this new world simple and believing like myself, but I found them as cunning and as cautious as those in the world I had left behind. They spunged up my money whilst it lasted, borrowed my coals and never paid them, and cheated me when I played at cribbage. All this was done because they believed me to be very good-natured and knew that I had no harm in me.

'Upon my first entrance into this mansion, which is to some the abode of despair, I felt no sensations different from those I experienced abroad. I was now on one side the door, and those who were unconfined were on the other; this was all the difference between us. At first indeed I felt some uneasiness, in considering how I should be able to provide this week for the wants of the week ensuing; but after some time, if I found myself sure of eating one day, I never troubled my head how I was to be supplied another. I seized every precarious meal with the utmost good humour, indulged no rants of spleen at my situation, never called down heaven and all the stars to behold me dining upon an halfpennyworth of radishes: my very companions were taught to believe that I liked salad better than mutton. I contented myself with thinking, that all my life I should either eat white bread or brown; considered that all that happened was best, laughed when I was not in pain, took the world as it went, and read Tacitus often, for want of more books and company.

'How long I might have continued in this torpid state of simplicity I cannot tell, had I not been roused by seeing an old acquaintance, whom I knew to be a prudent blockhead, preferred to a place in the government. I now found that I had pursued a wrong track, and that the true way of being able to relieve others, was first to aim at independence myself. My immediate care, therefore, was to leave my present habitation, and make an entire reformation in my conduct and behaviour. For a free, open, undesigning deportment, I put on that of closeness, prudence and economy. One of the most heroic actions I ever performed, and for which I shall praise myself as long as I live, was the refusing half a crown to an old acquaintance, at the time when he wanted it, and I had it to spare; for this alone I deserve to be decreed an ovation.

'I now therefore pursued a course of uninterrupted frugality, seldom wanted a dinner, and was consequently invited to twenty. I soon began to get the character of a saving hunks that had money; and insensibly grew into esteem. Neighbours have asked my advice in the disposal of their daughters, and I have always taken care not to give any. I have contracted a friendship with an alderman, only by observing, that if we take a farthing from a thousand pound, it will be a thousand pound no longer. I have been invited to a pawnbroker's table, by pretending to hate gravy; and am now actually upon treaty of marriage with a rich widow, for only having observed that the bread was rising. If ever I am asked a question, whether I know it or not, instead of answering, I only smile and look wise. If a charity is proposed, I go about with the hat, but put nothing in myself. If a wretch solicits my pity, I observe that the world is filled with impostors, and take a certain method of not being deceived by never relieving. In short, I now find the truest way of finding esteem even from the indigent, is *to give away nothing, and thus have much in our power to give.*'

LETTER XXVIII.—*To the same.*

LATELY in company with my friend in black, whose conversation is now both my amusement and instruction, I could not avoid observing the great numbers of old bachelors and maiden ladies with which this city seems to be over-run. Sure marriage, said I, is not sufficiently encouraged, or we should never behold such crowds of battered beaux and decayed coquets still attempting to drive a trade they have been so long unfit for, and swarming upon the gaiety of the age. I behold an old bachelor in the most contemptible light, as an animal that lives upon the common stock without contributing his share: he is a beast of prey, and the laws should make use of as many stratagems, and as much force to drive the reluctant savage into the toils, as the Indians when they hunt the rhinoceros. The mob should be permitted to hollo after him, boys might play tricks on him with impunity, every well-bred company should laugh at him, and if, when turned of sixty, he offered to make love, his mistress might spit in his face, or, what would be perhaps a greater punishment, should fairly grant the favour.

As for old maids, continued I, they should not be treated with so much severity, because I suppose none would be so if they could. No lady in her senses would choose to make a subordinate figure at christenings and lyings-in, when she might be the principal herself; nor curry favour with a sister-in-law, when she might command an husband, nor toil in preparing custards, when she might lie abed and give directions how they ought to be made, nor stifle all her sensations in demure formality, when she might with matrimonial freedom shake her acquaintance by the hand, and wink at a double entendre. No lady could be so very silly as to live single, if she could help it. I consider an unmarried lady declining into the vale of years, as one of those charming countries bordering on China that lies waste for want of proper inhabitants. We are not to accuse the country, but the ignorance of its neighbours, who are insensible of its beauties, though at liberty to enter and cultivate the soil.

'Indeed, Sir, replied my companion, you are very little acquainted with the English ladies to think they are old maids against their will. I dare venture to affirm that you can hardly select one of them all, but has had frequent offers of marriage, which, either pride or avarice has not made her reject. Instead of thinking it a disgrace, they take every occasion to boast of their former cruelty; a soldier does not exult more when he counts over the wounds he has received, than a female veteran when she relates the wounds she has formerly given: exhaustless when she begins a narrative of the former death-dealing power of her eyes. She tells of the knight in gold lace, who died with a single frown, and never rose again till—— he was married to his maid: Of the squire, who being cruelly denied, in a rage, flew to the window, and lifting up the sash, threw himself in an agony ——into his arm chair: Of the parson, who, crossed in love, resolutely swallowed opium, which banished the stings of despised love by——making him sleep. In short, she talks over her former losses with pleasure, and, like some tradesmen, finds consolation in the many bankruptcies she has suffered.

'For this reason, whenever I see a superannuated beauty still unmarried, I tacitly accuse her either of pride, avarice, coquetry, or affectation. There's Miss Jenny Tinderbox, I once remember her to have had some beauty, and a moderate fortune. Her elder sister happened to marry a man of quality, and this seemed as a statute of virginity against poor Jane. Because there was one lucky hit in the family, she was resolved not to disgrace it by introducing a tradesman; by thus rejecting her equals, and neglected or despised by her superiors, she now acts in the capacity of tutoress of her sister's children, and undergoes the drudgery of three servants, without receiving the wages of one.

'Miss Squeeze was a pawnbroker's daughter; her father had early taught her that money was a very good thing, and left her a moderate fortune at his death. She was so perfectly sensible of the value of what she had got, that she was resolved never to part with a farthing without an equality on the part of her suitor; she thus refused several offers made her by people who wanted to better themselves, as the saying is; and grew old and ill-natured, without ever considering that she should have made an abatement in her pretensions, from her face being pale, and marked with the small-pox.

'Lady Betty Tempest on the contrary had beauty, with fortune and family. But, fond of conquest, she passed from triumph to triumph; she had read plays and romances, and there had learned that a plain man of common sense was no better than a fool; such she refused, and sighed only for the gay, giddy, inconstant and thoughtless; after she had thus rejected hundreds who liked her, and sighed for hundreds who despised her, she found herself insensibly deserted: at present she is company only for her aunts and cousins, and sometimes makes one in a country-dance, with only one of the chairs for a partner, casts off round a joint-stool, and sets to a corner cupboard. In a word, she is treated with civil contempt from every quarter, and placed, like a piece of old-fashioned lumber, merely to fill up a corner.

'But Sophronia, the sagacious Sophronia; how shall I mention her? She was taught to love Greek, and hate the men from her very infancy: she has rejected fine gentlemen because they were not pedants, and pedants because they were not fine gentlemen; her exquisite sensibility has taught her to discover every fault in every lover, and her inflexible justice has prevented her pardoning them; thus she rejected several offers, till the wrinkles of age had overtaken her; and now, without one good feature in her face, she talks incessantly of the beauties of the mind.' Farewell.

LETTER XXIX.—*From the same.*

WERE we to estimate the learning of the English by the number of books that are every day published among them, perhaps no country, not even China itself, could equal them in this particular. I have reckoned not less than twenty-three new books published in one day; which upon computation, makes eight thousand three hundred and ninety-five in one year. Most of these are not confined to one single science, but embrace the whole circle. History, politics, poetry, mathematics, metaphysics, and the philosophy of Nature are all comprized in a manual not larger than that in which our children are taught the letters. If then we suppose the learned of England to read but an eighth part of the works which daily come from the press (and sure none can pretend to learning upon less easy terms) at this rate every scholar will read a thousand books in one year. From such a calculation you may conjecture what an amazing fund of literature a man must be possessed of, who thus reads three new books every day, not one of which but contains all the good things that ever were said or written.

And yet I know not how it happens, but the English are not in reality so learned as would seem from this calculation. We meet but few who know all arts and sciences to perfection; whether it is that the generality are incapable of such extensive knowledge, or that the authors of those books are not adequate instructors. In China, the emperor himself takes cognisance of all the doctors in the kingdom who profess authorship. In England, every man may be an author that can write; for they have by law a liberty not only of saying what they please, but of being as dull as they please.

Yesterday I testified my surprise to the man in black, where writers could be found in sufficient number to throw off the books I daily saw crowding from the press. I at first imagined that their learned seminaries might take this method of instructing the world. But to obviate this objection, my companion assured me, that the doctors of colleges never wrote, and that some of them had actually forgot their reading; but if you desire, continued he, to see a collection of authors, I fancy I can introduce you this evening to a club, which assembles every Saturday at seven, at the sign of the Broom near Islington, to talk over the business of the last, and the entertainment of the week ensuing. I accepted his invitation, we walked together, and entered the house some time before the usual hour for the company assembling.

My friend took this opportunity of letting me into the characters of the principal members of the club, not even the host excepted, who, it seems, was once an author himself, but preferred by a bookseller to this situation as a reward for his former services.

The first person, said he, of our society, is doctor Nonentity, a metaphysician. Most people think him a profound scholar; but as he seldom speaks, I cannot be positive in that particular; he generally spreads himself before the fire, sucks his pipe, talks little, drinks much, and is reckoned very good company. I 'm told he writes indexes to perfection, he makes essays on the origin of evil, philosophical enquiries upon any subject, and draws up an answer to any book upon twenty-four hours warning. You may distinguish him from the rest of the company by his long grey wig, and the blue handkerchief round his neck.

The next to him in merit and esteem is Tim Syllabub, a droll creature; he sometimes shines as a star of the first magnitude among the choice spirits of the age; he is reckoned equally excellent at a rebus, a riddle, a bawdy song, and an hymn for the tabernacle. You will know him by his shabby finery, his powdered wig, dirty shirt, and broken silk stockings.

After him succeeds Mr. Tibs, a very *useful hand*; he writes receipts for the bite of a mad dog, and throws off an eastern tale to perfection; he understands the *business* of an author as well as any man; for no bookseller alive can cheat him; you may distinguish him by the peculiar clumsiness of his figure and the coarseness of his coat: however, though it be coarse, (as he frequently tells the company,) he has paid for it.

Lawyer Squint is the politician of the society; he makes speeches for parliament, writes addresses to his fellow subjects, and letters to noble commanders, he gives the history of every new play, and finds *seasonable thoughts* upon every occasion.— My companion was proceeding in his description, when the host came running in with terror on his countenance to tell us, that the door was beset with bailiffs. If that be the case then, says my companion, we had as good be going; for I am positive we shall not see one of the company this night. Wherefore disappointed we were both obliged to return home, he to enjoy the oddities which compose his character alone, and I to write as usual to my friend the occurrences of the day. Adieu.

LETTER XXX.—*From the same.*

By my last advices from Moscow, I find the caravan has not yet departed from China: I still continue to write, expecting that you may receive a large number of my letters at once. In them you will find rather a minute detail of English peculiarities, than a general picture of their manners or disposition. Happy it were for mankind if all travellers would thus, instead of characterising a people in general terms, lead us into a detail of those minute circumstances which first influenced their opinion: the genius of a country should be investigated with a kind of experimental enquiry: by this means we should have more precise and just notions of foreign nations, and detect travellers themselves when they happened to form wrong conclusions.

My friend and I repeated our visit to the club of authors; where, upon our entrance, we found the members all assembled and engaged in a loud debate.

The poet, in shabby finery, holding a manuscript in his hand, was earnestly endeavouring to persuade the company to hear him read the first book of an heroic poem, which he had composed the day before. But against this, all the members very warmly objected. They knew no reason why any member of the club should be indulged with a particular hearing, when many of them had published whole volumes which had never been looked in. They insisted that the law should be observed, where reading in company was expressly noticed. It was in vain that the plaintiff pleaded the peculiar merit of his piece; he spoke to an assembly insensible to all his remonstrances; the book of laws was opened, and read by the secretary, where it was expressly enacted, 'That whatsoever poet, speechmaker, critic, or historian, should presume to engage the company by reading his own works, he was to lay down sixpence previous to opening the manuscript, and should be charged one shilling an hour while he continued reading; the said shilling to be equally distributed among the company as a recompence for their trouble.'

Our poet seemed at first to shrink at the penalty, hesitating for some time whether he should deposit the fine, or shut up the poem; but looking round, and perceiving two strangers in the room, his love of fame out-weighed his prudence, and laying down the sum by law established, he insisted on his prerogative.

A profound silence ensuing, he began by explaining his design. 'Gentlemen, says he, the present piece is not one of your common epic poems, which come from the press like paper kites in summer; there are none of your Turnuses or Dido's in it; it is an heroical description of Nature. I only beg you 'll endeavour to make your souls unison with mine, and hear with the same enthusiasm with which I have written. The poem begins with the description of an author's bedchamber: the picture was sketched in my own apartment; for you must know, gentlemen, that I am myself the hero. Then putting himself into the attitude of an orator, with all the emphasis of voice and action, he proceeded:

> Where the Red Lion flaring o'er the way,
> Invited each passing stranger that can pay;
> Where Calvert's butt, and Parson's black champaign,
> Regale the drabs and bloods of Drury lane;
> There in a lonely room, from bailiffs snug,
> The muse found Scroggen stretch'd beneath a rug.
> A window patch'd with paper lent a ray,
> That dimly shew'd the state in which he lay;

The sanded floor that grits beneath the tread;
The humid wall with paltry pictures spread:
The royal game of goose was there in view,
And the twelve rules the royal martyr drew;
The seasons fram'd with listing found a place,
And brave prince William shew'd his lamp-black face:
The morn was cold, he views with keen desire
The rusty grate unconscious of a fire;
With beer and milk arrears the frieze was scor'd
And five crack'd tea cups dress'd the chimney board,
A night cap deck'd his brows instead of bay,
A cap by night——a stocking all the day!'

With this last line he seemed to much elated, that he was unable to proceed: 'There gentlemen, cries he, there is a description for you; Rabelais's bed-chamber is but a fool to it:

A cap by night——a stocking all the day !

There is sound and sense, and truth, and nature in the trifling compass of ten little syllables.'

He was too much employed in self-admiration to observe the company; who by nods, winks, shrugs, and stifled laughter, testified every mark of contempt. He turned severally to each for their opinion, and found all however ready to applaud. One swore it was inimitable; another said it was damn'd fine; and a third cried out in a rapture Carissimo. At last addressing himself to the president, And pray, Mr. Squint, says he, let us have your opinion. Mine, answered the president (taking the manuscript out of the author's hands), may this glass suffocate me, but I think it equal to any thing I have seen; and I fancy (continued he, doubling up the poem and forcing it into the author's pocket) that you will get great honour when it comes out; so I shall beg leave to put it in. We will not intrude upon your good-nature, in desiring to hear more of it at present; *ex ungue Herculem*, we are satisfied, perfectly satisfied. The author made two or three attempts to pull it out a second time, and the president made as many to prevent him. Thus though with reluctance he was at last obliged to sit down, contented with the commendations for which he had paid.

When this tempest of poetry and praise was blown over, one of the company changed the subject, by wondering how any man can be so dull as to write poetry at present, since prose itself would hardly pay. Would you think it, gentlemen, continued he, I have actually written last week sixteen prayers, twelve bawdy jests, and three sermons, all at the rate of sixpence a-piece; and what is still more extraordinary, the bookseller has lost by the bargain. Such sermons would once have gained me a prebend's stall; but now alas we have neither piety, taste, nor humour among us. Positively if this season does not turn out better than it has begun, unless the ministry commit some blunders to furnish us with a new topic of abuse, I shall resume my old business of working at the press, instead of finding it employment.

The whole club seem to join in condemning the season, as one of the worst that had come for some time; a gentleman particularly observed that the nobility were never known to subscribe worse than at present. 'I know not how it happens, said he, though I follow them up as close as possible, yet I can hardly get a single subscription in a week. The houses of the great are as inaccessible as a frontier garrison at midnight. I never see a nobleman's door half opened that some surly porter or footman does not stand full in the breach. I was yesterday to wait with a subscription proposal upon my lord Squash, the Creolian. I had posted myself at his door the whole morning, and just as he was getting into his coach, thrust my proposal snug into his hand folded up in the form of a letter from myself. He just glanced at the superscription, and, not knowing the hand, consigned it to his valet de chambre; this respectable personage treated it as his master, and put it into the hands of the porter. The porter grasped my proposal frowning; and, measuring my figure from top to toe, put it back into my own hands unopened.

'To the devil I pitch all the nobility, cries a little man, in a peculiar accent, I am sure they have of late used me most scurvily. You must know, gentlemen, some time ago, upon the arrival of a certain noble duke from his travels, I set myself down, and vamped up a fine flaunting, poetical panegyric, which I had written in such a strain that I fancied it would have even wheedled milk from a mouse. In this I represented the whole kingdom welcoming his grace to his native soil, not forgetting the loss France and Italy would sustain in their arts by his departure. I expected to touch for a bank bill at least; so folding up my verses in gilt paper, I gave my last half crown to a genteel servant to be the bearer. My letter was safely conveyed to his grace, and the servant after four hours' absence, during which time I led the life of a fiend, returned with a letter four times as big as mine. Guess my extasy at the prospect of so fine a return. I eagerly took the pacquet into my hands, that trembled to receive it. I kept it some time unopened before me, brooding over the expected treasure it contained; when opening it, as I hope to be saved, gentlemen, his grace had sent me in payment for my poem no bank bills, but six copies of verse, each longer than mine, addressed to him upon the same occasion.'

'A nobleman, cries a member, who had hitherto been silent, is created as much for the confusion of us authors as the catchpole. I'll tell you a story, gentlemen, which is as true as that this pipe is made of clay. When I was delivered of my first book, I owed my tailor for a suit of clothes, but that is nothing new, you know, and may be any man's case as well as mine. Well, owing him for a suit of clothes, and hearing that my book took very well, he sent for his money, and insisted upon being paid immediately: though I was at that time rich in fame, for my book run like wild-fire, yet I was very short in money, and being unable to satisfy his demand, prudently resolved to keep my chamber, preferring a prison of my own choosing at home, to one of my tailor's choosing abroad. In vain the bailiffs used all their arts to decoy me from my citadel, in vain they sent to let me know that a gentleman wanted to speak with me at the next tavern, in vain they came with an urgent message from my aunt in the country; in vain I was told that a particular friend was at the point of death, and desired to take his last farewell; I was deaf, insensible, rock, adamant, the bailiffs could make no impression on my hard heart, for I effectually kept my liberty by never stirring out of the room.

'This was very well for a fortnight; when one morning I received a most splendid message from the earl of Doomsday, importing that he had read my book, and was in raptures with every line of it; he impatiently longed to see the author, and had some designs which might turn out greatly to my advantage. I paused upon the contents of this message, and found there could be no deceit, for the card was gilt at the edges, and the bearer, I was told, had quite the look of a gentleman. Witness, ye powers, how my heart triumphed at my own importance; I saw a long perspective of felicity before me, I applauded the taste of the times, which never saw genius forsaken; I had prepared a set introductory speech for the occasion, five glaring compliments for his lordship, and two more modest for myself. The next morning, therefore, in order to be punctual to my appointment, I took coach, and ordered the fellow to drive to the street and house mentioned in his lordship's address. I had the precaution to pull up the windows as I went along to keep off the busy part of mankind, and, big with expectation, fancied the coach never went fast enough. At length, however, the wished for moment of its stopping arrived, this for some time I impatiently expected, and letting down the door in a transport, in order to take a previous view of his lordship's magnificent palace and situation, I found poison to my sight! I found myself, not in an elegant street, but a paltry lane, not at a nobleman's door, but the door of a spunging-house; I found the coachman had all this while been just driving me to jail, and I saw the bailiff with a devil's face, coming out to secure me.'

To a philosopher, no circumstance, however trifling, is too minute; he finds instruction and entertainment in occurrences, which are passed over by the rest of mankind as low, trite, and indifferent; it is from the number of these particulars, which, to many, appear insignificant, that he is at last enabled to form general conclusions; this, therefore, must be my excuse for sending so far as China accounts of manners and follies, which, though minute in their own nature, serve more truly to characterise this people than histories of their public treaties, courts, ministers, negotiations, and ambassadors.   Adieu.

LETTER XXXI.—*From the same.*

THE English have not yet brought the art of gardening to the same perfection with the Chinese, but have lately begun to imitate them; Nature is now followed with greater assiduity than formerly; the trees are suffered to shoot out into the utmost luxuriance; the streams no longer forced from their native beds, are permitted to wind along the vallies; spontaneous flowers take place of the finished parterre, and the enamelled meadow of the shaven green.

Yet still the English are far behind us in this charming art; their designers have not yet attained a power of uniting instruction with beauty. An European will scarcely conceive my meaning, when I say that there is scarce a garden in China which does not contain some fine moral, couched under the general design, where one is not taught wisdom as he walks, and feels the force of some noble truth, or delicate precept resulting from the disposition of the groves, streams or grottos. Permit me to illustrate what I mean by a description of my gardens at Quamsi. My heart still hovers round those scenes of former happiness with pleasure; and I find a satisfaction in enjoying them at this distance, though but in imagination.

* D 902

You descended from the house between two groves of trees, planted in such a manner, that they were impenetrable to the eye; while on each hand the way was adorned with all that was beautiful in porcelain, statuary, and painting. This passage from the house opened into an area surrounded with rocks, flowers, trees, and shrubs, but all so disposed as if each was the spontaneous production of Nature. As you proceeded forward on this lawn, to your right and left hand were two gates, opposite each other, of very different architecture and design; and before you lay a temple built rather with minute elegance than ostentation.

The right-hand gate was planned with the utmost simplicity, or rather rudeness; ivy clasped round the pillars, the baleful cypress hung over it; time seemed to have destroyed all the smoothness and regularity of the stone: two champions with lifted clubs appeared in the act of guarding its access; dragons and serpents were seen in the most hideous attitudes, to deter the spectator from approaching; and the perspective view that lay behind, seemed dark and gloomy to the last degree; the stranger was tempted to enter only from the motto: PERVIA VIRTUTI.

The opposite gate was formed in a very different manner; the architecture was light, elegant, and inviting; flowers hung in wreaths round the pillars; all was finished in the most exact and masterly manner; the very stone of which it was built, still preserved its polish; nymphs, wrought by the hand of a master, in the most alluring attitudes, beckoned the stranger to approach; while all that lay behind, as far as the eye could reach, seemed gay, luxuriant, and capable of affording endless pleasure. The motto itself contributed to invite him; for over the gate was written these words, FACILIS DESCENSUS.

By this time I fancy you begin to perceive that the gloomy gate was designed to represent the road to Virtue; the opposite, the more agreeable passage to Vice. It is but natural to suppose, that the spectator was always tempted to enter by the gate which offered him so many allurements; I always in these cases left him to his choice; but generally found that he took to the left, which promised most entertainment.

Immediately upon his entering the gate of Vice, the trees and flowers were disposed in such a manner as to make the most pleasing impression; but as he walked farther on, he insensibly found the garden assume the air of a wilderness, the landskips began to darken, the paths grew more intricate, he appeared to go downwards, frightful rocks seemed to hang over his head, gloomy caverns, unexpected precipices, awful ruins, heaps of unburied bones, and terrifying sounds, caused by unseen waters, began to take place of what at first appeared so lovely; it was in vain to attempt returning, the labyrinth was too much perplexed for any but myself to find the way back. In short, when sufficiently impressed with the horrors of what he saw, and the imprudence of his choice, I brought him by an hidden door, a shorter way back into the area from whence at first he had strayed.

The gloomy gate now presented itself before the stranger; and though there seemed little in its appearance to tempt his curiosity, yet encouraged by the motto, he generally proceeded. The darkness of the entrance, the frightful figures that seemed to obstruct his way, the trees of a mournful green, conspired at first to disgust him: as he went forward, however, all began to open and wear a more pleasing appearance, beautiful cascades, beds of flowers, trees loaded with fruit or blossoms, and unexpected brooks, improved the scene: he now found that he was ascending, and, as he proceeded, all Nature grew more beautiful, the prospect widened as he went higher, even the air itself, seemed to become more pure. Thus pleased, and happy from unexpected beauties, I at last led him to an arbour, from whence he could view the garden, and the whole country around, and where he might own, that the road to Virtue terminated in Happiness.

Though from this description you may imagine, that a vast tract of ground was necessary to exhibit such a pleasing variety in, yet be assured I have seen several gardens in England take up ten times the space which mine did, without half the beauty. A very small extent of ground is enough for an elegant taste; the greater room is required if magnificence is in view. There is no spot, tho' ever so little, which a skilful designer might not thus improve, so as to convey a delicate allegory, and impress the mind with truths the most useful and necessary.   Adieu.

LETTER XXXII.—*From the same.*

IN a late excursion with my friend into the country, a gentleman with a blue ribbon tied round his shoulder, and in a chariot drawn by six horses passed swiftly by us, attended with a numerous train of captains, lacquies, and coaches filled with women. When we were recovered from the dust raised by this cavalcade, and could continue our discourse without danger of suffocation, I observed to my companion, that all this state and equipage which he seemed to despise, would in China be regarded with the utmost reverence, because such distinctions were always the reward of merit; the greatness of a Mandarine's retinue being a most certain mark of the superiority of his abilities or virtue.

The gentleman who has now passed us, replied my companion, has no claims from his own merit to distinction; he is possessed neither of abilities nor virtue; it is enough for him that one of his ancestors was possessed of these qualities two hundred years before him.   There was a time, indeed, when his family deserved their title, but they are long since degenerated, and his ancestors for more than a century have been more and more solicitous to keep up the breed of their dogs and horses, than that of their children.   This very nobleman, simple as he seems, is descended from a race of statesmen and heroes; but unluckily his great grandfather marrying a cook maid, and she having a trifling passion for his lordship's groom, they somehow crossed the strain, and produced an heir, who took after his mother in his great love to *good eating*, and his father in a violent affection for *horse flesh*.   These passions have for some generations passed on from father to son, and are now become characteristics of the family, his present lordship being equally remarkable for his kitchen and his stable.

But such a nobleman, cried I, deserves our pity thus placed in so high a sphere of life, which only the more exposes to contempt.   A king may confer titles, but it is personal merit alone that insures respect.   I suppose, added I, that such men who are despised by their equals, neglected by their inferiors, are condemned to live among involuntary dependants in irksome solitude?

You are still under a mistake, replied my companion, for though this nobleman is a stranger to generosity; though he takes twenty opportunities in a day of letting his guests know how much he despises them; though he is possessed neither of taste, wit, nor wisdom: though incapable of improving others by his conversation, and never known to enrich any by his bounty, yet for all this, his company is eagerly sought after: he is a lord, and that is as much as most people desire in a companion. Quality and title have such allurements, that hundreds are ready to give up all their own importance, to cringe, to flatter, to look little, and to pall every pleasure in constraint, merely to be among the great, though without the least hopes of improving their understanding, or sharing their generosity; they might be happy among their equals, but those are despised for company, where they are despised in turn. You saw what a crowd of humble cousins, card-ruined beaus, and captains on half-pay, were willing to make up this great man's retinue down to his country seat. Not one of all these that could not lead a more comfortable life at home in their little lodging of three shillings a week, with their luke-warm dinner, served up between two pewter plates from a cook's shop. Yet poor devils, they are willing to undergo the impertinence and pride of their entertainer, merely to be thought to live among the great: they are willing to pass the summer in bondage, though conscious they are taken down only to approve his lordship's taste upon every occasion, to tag all his stupid observations with a *very true*, to praise his stable, and descant upon his claret and cookery.

The pitiful humiliations of the gentlemen you are now describing, said I, puts me in mind of a custom among the Tartars of Koreki, not entirely dissimilar to this we are now considering.[1] The Russians, who trade with them, carry thither a kind of mushrooms, which they exchange for furs of squirrels, ermines, sables, and foxes. These mushrooms the rich Tartars lay up in large quantities for the winter; and when a nobleman makes a mushroom feast, all the neighbours around are invited. The mushrooms are prepared by boiling, by which the water acquires an intoxicating quality, and is a sort of drink which the Tartars prize beyond all other. When the nobility and ladies are assembled, and the ceremonies usual between people of distinction over, the mushroom broth goes freely round; they laugh, talk double entendre, grow fuddled, and become excellent company. The poorer sort, who love mushroom broth to distraction as well as the rich, but cannot afford it at the first hand, post themselves on these occasions round the huts of the rich, and watch the opportunity of the ladies and gentlemen as they come down to pass their liquor, and holding a wooden bowl, catch the delicious fluid, very little altered by filtration, being still strongly tinctured with the intoxicating quality. Of this they drink with the utmost satisfaction, and thus they get as drunk and as jovial as their betters.

Happy nobility, cries my companion, who can fear no diminu-

---

[1] Van Stralenberg, a writer of credit, gives the same account of this people. Vid. an Historico-Geographical Description of the north eastern parts of Europe and Asia, p. 397

tion of respect, unless by being seized with a strangury; and who when most drunk are most useful; though we have not this custom among us, I foresee, that if it were introduced, we might have many a toad-eater in England ready to drink from the wooden bowl on these occasions, and to praise the flavour of his lordship's liquor: As we have different classes of gentry, who knows but we may see a lord holding the bowl to a minister, a knight holding it to his lordship, and a simple 'squire drinking it double distilled from the loins of knighthood. For my part, I shall never for the future hear a great man's flatterers haranguing in his praise that I shall not fancy I behold the wooden bowl; for I can see no reason why a man, who can live easily and happily at home, should bear the drudgery of decorum and the impertinence of his entertainer, unless intoxicated with a passion for all that was quality; unless he thought that whatever came from the great was delicious, and had the tincture of the mushroom in it.   Adieu.

LETTER XXXIII.—*From the same.*

I am disgusted, O Fum Hoam, even to sickness disgusted. Is it possible to bear the presumption of those islanders, when they pretend to instruct me in the ceremonies of China! They lay it down as a maxim, that every person who comes from thence must express himself in metaphor; swear by Alla, rail against wine, and behave, and talk and write like a Turk or Persian They make no distinction between our elegant manners, and the voluptuous barbarities of our eastern neighbours. Wherever I come, I raise either diffidence or astonishment; some fancy me no Chinese, because I am formed more like a man than a monster; and others wonder to find one born five thousand miles from England endued with common sense. Strange, say they, that a man who has received his education at such a distance from London, should have common sense: to be born out of England, and yet have common sense! impossible! He must be some Englishman in disguise; his very visage has nothing of the true exotic barbarity.

I yesterday received an invitation from a lady of distinction, who it seems had collected all her knowledge of eastern manners from fictions every day propagated here, under the titles of eastern tales, and oriental histories: she received me very politely, but seemed to wonder that I neglected bringing opium and a tobacco box; when chairs were drawn for the rest of the company, I was assigned my place on a cushion on the floor. It was in vain that I protested the Chinese used chairs as in Europe; she understood decorums too well to entertain me with the ordinary civilities.

I had scarce been seated according to her directions, when the footman was ordered to pin a napkin under my chin; this I protested against, as being no way Chinese; however, the whole company, who it seems were a club of connoisseurs, gave it unanimously against me, and the napkin was pinned accordingly.

It was impossible to be angry with people, who seemed to err only from an excess of politeness, and I sat contented, expecting their importunities were now at an end; but as soon as ever dinner was served, the lady demanded whether I was for a plate of *Bear's claws*, or a slice of *Bird's nests*? As these were dishes with which I was utterly unacquainted, I was desirous of eating only what I knew, and therefore begged to be helped from a piece of beef that lay on the side table: my request at once disconcerted the whole company. A Chinese eat beef! that could never be! there was no local propriety in Chinese beef, whatever there might be in Chinese pheasant. Sir, said my entertainer, I think I have some reason to fancy myself a judge of these matters: in short, the Chinese never eat beef; so that I must be permitted to recommend the Pilaw, there was never better dressed at Pekin; the saffron and rice well boiled, and the spices in perfection.

I had no sooner began to eat what was laid before me, than I found the whole company as much astonished as before; it seems I made no use of my chop-sticks. A grave gentleman, whom I take to be an author, harangued very learnedly (as the company seemed to think) upon the use which was made of them in China: he entered into a long argument with himself about their first introduction, without once appealing to me, who might be supposed best capable of silencing the enquiry. As the gentleman therefore took my silence for a mark of his own superior sagacity, he was resolved to pursue the triumph: he talked of our cities, mountains and animals, as familiarly as if he had been born in Quamsi, but as erroneously as if a native of the moon; he attempted to prove that I had nothing of the true Chinese cut in my visage; shewed that my cheek bones should have been higher, and my forehead broader; in short, he almost reasoned me out of my country, and effectually persuaded the rest of the company to be of his opinion.

I was going to expose his mistakes, when it was insisted that I had nothing of the true eastern manner in my delivery. This gentleman's conversation (says one of the ladies, who was a great reader) is like our own, mere chit chat and common sense; there is nothing like sense in the true eastern style, where nothing more is required but sublimity. Oh, for an history of Aboulfaouris, the grand voyager, of genii, magicians, rocks, bags of bullets, giants, and enchanters, where all is great, obscure, magnificent, and unintelligible! I have written many a sheet of eastern tale myself, interrupts the author, and I defy the severest critic to say but that I have stuck close to the true manner. I have compared a lady's chin to the snow upon the mountains of Bomek; a soldier's sword, to the clouds that obscure the face of heaven. If riches are mentioned, I compare them to the flocks that graze the verdant Tefflis; if poverty, to the mists that veil the brow of mount Baku. I have used *thee* and *thou* upon all occasions, I have described fallen stars, and splitting mountains, not forgetting the little Houries who make a pretty figure in every description. But you shall hear how I generally begin. 'Eben-ben-bolo, who was the son of Ban, was born on the foggy summits of Benderabassi. His beard was whiter than the feathers which veil the breast of the Penguin; his eyes were like the eyes of doves, when washed by the dews of the morning; his hair, which hung like the willow weeping over the glassy stream, was so beautiful that it seemed to reflect its own brightness; and his feet were as the feet of a wild deer which fleeth to the tops of the mountains.' There, there, is the true eastern taste for you; every advance made towards sense, is only a deviation from sound. Eastern tales should always be sonorous, lofty, musical, and unmeaning.

I could not avoid smiling to hear a native of England attempt to instruct me in the true eastern idiom, and after he looked round some time for applause, I presumed to ask him whether he had ever travelled into the east; to which he replied in the negative; I demanded whether he understood Chinese or Arabic, to which also he answered as before. Then how, Sir, said I, can you pretend to determine upon the eastern style, who are entirely unacquainted with the eastern writings? Take, Sir, the word of one who is *professedly* a Chinese, and who is *actually* acquainted with the Arabian writers, that what is palmed upon you daily for an imitation of eastern writing, no ways resembles their manner, either in sentiment or diction. In the east, similes are seldom used, and metaphors almost wholly unknown;

but in China particularly, the very reverse of what you allude to, takes place; a cool phlegmatic method of writing prevails there. The writers of that country, ever more assiduous to instruct than to please, address rather the judgment than the fancy. Unlike many authors of Europe, who have no consideration of the reader's time, they generally leave more to be understood than they express.

Besides, Sir, you must not expect from an inhabitant of China the same ignorance, the same unlettered simplicity, that you find in a Turk, Persian, or native of Peru. The Chinese are versed in the sciences as well as you, and are masters of several arts unknown to the people of Europe. Many of them are instructed not only in their own national learning, but are perfectly well acquainted with the languages and learning of the west. If my word in such a case, is not to be taken, consult your own travellers on this head, who affirm, that the scholars of Pekin and Siam sustain theological theses in Latin. *The college of Masprend, which is but a league from Siam* (says one of your travellers [1]) *came in a body to salute our ambassador. Nothing gave me more sincere pleasure than to behold a number of priests venerable both from age and modesty, followed by a number of youths of all nations, Chinese, Japanese, Tonquinese, of Cochin China, Pegu and Siam, all willing to pay their respects in the most polite manner imaginable. A Cochin Chinese made an excellent Latin oration upon this occasion: he was succeeded, and even outdone, by a student of Tonquin, who was as well skilled in the western learning as any scholar of Paris.* Now, Sir, if youths who never stirred from home, are so perfectly skilled in your laws and learning, surely more must be expected from one like me, who have travelled so many thousand miles, who have conversed familiarly for several years with the English factors established at Canton, and the missionaries sent us from every part of Europe. The unaffected of every country nearly resemble each other, and a page of our Confucius and of your Tillotson have scarce any material difference. Paltry affectation, strained allusions, and disgusting finery, are easily attained by those who choose to wear them; and they are but too frequently the badges of ignorance, or of stupidity whenever it would endeavour to please.

I was proceeding in my discourse, when, looking round, I perceived the company no way attentive to what I attempted,

---

[1] Journal ou suite du Voyage de Siam en forme de Lettres familieres fait en 1685, et 1686, par N. L. D. C., p. 174, edit. Amstelod. 1686.

with so much earnestness, to enforce. One lady was whispering her that sat next, another was studying the merits of a fan, a third began to yawn, and the author himself fell fast asleep: I thought it, therefore, high time to make a retreat, nor did the company seem to shew any regret at my preparations for departure; even the lady who had invited me, with the most mortifying insensibility, saw me seize my hat and rise from my cushion; nor was I invited to repeat my visit, because it was found that I aimed at appearing rather a reasonable creature, than an outlandish idiot. Adieu.

LETTER XXXIV.—*To the same.*

THE polite arts are in this country subject to as many revolutions as its laws or politics; not only the object of fancy and dress, but even of delicacy and taste are directed by the capricious influence of fashion. I am told there has been a time when poetry was universally encouraged by the great, when men of the first rank not only patronised the poet, but produced the finest models for his imitation: it was then the English sent forth those glowing rhapsodies, which we have so often read over together with rapture; poems big with all the sublimity of Mentius, and supported by reasoning as strong as that of Zimpo.

The nobility are fond of wisdom, but they are also fond of having it without study; to read poetry required thought, and the English nobility were not fond of thinking; they soon therefore placed their affections upon music, because in this they might indulge an happy vacancy, and yet still have pretensions to delicacy and taste as before. They soon brought their numerous dependants into an approbation of their pleasures; who in turn led their thousand imitators to feel or feign a similitude of passion. Colonies of singers were now imported from abroad at a vast expense, and it was expected the English would soon be able to set examples to Europe; all these expectations however were soon dissipated; in spite of the zeal which fired the great, the ignorant vulgar refused to be taught to sing; refused to undergo the ceremonies which were to initiate them in the singing fraternity; thus the colony from abroad dwindled by degrees; for they were of themselves unfortunately incapable of propagating the idea.

Music having thus lost its splendour, Painting is now become the sole object of fashionable care; the title of connoisseur in

that art is at present the safest passport in every fashionable
society; a well timed shrug, an admiring attitude, and one or
two exotic tones of exclamation are sufficient qualifications
for men of low circumstances to curry favour; even some of the
young nobility are themselves early instructed in handling the
pencil, while their happy parents, big with expectation, foresee
the walls of every apartment covered with the manufactures
of their posterity.

But many of the English are not content with giving all their
time to this art at home; some young men of distinction are
found to travel thro' Europe with no other intent than that
of understanding and collecting pictures; studying seals, and
describing statues; on they travel from this cabinet of curiosities
to that gallery of pictures, waste the prime of life in wonder,
skilful in pictures, ignorant in men; yet impossible to be reclaimed, because their follies take shelter under the names of
delicacy and taste.

It is true, Painting should have due encouragement; as the
painter can undoubtedly fit up our apartments in a much more
elegant manner than the upholsterer; but I should think a man
of fashion makes but an indifferent exchange, who lays out all
that time in furnishing his house which he should have employed
in the furniture of his head; a person who shews no other
symptoms of taste than his cabinet or gallery, might as well
boast to me of the furniture of his kitchen.

I know no other motive but vanity that induces the great
to testify such an inordinate passion for pictures; after the piece
is bought, and gazed at eight or ten days successively, the purchaser's pleasure must surely be over; all the satisfaction he
can then have, is to shew it to others; he may be considered as
the guardian of a treasure of which he makes no manner of use;
his gallery is furnished not for himself, but the connoisseur,
who is generally some humble flatterer, ready to feign a
rapture he does not feel; and as necessary to the happiness of
a picture buyer, as gazers are to the magnificence of an Asiatic
procession.

I have enclosed a letter from a youth of distinction, on his
travels, to his father in England; in which he appears addicted
to no vice, seems obedient to his governor, of a good natural
disposition, and fond of improvement; but at the same time
early taught to regard cabinets and galleries as the only proper
schools of improvement, and to consider a skill in pictures as
the properest knowledge for a man of quality.

My Lord,

We have been but two days at Antwerp, wherefore I have sat down as soon as possible to give you some account of what we have seen since our arrival, desirous of letting no opportunity pass without writing to so good a father. Immediately upon alighting from our Rotterdam machine, my governor who is immoderately fond of paintings, and at the same time an excellent judge, would let no time pass till we paid our respects to the church of the Virgin-Mother, which contains treasure beyond estimation. We took an infinity of pains in knowing its exact dimensions, and differed half a foot in our calculations; so I leave that to some succeeding information. I really believe my governor and I could have lived and died there. There is scarce a pillar in the whole church that is not adorned by a Rubens, a Vander Meuylen, a Vandyke, or a Wouverman. What attitudes, carnations, and draperies! I am almost induced to pity the English who have none of those exquisite pieces among them. As we are willing to let slip no opportunity of doing business, we immediately after went to wait on Mr. Hogendorp, whom you have so frequently commended for his judicious collection. His cameos are indeed beyond price; his intaglios not so good. He showed us one of an officiating flamen, which he thought to be an antique; but my governor, who is not to be deceived in these particulars, soon found it to be an arrant *cinque cento*. I could not, however, sufficiently admire the genius of Mr. Hogendorp, who has been able to collect from all parts of the world a thousand things which nobody knows the use of. Except your lordship and my governor, I do not know any body I admire so much. He is indeed a surprizing genius. The next morning early, as we were resolved to take the whole day before us, we sent our compliments to Mr. Van Sprockken, desiring to see his gallery, which request he very politely complied with. His gallery measures fifty feet by twenty, and is well filled; but what surprized me most of all, was to see an holy family just like your lordship's, which this ingenious gentleman assures me is the true original. I own this gave me inexpressible uneasiness, and I fear it will to your lordship, as I had flattered myself that the only original was in your lordship's possession; I would advise you, however, to take yours down till its merit can be ascertained, my governor assuring me, that he intends to write a long dissertation to prove its originality. One might study in this city for ages, and still find something new: we went from this to view the cardinal's statues, which are really very fine; there were three spintria executed in a very masterly manner, all arm in arm: the torse which I heard you talk so much of, is at last discovered to be a Hercules spinning, and not a Cleopatra bathing, as your lordship had conjectured: there has been a treatise written to prove it.

My lord Firmly is certainly a Goth, a Vandal, no taste in the world for painting. I wonder how any call him a man of taste; passing through the streets of Antwerp a few days ago, and observing the nakedness of the inhabitants, he was so barbarous as to observe, that he thought the best method the Flemings could take, was to sell their pictures, and buy clothes. Ah, Coglione! We shall go to-morrow to Mr. Carwarden's cabinet, and the next day we shall see the curiosities collected by Van Ran, and the day after we shall pay a visit to Mount Calvary, and after that——but I find my paper finished; so with the most sincere wishes to your lordship's happiness, and with hopes after having seen Italy, that centre of pleasure, to return home worthy the care and expense which has been generously laid out in my improvement,

I remain, my Lord,

Yours, etc.

LETTER XXXV.—*From Hingpo, a slave in Persia, to Altangi, a travelling philosopher of China, by the way of Moscow.*

FORTUNE has made me the slave of another, but nature and inclination render me entirely subservient to you; a tyrant commands my body, but you are master of my heart. And yet let not thy inflexible nature condemn me when I confess that I find my soul shrink with my circumstances. I feel my mind, not less than my body, bend beneath the rigours of servitude; the master whom I serve grows every day more formidable. In spite of reason which should teach me to despise him, his hideous image fills even my dreams with horror.

A few days ago a Christian slave, who wrought in the gardens, happening to enter an arbour where the tyrant was entertaining the ladies of his Haram with coffee, the unhappy captive was instantly stabbed to the heart for his intrusion. I have been preferred to his place, which tho' less laborious than my former station, is yet more ungrateful, as it brings me nearer him whose presence excites sensations at once of disgust and apprehension.

Into what a state of misery are the modern Persians fallen!

A nation famous for setting the world an example of freedom, is now become a land of tyrants, and a den of slaves. The houseless Tartar of Kamkatska, who enjoys his herbs and his fish in unmolested freedom, may be envied, if compared to the thousands who pine here in hopeless servitude, and curse the day that gave them being. Is this just dealing, Heaven! to render millions wretched to swell up the happiness of a few; cannot the powerful of this earth be happy without our sighs and tears; must every luxury of the great be woven from the calamities of the poor! It must, it must surely be, that this jarring discordant life is but the prelude to some future harmony; the soul attuned to virtue here, shall go from hence to fill up the universal choir where Tien presides in person, where there shall be no tyrants to frown, no shackles to bind, nor no whips to threaten, where I shall once more meet my father with rapture, and give a loose to filial piety, where I shall hang on his neck, and hear the wisdom of his lips, and thank him for all the happiness to which he has introduced me.

The wretch whom fortune has made my master, has lately purchased several slaves of both sexes; among the rest I hear a Christian captive talked of with admiration. The eunuch who bought her, and who is accustomed to survey beauty with indifference, speaks of her with emotion! Her pride, however, astonishes her attendant slaves not less than her beauty; it is reported that she refuses the warmest solicitations of her haughty lord; he has even offered to make her one of his four wives upon changing her religion, and conforming to his. It is probable she cannot refuse such extraordinary offers, and her delay is perhaps intended to enhance her favours.

I have just now seen her, she inadvertently approached the place without a veil, where I sat writing. She seemed to regard the heavens alone with fixed attention; there her most ardent gaze was directed. Genius of the sun! what unexpected softness! what animated grace! her beauty seemed the transparent covering of virtue. Celestial beings could not wear a look of more perfection while sorrow humanised her form, and mixed my admiration with pity. I rose from the bank on which I sat, and she retired; happy that none observed us, for such an interview might have been fatal.

I have regarded, till now, the opulence and the power of my tyrant, without envy; I saw him with a mind incapable of enjoying the gifts of fortune, and consequently regarded him as one loaded, rather than enriched with its favours. But at present, when I think that so much beauty is reserved only for him, that so many charms shall be lavished on a wretch incapable of feeling the greatness of the blessing, I own I feel a reluctance to which I have hitherto been a stranger.

But let not my father impute those uneasy sensations to so trifling a cause as love. No, never let it be thought that *your* son, and the pupil of the wise Fum Hoam, could stoop to so degrading a passion. I am only displeased at seeing so much excellence so unjustly disposed of.

The uneasiness which I feel is not for myself, but for the beautiful Christian. When I reflect on the barbarity of him for whom she is designed, I pity, indeed I pity her. When I think that she must only share one heart, who deserves to command a thousand, excuse me, if I feel an emotion, which universal benevolence extorts from me. As I am convinced, that you take a pleasure in those sallies of humanity, and are particularly pleased with compassion, I could not avoid discovering the sensibility with which I felt this beautiful stranger's distress. I have for a while forgot in hers, the miseries of my own hopeless situation. The tyrant grows every day more severe, and love which softens all other minds into tenderness, seems only to have encreased his severity. Adieu.

LETTER XXXVI.—*To the same.*

THE whole Haram is filled with a tumultuous joy; Zelis, the beautiful captive, has consented to embrace the religion of Mahomet, and become one of the wives of the fastidious Persian. It is impossible to describe the transport that sits on every face on this occasion. Music and feasting fill every apartment, the most miserable slave seems to forget his chains, and sympathizes with the happiness of Mostadad. The herb we tread beneath our feet is not made more for our use, than every slave around him for their imperious master; mere machines of obedience, they wait with silent assiduity, feel his pains, and rejoice in his exultation. Heavens! how much is requisite to make one man happy!

Twelve of the most beautiful slaves, and I among the number, have got orders to prepare for carrying him in triumph to the bridal apartment. The blaze of perfumed torches are to imitate the day; the dancers and singers are hired at a vast expence. The nuptials are to be celebrated on the approaching feast of

Barboura, when an hundred taels in gold are to be distributed among the barren wives, in order to pray for fertility from the approaching union.

What will not riches procure! an hundred domestics, who curse the tyrant in their souls, are commanded to wear a face of joy, and they are joyful. An hundred flatterers are ordered to attend, and they fill his ears with praise. Beauty, all-commanding beauty, sues for admittance, and scarcely receives an answer; even love itself seems to wait upon fortune, or though the passion be only feigned, yet it wears every appearance of sincerity; and what greater pleasure can even true sincerity confer, or what would the rich have more?

Nothing can exceed the intended magnificence of the bridegroom, but the costly dresses of the bride; six eunuchs in the most sumptuous habits are to conduct him to the nuptial couch, and wait his orders. Six ladies, in all the magnificence of Persia, are directed to undress the bride. Their business is to assist to encourage her, to divest her of every encumbering part of her dress, all but the last covering, which, by an artful complication of ribbons, is purposely made difficult to unloose, and with which she is to part reluctantly even to the joyful possessor of her beauty.

Mostadad, O my father, is no philosopher; and yet he seems perfectly contented with ignorance. Possessed of numberless slaves, camels, and women, he desires no greater possession. He never opened the page of Mencius, and yet all the slaves tell me that he is happy.

Forgive the weakness of my nature, if I sometimes feel my heart rebellious to the dictates of wisdom, and eager for happiness like his. Yet why wish for his wealth with his ignorance; to be like him, incapable of sentimental pleasures, incapable of feeling the happiness of making others happy, incapable of teaching the beautiful Zelis philosophy?

What, shall I in a transport of passion give up the golden mean, the universal harmony, the unchanging essence for the possession of an hundred camels; as many slaves, thirty-five beautiful horses, and seventy-three fine women: first blast me to the centre! Degrade me beneath the most degraded! Pare my nails, ye powers of heaven! ere I would stoop to such an exchange. What, part with philosophy, which teaches me to suppress my passions instead of gratifying them, which teaches me even to divest my soul of passion, which teaches serenity in the midst of tortures; philosophy, by which even now I am so very serene, and so very much at ease, to be persuaded to part with it for any other enjoyment! Never, never, even though persuasion spoke in the accents of Zelis!

A female slave informs me that the bride is to be arrayed in a tissue of silver, and her hair adorned with the largest pearls of Ormus; but why tease you with particulars, in which we both are so little concerned? The pain I feel in separation throws a gloom over my mind, which in this scene of universal joy I fear may be attributed to some other cause; how wretched are those who are like me, denied even the last resource of misery, their tears. Adieu.

LETTER XXXVII.—*From the same.*

I BEGIN to have doubts whether wisdom be alone sufficient to make us happy, whether every step we make in refinement is not an inlet into new disquietudes. A mind too vigorous and active, serves only to consume the body to which it is joined, as the richest jewels are soonest found to wear their settings.

When we rise in knowledge as the prospect widens, the objects of our regard become more obscure, and the unlettered peasant, whose views are only directed to the narrow sphere around him, beholds Nature with a finer relish, and tastes her blessings with a keener appetite than the philosopher, whose mind attempts to grasp an universal system.

As I was some days ago pursuing this subject among a circle of my fellow slaves, an ancient Guebre of the number, equally remarkable for his piety and wisdom, seemed touched with my conversation, and desired to illustrate what I had been saying with an allegory taken from the Zendavesta of Zoroaster; by this shall we be taught, says he, that they who travel in pursuit of wisdom, walk only in a circle; and after all their labour, at last return to their pristine ignorance; and in this also we shall see that enthusiastic confidence or unsatisfying doubts terminate all our enquiries.

In early times, before myriads of nations covered the earth, the whole human race lived together in one valley. The simple inhabitants, surrounded on every side by lofty mountains, knew no other world but the little spot to which they were confined. They fancied the heavens bent down to meet the mountain tops, and formed an impenetrable wall to surround them. None had ever yet ventured to climb the steepy cliff, in order to explore those regions that lay beyond it; they knew the nature of the skies only from a tradition, which mentioned their being made of adamant; traditions make up the reasonings of the simple, and serve to silence every enquiry.

In this sequestered vale, blessed with all the spontaneous productions of Nature, the honeyed blossom, the refreshing breeze, the gliding brook, and golden fruitage, the simple inhabitants seemed happy in themselves, in each other; they desired no greater pleasures, for they knew of none greater; ambition, pride and envy, were vices unknown among them; and from this peculiar simplicity of its possessors, the country was called *the Valley of Ignorance*.

At length, however, an unhappy youth, more aspiring than the rest, undertook to climb the mountain's side, and examine the summits which were hitherto deemed inaccessible. The inhabitants from below, gazed with wonder at his intrepidity, some applauded his courage, others censured his folly, still however he proceeded towards the place where the earth and heavens seemed to unite, and at length arrived at the wished for height with extreme labour and assiduity.

His first surprise was to find the skies, not as he expected within his reach, but still as far off as before; his amazement increased when he saw a wide extended region lying on the opposite side of the mountain, but it rose to astonishment when he beheld a country at a distance more beautiful and alluring than even that he had just left behind.

As he continued to gaze with wonder, a genius, with a look of infinite modesty, approaching, offered to be his guide and instructor. The distant country which you so much admire, says the angelic being, is called *the Land of Certainty*, in that charming retreat, sentiment contributes to refine every sensual banquet; the inhabitants are blessed with every solid enjoyment, and still more blessed in a perfect consciousness of their own felicity; ignorance in that country is wholly unknown, all there is satisfaction without alloy, for every pleasure first undergoes the examination of reason. As for me I am called the genius of *Demonstration*, and am stationed here in order to conduct every adventurer to that land of happiness through those intervening regions you see over-hung with fogs and darkness, and horrid with forests, cataracts, caverns, and various other shapes of danger. But follow me, and in time I may lead you to that distant desirable land of tranquillity.

The intrepid traveller immediately put himself under the

direction of the genius, and both journeying on together with a slow but agreeable pace, deceived the tediousness of the way by conversation. The beginning of the journey seemed to promise true satisfaction, but as they proceeded forward, the skies became more gloomy and the way more intricate, they often inadvertently approached the brow of some frightful precipice, or the brink of a torrent, and were obliged to measure back their former way; the gloom increasing as they proceeded, their pace became more slow; they paused at every step, frequently stumbled, and their distrust and timidity encreased. The genius of Demonstration now, therefore, advised his pupil to grope upon hands and feet, as a method though more slow, yet less liable to error.

In this manner they attempted to pursue their journey for some time, when they were overtaken by another genius, who, with a precipitate pace seemed travelling the same way. He was instantly known by the other to be the *genius of Probability*. He wore two wide extended wings at his back, which incessantly waved, without increasing the rapidity of his motion; his countenance betrayed a confidence that the ignorant might mistake for sincerity, and he had but one eye, which was fixed in the middle of his forehead.

Servant of Hormizda, cried he, approaching the mortal pilgrim, if thou art travelling to the *Land of Certainty*, how is it possible to arrive there under the guidance of a genius, who proceeds forward so slowly, and is so little acquainted with the way; follow me, we shall soon perform the journey to where every pleasure awaits our arrival.

The peremptory tone in which this genius spoke, and the speed which with he moved forward, induced the traveller to change his conductor, and leaving his modest companion behind, he proceeded forward with his more confident director, seeming not a little pleased at the increased velocity of his motion.

But soon he found reasons to repent. Whenever a torrent crossed their way, his guide taught him to despise the obstacle by plunging him in; whenever a precipice presented, he was directed to fling himself forward. Thus each moment miraculously escaping; his repeated escapes only served to increase his temerity. He led him therefore forward, amidst infinite difficulties, till they arrived at the borders of an ocean which appeared unnavigable from the black mists that lay upon its surface. Its unquiet waves were of the darkest hue, and gave a lively representation of the various agitations of the human mind.

The genius of Probability now confessed his temerity, owned his being an improper guide to the *Land of Certainty*, a country where no mortal has ever been permitted to arrive; but at the same time offered to supply the traveller with another conductor, who should carry him to *the Land of Confidence*, a region where the inhabitants lived with the utmost tranquillity, and tasted almost as much satisfaction as if in the Land of Certainty. Not waiting for a reply, he stamped three times on the ground, and called forth *the Dæmon of Error*, a gloomy fiend of the servants of Arimanes. The yawning earth gave up the reluctant savage, who seemed unable to bear the light of the day. His stature was enormous, his colour black and hideous, his aspect betrayed a thousand varying passions, and he spread forth pinions that were fitted for the most rapid flight. The traveller at first was shocked at the spectre; but finding him obedient to superior power, he assumed his former tranquillity.

I have called you to duty, cries the genius to the dæmon, to bear on your back a son of mortality over the *Ocean of Doubt*, into *the Land of Confidence*: I expect you 'll perform your commission with punctuality. And as for you, continued the genius, addressing the traveller, when once I have bound this fillet round your eyes, let no voice of persuasion, nor threats the most terrifying, persuade you to unbind it in order to look round; keep the fillet fast, look not at the ocean below, and you may certainly expect to arrive at a region of pleasure.

Thus saying, and the traveller's eyes being covered, the dæmon, muttering curses, raised him on his back, and instantly up-borne by his strong pinions, directed his flight among the clouds. Neither the loudest thunder, nor the most angry tempest, could persuade the traveller to unbind his eyes. The dæmon directed his flight downwards, and skimmed the surface of the ocean; a thousand voices, some with loud invectives, others in the sarcastic tones of contempt, vainly endeavoured to persuade him to look round; but he still continued to keep his eyes covered, and would in all probability have arrived at the happy land, had not flattery effected what other means could not perform. For now he heard himself welcomed on every side to the promised land, and an universal shout of joy was sent forth at his safe arrival; the wearied traveller, desirous of seeing the long wished for country, at length pulled the fillet from his eyes, and ventured to look round him. But he had unloosed the band too soon; he was not yet above half way over. The dæmon, who was still hovering in the air, and had produced those sounds only in order to deceive, was now freed from his commission; wherefore throwing the astonished traveller from his back, the unhappy youth fell headlong into the subjacent Ocean of Doubts, from whence he never after was seen to rise.

LETTER XXXVIII.—*From Lien Chi Altangi, to Fum Hoam, first President of the Ceremonial Academy at Pekin, in China.*

WHEN Parmenio, the Grecian, had done something which excited an universal shout from the surrounding multitude, he was instantly struck with the doubt, that what had their approbation must certainly be wrong; and turning to a philosopher who stood near him, *Pray, Sir*, says he, *pardon me; I fear I have been guilty of some absurdity*.

You know that I am not less than him a despiser of the multitude; you know that I equally detest flattery to the great; yet so many circumstances have concurred to give a lustre to the latter part of the present English monarch's reign, that I cannot withhold my contribution of praise; I cannot avoid the acknowledging the crowd for once just, in their unanimous approbation.

Yet think not that battles gained, dominion extended, or enemies brought to submission, are the virtues which at present claim my admiration. Were the reigning monarch only famous for his victories, I should regard his character with indifference; the boast of heroism in this enlightened age is justly regarded as a qualification of a very subordinate rank, and mankind now begin to look with becoming horror on these foes to man; the virtue in this aged monarch which I have at present in view, is one of a much more exalted nature, is one of the most difficult of attainment, is the least praised of all kingly virtues, and yet deserves the greatest praise; the virtue I mean is JUSTICE; a strict administration of justice, without severity and without favour.

Of all virtues this is the most difficult to be practised by a king who has a power to pardon. All men, even tyrants themselves, lean to mercy when unbiassed by passions or interest, the heart naturally persuades to forgiveness, and pursuing the dictates of this pleasing deceiver, we are led to prefer our private satisfaction to public utility; what a thorough love for the public, what a strong command over the passions, what a finely conducted judgment must he possess who opposes the dictates of reason to those of his heart, and prefers the future interest of his people to his own immediate satisfaction.

If still to a man's own natural bias for tenderness, we add the numerous solicitations made by a criminal's friends for mercy; if we survey a king not only opposing his own feelings, but reluctantly refusing those he regards, and this to satisfy the public, whose cries he may never hear, whose gratitude he may never receive, this surely is true greatness! Let us fancy ourselves for a moment in this just old man's place, surrounded by numbers, all soliciting the same favour, a favour that Nature disposes us to grant, where the inducements to pity are laid before us in the strongest light, suppliants at our feet, some ready to resent a refusal, none opposing a compliance; let us, I say, suppose ourselves in such a situation, and I fancy we should find ourselves more apt to act the character of good-natured men than of upright magistrates.

What contributes to raise justice above all other kingly virtues is, that it is seldom attended with a due share of applause, and those who practise it must be influenced by greater motives than empty fame; the people are generally well pleased with a remission of punishment, and all that wears the appearance of humanity; it is the wise alone who are capable of discerning that impartial justice is the truest mercy: they know it to be very difficult, at once to compassionate, and yet condemn an object that pleads for tenderness.

I have been led into this common-place train of thought by a late striking instance in this country of the impartiality of justice, and of the king's inflexible resolution of inflicting punishment where it was justly due. A man of the first quality in a fit either of passion, melancholy, or madness, murdered his servant; it was expected that his station in life would have lessened the ignominy of his punishment; however, he was arraigned, condemned, and underwent the same degrading death with the meanest malefactor. It was well considered that virtue alone is true nobility; and that he whose actions sink him even beneath the vulgar, has no right to those distinctions which should be the rewards only of merit; it was perhaps considered that crimes were more heinous among the higher classes of people, as necessity exposes them to fewer temptations.

Over all the east, even China not excepted, a person of the same quality guilty of such a crime, might, by giving up a share of his fortune to the judge, buy off his sentence; there are several countries, even in Europe, where the servant is entirely the

property of his master; if a slave kills his lord, he dies by the
most excruciating tortures; but if the circumstances are reversed,
a small fine buys off the punishment of the offender. Happy
the country where all are equal, and where those who sit as
judges have too much integrity to receive a bribe, and too much
honour to pity from a similitude of the prisoner's title or
circumstances with their own. Such is England; yet think not
that it was always equally famed for this strict impartiality.
There was a time even here when title softened the rigours of
the law, when dignified wretches were suffered to live, and
continue for years an equal disgrace to justice and nobility.

To this day in a neighbouring country, the great are often most
scandalously pardoned for the most scandalous offences. A
person is still alive among them who has more than once deserved
the most ignominious severity of justice. His being of the
blood royal, however, was thought a sufficient atonement for
his being a disgrace to humanity. This remarkable personage
took pleasure in shooting at the passengers below, from the top
of his palace; and in this most princely amusement he usually
spent some time every day. He was at length arraigned by the
friends of a person whom in this manner he had killed, was found
guilty of the charge, and condemned to die. His merciful
monarch pardoned him in consideration of his rank and quality.
The unrepenting criminal soon after renewed his usual entertainment, and in the same manner killed another man. He
was a second time condemned; and strange to think, a second
time received his majesty's pardon! Would you believe it? A
third time the very same man was guilty of the very same
offence; a third time therefore the laws of his country found him
guilty—I wish for the honour of humanity I could suppress the
rest!—A third time he was pardoned! Will you not think such
a story too extraordinary for belief, will you not think me describing the savage inhabitants of Congo; alas, the story is but
too true, and the country where it was transacted, regards itself
as the politest in Europe! Adieu.

LETTER XXXIX.—*From Lien Chi Altangi to * * *, Merchant
in Amsterdam.*

CEREMONIES are different in every country, but true politeness
is every where the same. Ceremonies, which take up so much of
our attention, are only artificial helps which ignorance assumes,
in order to imitate politeness, which is the result of good sense

and good-nature. A person possessed of these qualities, though he had never seen a court, is truly agreeable; and if without them, would continue a clown, though he had been all his life a gentleman usher.

How would a Chinese, bred up in the formalities of an eastern court, be regarded, should he carry all his good manners beyond the Great Wall? How would an Englishman, skilled in all the decorums of Western good breeding, appear at an Eastern entertainment? Would he not be reckoned more fantastically savage than even his unbred footman?

Ceremony resembles that base coin which circulates through a country by the royal mandate; it serves every purpose of real money at home, but is entirely useless if carried abroad; a person who should attempt to circulate his native trash in another country, would be thought either ridiculous or culpable. He is truly well bred who knows when to value and when to despise those national peculiarities which are regarded by some with so much observance; a traveller of taste at once perceives that the wise are polite all the world over; but that fools are polite only at home.

I have now before me two very fashionable letters upon the same subject, both written by ladies of distinction; one of whom leads the fashion in England, and the other sets the ceremonies of China; they are both regarded in their respective countries by all the beau monde, as standards of taste, and models of true politeness, and both give us a true idea of what they imagine elegant in their admirers; which of them understands true politeness or whether either, you shall be at liberty to determine: the English lady writes thus to her female confidante.

As I live, my dear Charlotte, I believe the colonel will carry it at last; he is a most irresistible fellow, that is flat. So well dressed, so neat, so sprightly, and plays about one so agreeably, that I vow, he has as much spirits as the marquis of Monkey-man's Italian greyhound. I first saw him at Ranelagh; he shines there; he is nothing without Ranelagh, and Ranelagh nothing without him. The next day he sent a card, and compliments, desiring to wait on mamma and me to the music subscription. He looked all the time with such irresistible impudence, that positively he had something in his face gave me as much pleasure as a pair-royal of naturals in my own hand. He waited on mamma and me the next morning to know how we got home: you must know the insidious devil makes love to us both. Rap went the footman at the door; bounce went my heart; I thought he would have rattled the house down. Chariot drove up to the window, with his footmen in the prettiest liveries: he has infinite taste, that is flat. Mamma had spent all the morning at her head; but for my part, I was in an undress to receive him; quite easy, mind that; no way disturbed at his approach: mamma pretended to be as degagée as I, and yet I saw her blush in spite of her. Positively he is a most killing devil! We did nothing but laugh all the time he staid with us; I never heard so many very good things before: at first he mistook mamma for my sister; at which she laughed: then he mistook my natural complexion for paint; at which I laughed: and then he shewed us a picture on the lid of his snuff-box, at which we all laughed. He plays picquet so very ill, and is so very fond of cards, and loses with such a grace, that positively he has won me; I have got a cool hundred, but have lost my heart. I need not tell you that he is only a colonel of the trainbands.

> I am, dear Charlotte,
> Yours for ever,
> BELINDA.

The Chinese lady addresses her confidante, a poor relation of the family, upon the same occasion; in which she seeems to understand decorums even better than the western beauty. You have who resided so long in China will readily acknowledge the picture to be taken from Nature; and, by being acquainted with the Chinese customs, will better apprehend the lady's meaning.

From YAOUA to YAYA

PAPA insists upon one, two, three, four hundred taels from the colonel my lover, before he parts with a lock of my hair. Ho, how I wish the dear creature may be able to produce the money, and pay papa my fortune. The colonel is reckoned the politest man in all Shensi. The first visit he paid at our house; mercy, what stooping, and cringing, and stopping, and fidgeting, and going back, and creeping forward, there was between him and papa, one would have thought he had got the seventeen books of ceremonies all by heart. When he was come into the hall he flourished his hands three times in a very graceful manner. Papa, who would not be outdone, flourished his four times; upon this the colonel began again, and both thus continued flourishing for some minutes in the politest manner imaginable. I was posted in the usual place behind the screen, where I saw the whole ceremony through a slit. Of this the colonel was sensible, for papa informed him. I would have given the world to have shewn him my little shoes, but had no opportunity. It was the first time I had ever the happiness of seeing any man but papa and I vow my dear Yaya, I thought my three souls would have actually have fled from my lips. Ho, but he looked most charmingly, he is reckoned the best shaped man in the whole province, for he is very fat, and very short; but even those natural advantages are improved by his dress, which is fashionable past description. His head was close shaven, all but the crown, and the hair of that was braided into a most beautiful tail, that reached down to his heels, was terminated by a bunch of yellow roses. Upon his first entering the room, I could easily perceive he had been highly perfumed with assafœtida. But then his looks, his looks, my dear Yaya, were irresistible. He kept his eyes steadfastly fixed on the wall during the whole ceremony, and I sincerely believe no accident could have discomposed his gravity, or drawn his eyes away. After a polite silence of two hours, he gallantly begged to have the singing women introduced, purely for my amusement. After one of them had for some time entertained us with her voice, the colonel and she retired for some minutes together. I thought they would never have come back; I must own he is a most agreeable creature. Upon his return, they again renewed the concert, and he continued to gaze upon the wall as usual, when, in less than half an hour more! Ho, but he retired out of the room with another. He is indeed a most agreeable creature.

When he came to take his leave, the whole ceremony began afresh; papa would see him to the door, but the colonel swore he would rather see the earth turned upside down than permit him to stir a single step, and papa was at last obliged to comply. As soon as he was got to the door, papa went out to see him on horse-back; here they continued half an hour bowing and cringing, before one would mount or the other go in, but the colonel was at last victorious. He had scarce gone an hundred paces from the house when papa running out halloo'd after him, A good journey. Upon which the colonel returned, and would see papa into his house before ever he would depart. He was no sooner got home than he sent me a very fine present of duck eggs painted of twenty different colours. His generosity I own has won me. I have ever since been trying over the eight letters of good fortune, and have great hopes. All I have to apprehend is that after he has married me, and that I am carried to his house close shut up in my chair, when he comes to have the first sight of my face, he may shut me up a second time and send me back to papa. However I shall appear as fine as possible; mamma and I have been to buy the clothes for my wedding. I am to have a new *fong whang* in my hair, the beak of which will reach down to my nose; the milliner from whom we bought that and our ribbons cheated us as if she had no conscience, and so to quiet mine I cheated her. All this is fair you know. I remain, my dear Yaya,

Your ever faithful,

YAOUA.

LETTER XL.—*From the same.*

You have always testified the highest esteem for the English poets, and thought them not inferior to the Greeks, Romans, or even the Chinese in the art. But it is now thought even by the English themselves that the race of their poets is extinct, every day produces some pathetic exclamation upon the decadence of taste and genius. Pegasus, say they, has slipped the bridle from his mouth, and our modern bards attempt to direct his flight by catching him by the tail.

Yet, my friend, it is only among the ignorant that such discourses prevail; men of true discernment can see several poets still among the English, some of whom equal if not surpass their predecessors. The ignorant term that alone poetry which is couched in a certain number of syllables in every line, where a vapid thought is drawn out into a number of verses of equal length, and perhaps pointed with rhymes at the end. But glowing sentiment, striking imagery, concise expression, natural description, and modulated periods are full sufficient entirely to fill up my idea of this art, and make way to every passion.

If my idea of poetry therefore be just, the English are not at present so destitute of poetical merit as they seem to imagine. I can see several poets in disguise among them; men furnished with that strength of soul, sublimity of sentiment, and grandeur of expression, which constitutes the character. Many of the writers of their modern odes, sonnets, tragedies, or rebusses, it is true, deserve not the name, though they have done nothing but clink rhymes and measure syllables for years together;

their Johnsons and Smolletts are truly poets; though for aught I know they never made a single verse in their whole lives.

In every incipient language the poet and the prose writer are very distinct in their qualifications: the poet ever proceeds first, treading unbeaten paths, enriching his native funds, and employed in new adventures. The other follows with more cautious steps, and though slow in his motions, treasures up every useful or pleasing discovery. But when once all the extent and the force of the language is known, the poet then seems to rest from his labour, and is at length overtaken by his assiduous pursuer. Both characters are then blended into one, the historian and orator catch all the poet's fire, and leave him no real mark of distinction except the iteration of numbers regularly returning. Thus in the decline of ancient European learning, Seneca, though he wrote in prose, is as much a poet as Lucan, and Longinus, though but a critic, more sublime than Apollonius.

From this then it appears that poetry is not discontinued, but altered among the English at present; the outward form seems different from what it was, but poetry still continues internally the same; the only question remains whether the metric feet used by the good writers of the last age, or the prosaic numbers employed by the good writers of this, be preferable. And here the practice of the last age appears to me superior; they submitted to the restraint of numbers and similar sounds; and this restraint, instead of diminishing, augmented the force of their sentiment and style. Fancy restrained may be compared to a fountain which plays highest by diminishing the aperture. Of the truth of this maxim in every language, every fine writer is perfectly sensible from his own experience, and yet to explain the reason would be perhaps as difficult as to make a frigid genius profit by the discovery.

There is still another reason in favour of the practice of the last age, to be drawn from the variety of modulation. The musical period in prose is confined to a very few changes; the numbers in verse are capable of infinite variation. I speak not now from the practice of modern verse writers, few of whom have any idea of musical variety, but run on in the same monotonous flow through the whole poem; but rather from the example of their former poets, who were tolerable masters of this variety, and also from a capacity in the language of still admitting various unanticipated music.

Several rules have been drawn up for varying the poetic

measure, and critics have elaborately talked of accents and
syllables, but good sense and a fine ear, which rules can never
teach, are what alone can in such a case determine.   The
rapturous flowings of joy, or the interruptions of indignation,
require accents placed entirely different, and a structure con-
sonant to the emotions they would express.   Changing passions,
and numbers changing with those passions, make the whole
secret of western as well as eastern poetry.   In a word, the
great faults of the modern professed English poets are, that they
seem to want numbers which should vary with the passion, and
are more employed in describing to the imagination than
striking at the heart.

LETTER XLI.—*From the same.*

SOME time since I sent thee, oh holy disciple of Confucius, an
account of the grand abbey or mausoleum of the kings and heroes
of this nation.   I have since been introduced to a temple not so
ancient, but far superior in beauty and magnificence.   In this,
which is the most considerable of the empire, there are no
pompous inscriptions, no flattery paid the dead, but all is elegant
and awfully simple.   There are however a few rags hung round
the walls, which have at a vast expence been taken from the
enemy in the present war.   The silk of which they are composed,
when new, might be valued at half a string of copper money in
China; yet this wise people fitted out a fleet and an army in
order to seize them; though now grown old, and scarce capable
of being patched up into a handkerchief.   By this conquest the
English are said to have gained, and the French to have lost,
much honour.   Is the honour of European nations placed only
in tattered silk?

In this temple I was permitted to remain during the whole
service; and were you not already acquainted with the religion
of the English, you might, from my description, be inclined to
believe them as grossly idolatrous as the disciples of Lao.   The
idol which they seem to address, strides like a colossus over the
door of the inner temple, which here, as with the Jews, is esteemed the most sacred part of the building.   Its oracles are
delivered in an hundred various tones, which seem to inspire
the worshippers with enthusiasm and awe: an old woman who
appeared to be the priestess, was employed in various attitudes,
as she felt the inspiration.   When it began to speak, all the

people remained fixed in silent attention, nodding assent, looking approbation, appearing highly edified by those sounds, which to a stranger might seem inarticulate and unmeaning.

When the idol had done speaking, and the priestess had locked up its lungs with a key, observing almost all the company leaving the temple, I concluded the service was over, and taking my hat, was going to walk away with the crowd, when I was stopt by the man in black, who assured me that the ceremony had scarcely yet begun! What, cried I, do I not see almost the whole body of the worshippers leaving the church? Would you persuade me that such numbers who profess religion and morality would in this shameless manner quit the temple before the service was concluded? you surely mistake; not even the Kalmouks would be guilty of such an indecency, though all the object of their worship was but a joint stool. My friend seemed to blush for his countrymen, assuring me that those whom I saw running away, were only a parcel of musical blockheads, whose passion was merely for sounds, and whose heads were as empty as a fiddle case; those who remain behind, says he, are the true Religious; they make use of music to warm their hearts, and to lift them to a proper pitch of rapture; examine their behaviour, and you will confess there are some among us who practise true devotion.

I now looked round me as he directed, but saw nothing of that fervent devotion which he had promised; one of the worshippers appeared to be ogling the company through a glass; another was fervent not in addresses to heaven, but to his mistress; a third whispered, a fourth took snuff, and the priest himself, in a drowsy tone, read over the *duties* of the day.

Bless my eyes, cried I, as I happened to look towards the door, what do I see; one of the worshippers fallen fast asleep, and actually sunk down on his cushion: is he now enjoying the benefit of a trance, or does he receive the influence of some mysterious vision! *Alas, alas,* replied my companion, *no such thing; he has only had the misfortune of eating too hearty a dinner, and finds it impossible to keep his eyes open.* Turning to another part of the temple, I perceived a young lady just in the same circumstances and attitude; Strange, cried I, can she too have over-eaten herself? *O fie,* replied my friend, *you now grow censorious. She grow drowsy from eating too much! that would be profanation! She only sleeps now from having sat up all night at a brag party.* Turn me where I will then, says I, I can perceive no single sympton of devotion among the worshippers, except from that old woman in the corner, who sits groaning behind the long sticks of a mourning fan; she indeed seems greatly edified with what she hears. *Aye,* replied my friend, *I knew we should find some to catch you; I know her; that is the deaf lady who lives in the cloysters.*

In short, the remissness of behaviour in almost all the worshippers, and some even of the guardians, struck me with surprise: I had been taught to believe that none were ever promoted to offices in the temple, but men remarkable for their superior sanctity, learning, and rectitude; that there was no such thing heard of as persons being introduced into the church merely to oblige a senator, or provide for the younger branch of a noble family: I expected, as their minds were continually set upon heavenly things, to see their eyes directed there also, and hoped from their behaviour to perceive their inclinations corresponding with their duty. But I am since informed, that some are appointed to preside over temples they never visit; and, while they receive all the money, are contented with letting others do all the good. Adieu.

LETTER XLII.—*From Fum Hoam, to Lien Chi Altangi, the discontented wanderer, by the way of Moscow.*

Must I ever continue to condemn thy perseverance, and blame that curiosity, which destroys thy happiness! What yet untasted banquet, what luxury yet unknown, has rewarded thy painful adventures! Name a pleasure which thy native country could not amply procure; frame a wish that might not have been satisfied in China! Why then such toil, and such danger, in pursuit of raptures within your reach at home.

The Europeans, you will say, excel us in sciences and in arts; those sciences which bound the aspiring wish, and those arts which tend to gratify even unrestrained desire. They may perhaps outdo us in the arts of building ships, casting cannons, or measuring mountains, but are they superior in the greatest of all arts, the art of governing kingdoms and ourselves?

When I compare the history of China with that of Europe, how do I exult in being a native of that kingdom which derives its original from the sun. Upon opening the Chinese history, I there behold an ancient extended empire, established by laws which Nature and reason seem to have dictated. The duty of children to their parents, a duty which Nature implants in every breast, forms the strength of that government which has subsisted for time immemorial. Filial obedience is the first and greatest requisite of a state; by this we become good subjects to our emperors, capable of behaving with just subordination to our superiors, and grateful dependents on heaven; by this we become fonder of marriage, in order to be capable of exacting obedience from others in our turn: by this we become good magistrates; for early submission is the truest lesson to those who would learn to rule. By this the whole state may be said to resemble one family, of which the emperor is the protector, father, and friend.

In this happy region, sequestered from the rest of mankind, I see a succession of princes who in general considered themselves as the fathers of their people; a race of philosophers who bravely combated idolatry, prejudice, and tyranny, at the expense of their private happiness and immediate reputation. Whenever an usurper or a tyrant intruded into the administration, how have all the good and great been united against him! Can European history produce an instance like that of the twelve mandarines, who all resolved to apprize the vicious emperor Tisaing of the irregularity of his conduct? He who first undertook the dangerous task was cut in two by the emperor's order; the second was ordered to be tormented, and then put to a cruel death; the third undertook the task with intrepidity, and was instantly stabbed by the tyrant's hand: in this manner they all suffered, except one. But not to be turned from his purpose, the brave survivor entering the palace with the instruments of torture in his hand, *Here*, cried he addressing himself to the throne, *here, O Tisiang, are the marks your faithful subjects receive for their loyalty; I am wearied with serving a tyrant, and now come for my reward.* The emperor, struck with his intrepidity, instantly forgave the boldness of his conduct, and reformed his own. What European annals can boast of a tyrant thus reclaimed to lenity!

When five brethren had set upon the great emperor Ginsong alone; with his sabre he slew four of them; he was struggling with the fifth, when his guards coming up were going to cut the conspirator into a thousand pieces. *No, no*, cried the emperor, with a calm and placid countenance, *of all his brothers he is the only one remaining, at least let one of the family be suffered to live, that his aged parents may have some body left to feed and comfort them.*

When Haitong, the last emperor of the house of Ming, saw himself besieged in his own city by the usurper, he was resolved to issue from his palace with six hundred of his guards, and give the enemy battle; but they forsook him. Being thus without hopes and chusing death rather than to fall alive into the hands of a rebel, he retired to his garden, conducting his little daughter an only child in his hand, there, in a private arbour, unsheathing his sword, he stabbed the young innocent to the heart, and then dispatching himself, left the following words written with his blood on the border of his vest. *Forsaken by my subjects, abandoned by my friends, use my body as you will, but spare, O spare, my people.*

An empire which has thus continued invariably the same for such a long succession of ages, which though at last conquered by the Tartars, still preserves its ancient laws and learning; and may more properly be said to annex the dominions of Tartary to its empire, than to admit a foreign conqueror; an empire as large as Europe, governed by one law, acknowledging subjection to one prince, and experiencing but one revolution of any continuance in the space of four thousand years; that is something so peculiarly great, that I am naturally led to despise all other nations on the comparison. Here we see no religious persecutions, no enmity between mankind, for difference in opinion. The disciples of Lao Kium, the idolatrous sectaries of Fohi, and the philosophical children of Confucius, only strive to show by their actions the truth of their doctrines.

Now turn from this happy peaceful scene to Europe the theatre of intrigue, avarice, and ambition. How many revolutions does it not experience in the compass even of one age; and to what do these revolutions tend but the destruction of thousands? Every great event is replete with some new calamity. The seasons of serenity are passed over in silence, their histories seem to speak only of the storm.

There we see the Romans extending their power over barbarous nations, and in turn becoming a prey to those whom they had conquered. We see those barbarians, when become Christians, engaged in continual wars with the followers of Mahomet; or more dreadful still, destroying each other. We see councils in the earlier ages authorising every iniquity; crusades spreading desolation in the country left, as well as that to be conquered. Excommunications freeing subjects from natural allegiance, and persuading to sedition; blood flowing in the fields and on scaffolds; tortures used as arguments to convince the recusant: to heighten the horror of the piece, behold it shaded with wars, rebellions, treasons, plots, politics, and poison.

And what advantage has any country of Europe obtained from such calamities? Scarce any. Their dissensions for more than a thousand years have served to make each other unhappy, but have enriched none. All the great nations still nearly preserve their ancient limits; none have been able to subdue the other, and so terminate the dispute. France, in spite of the conquests of Edward the third, and Henry the fifth, notwithstanding the efforts of Charles the fifth and Philip the second, still remains within its ancient limits. Spain, Germany, Great Britain, Poland, the states of the north, are nearly still the same. What effect then has the blood of so many thousands, the destruction of so many cities, produced? Nothing either great or considerable. The Christian princes have lost indeed much from the enemies of Christendom, but they have gained nothing from each other. Their princes, because they preferred ambition to justice, deserve the character of enemies to mankind; and their priests, by neglecting morality for opinion, have mistaken the interests of society.

On whatever side we regard the history of Europe, we shall perceive it to be a tissue of crimes, follies, and misfortunes, of politics without design, and wars without consequence; in this long list of human infirmity, a great character, or a shining virtue, may sometimes happen to arise, as we often meet a cottage or a cultivated spot in the most hideous wilderness. But for an Alfred, an Alphonso, a Frederic, or an Alexander III we meet a thousand princes who have disgraced humanity.

LETTER XLIII.—*From Lien Chi Altangi, to Fum Hoam, first President of the Ceremonial Academy at Pekin, in China.*

WE have just received accounts here, that Voltaire the poet and philosopher of Europe is dead! He is now beyond the reach of the thousand enemies, who while living, degraded his writings, and branded his character. Scarce a page of his latter productions that does not betray the agonies of an heart bleeding under the scourge of unmerited reproach. Happy therefore at last in escaping from calumny, happy in leaving a world that was unworthy of him and his writings.

Let others, my friend, bestrew the hearses of the great with panegyric; but such a loss as the world has now suffered affects me with stronger emotions. When a philosopher dies, I consider myself as losing a patron, an instructor, and a friend.

I consider the world as losing one who might serve to console her amidst the desolations of war and ambition. Nature every day produces in abundance men capable of filling all the requisite duties of authority; but she is niggard in the birth of an exalted mind, scarcely producing in a century a single genius to bless and enlighten a degenerate age. Prodigal in the production of kings, governors, mandarines, chams, and courtiers, she seems to have forgotten for more than three thousand years, the manner in which she once formed the brain of a Confucius; and well it is she has forgotten, when a bad world gave him so very bad a reception.

Whence, my friend, this malevolence which has ever pursued the great even to the tomb; whence this more than fiend-like disposition of embittering the lives of those who would make us more wise and more happy?

When I cast my eye over the fates of several philosophers, who have at different periods enlightened mankind, I must confess it inspires me with the most degrading reflections on humanity. When I read of the stripes of Mencius, the tortures of Tchin, the bowl of Socrates, and the bath of Seneca; when I hear of the persecutions of Dante, the imprisonment of Galileo, the indignities suffered by Montaigne, the banishment of Cartesius, the infamy of Bacon; and that even Locke himself escaped not without reproach; when I think on such subjects, I hesitate whether most to blame, the ignorance or the villainy of my fellow creatures.

Should you look for the character of Voltaire among the journalists and illiterate writers of the age, you will there find him characterised as a monster, with a head turned to wisdom, and an heart inclined to vice; the powers of his mind and the baseness of his principles forming a detestable contrast. But seek for his character among writers like himself, and you find him very differently described. You perceive him in their accounts possessed of good-nature, humanity, greatness of soul, fortitude, and almost every virtue: in this description those who might be supposed best acquainted with his character are unanimous. The royal Prussian,[1] D'Argens,[2] Diderot,[3] D'Alembert, and Fontenelle conspire in drawing the picture, in describing the friend of man and the patron of every rising genius.

An inflexible perseverance in what he thought was right, and a generous detestation of flattery, formed the ground-work of this great man's character. From these principles many

---

[1] Philosophe sans souci.   [2] Let. Chin.   [3] Encycloped.

strong virtues and few faults arose; as he was warm in his friendship, and severe in resentment, all that mention him seem possessed of the same qualities, and speak of him with rapture or detestation. A person of his eminence can have few indifferent as to his character; every reader must be an enemy or an admirer.

This poet began the course of glory so early as the age of eighteen, and even then was author of a tragedy which deserves applause; possessed of a small patrimony he preserved his independence in an age of venality, and supported the dignity of learning, by teaching his cotemporary writers to live like him, above the favours of the great. He was banished his native country for a satire upon the royal concubine. He had accepted the place of historian to the French king, but refused to keep it when he found it was presented only in order that he should be the first flatterer of the state.

The great Prussian received him as an ornament to this kingdom, and had sense enough to value his friendship, and profit by his instructions. In this court he continued till an intrigue, with which the world seems hitherto unacquainted, obliged him to quit that country. His own happiness, the happiness of the monarch, *of his sister*, of a part of the court, rendered his departure necessary.

Tired at length of courts, and all the follies of the great, he retired to Switzerland, a country of liberty, where he enjoyed tranquillity and the muse. Here, though without any taste for magnificence himself, he usually entertained at his table the learned and polite of Europe, who were attracted by a desire of seeing a person from whom they had received so much satisfaction. The entertainment was conducted with the utmost elegance, and the conversation was that of philosophers. Every country that at once united liberty and science were his peculiar favourites. The being an Englishman was to him a character that claimed admiration and respect.

Between Voltaire and the disciples of Confucius, there are many differences; however, being of a different opinion, does not in the least diminish my esteem; I am not displeased with my brother, because he happens to ask our father for favours in a different manner from me. Let his errors rest in peace, his excellences deserve admiration; let me with the wise admire his wisdom; let the envious and the ignorant ridicule his foibles; the folly of others is ever most ridiculous to those who are themselves most foolish. Adieu.

LETTER XLIV.—*From Lien Chi Altangi to Hingpo, a slave in Persia.*

It is impossible to form a philosophic system of happiness which is adapted to every condition in life, since every person who travels in this great pursuit takes a separate road. The differing colours which suit different complexions, are not more various than the different pleasures appropriated to different minds. The various sects who have pretended to give lessons to instruct me in happiness, have described their own particular sensations without considering ours, have only loaded their disciples with constraint, without adding to their real felicity.

If I find pleasure in dancing, how ridiculous would it be in me to prescribe such an amusement for the entertainment of a cripple; should he, on the other hand, place his chief delight in painting, yet would he be absurd in recommending the same relish to one who had lost the power of distinguishing colours. General directions are therefore commonly useless; and to be particular would exhaust volumes, since each individual may require a particular system of precepts to direct his choice.

Every mind seems capable of entertaining a certain quantity of happiness, which no institutions can encrease, no circumstances alter, and entirely independent of fortune. Let any man compare his present fortune with the past, and he will probably find himself, upon the whole, neither better nor worse than formerly.

Gratified ambition, or irreparable calamity, may produce transient sensations of pleasure or distress. Those storms may discompose in proportion as they are strong, or the mind is pliant to their impression. But the soul, though at first lifted up by the event, is every day operated upon with diminished influence; and at length subsides into the level of its usual tranquillity. Should some unexpected turn of fortune take thee from fetters, and place thee on a throne, exultation would be natural upon the change; but the temper, like the face, would soon resume its native serenity.

Every wish therefore which leads us to expect happiness somewhere else but where we are, every institution which teaches us that we should be better, by being possessed of something new, which promises to lift us a step higher than we are, only lays a foundation for uneasiness, because it contracts debts which we cannot repay; it calls that a good, which when we have found it, will in fact, add nothing to our happiness.

To enjoy the present, without regret for the past, or solicitude for the future, has been the advice rather of poets than philosophers. And yet the precept seems more rational than is generally imagined. It is the only general precept respecting the pursuit of happiness, that can be applied with propriety to every condition of life. The man of pleasure, the man of business, and the philosopher are equally interested in its disquisition. If we do not find happiness in the present moment, in what shall we find it? Either in reflecting on the past, or prognosticating the future. But let us see how these are capable of producing satisfaction.

A remembrance of what is past, and an anticipation of what is to come, seem to be the two faculties by which man differs most from other animals. Though brutes enjoy them in a limited degree, yet their whole life seems taken up in the present, regardless of the past and the future. Man, on the contrary, endeavours to derive his happiness, and experiences most of his miseries, from these two sources.

Is this superiority of reflection a prerogative of which we should boast, and for which we shall thank Nature; or is it a misfortune of which we should complain and be humble? Either from the abuse, or from the nature of things, it certainly makes our condition more miserable.

Had we a privilege of calling up, by the power of memory, only such passages as were pleasing, unmixed with such as were disagreeable, we might then excite at pleasure an ideal happiness, perhaps more poignant than actual sensation. But this is not the case; the past is never represented without some disagreeable circumstance, which tarnishes all its beauty; the remembrance of an evil carries in it nothing agreeable, and to remember a good is always accompanied with regret. Thus we lose more than we gain by remembrance.

And we shall find our expectation of the future to be a gift more distressful even than the former. To fear an approaching evil is certainly a most disagreeable sensation; and in expecting an approaching good, we experience the inquietude of wanting actual possession.

Thus, whichever way we look, the prospect is disagreeable. Behind, we have left pleasures we shall never more enjoy, and therefore regret; and before, we see pleasures which we languish to possess, and are consequently uneasy till we possess them. Was there any method of seizing the present, unembittered by such reflections, then would our state be tolerably easy.

This, indeed, is the endeavour of all mankind, who untutored by philosophy, pursue as much as they can a life of amusement and dissipation. Every rank in life, and every size of understanding, seems to follow this alone; or not pursuing it, deviates from happiness. The man of pleasure pursues dissipation by profession; the man of business pursues it not less, as every voluntary labour he undergoes is only dissipation in disguise. The philosopher himself, even while he reasons upon the subject, does it unknowingly with a view of dissipating the thoughts of what he was, or what he must be.

The subject therefore comes to this. Which is the most perfect sort of dissipation: pleasure, business, or philosophy? which best serves to exclude those uneasy sensations which *memory* or *anticipation* produce?

The enthusiasm of pleasure charms only by intervals. The highest rapture lasts only for a moment, and all the senses seem so combined, as to be soon tired into languor by the gratification of any one of them. It is only among the poets we hear of men changing to one delight, when satisfied with another. In Nature, it is very different: the glutton, when sated with the full meal, is unqualified to feel the real pleasure of drinking; the drunkard in turn finds few of those transports which lovers boast in enjoyment; and the lover, when cloyed, finds a diminution of every other appetite. Thus, after a full indulgence of any one sense, the man of pleasure finds a languor in all, is placed in a chasm between past and expected enjoyment, perceives an interval which must be filled up. The present can give no satisfaction, because he has already robbed it of every charm: a mind thus left without immediate gratification. Instead of a life of dissipation, none has more frequent conversations with disagreeable *self* than he: his enthusiasms are but few and transient; his appetites, like angry creditors, continually making fruitless demands for what he is unable to pay; and the greater his former pleasure, the more impatient his expectations; a life of pleasure is therefore the most unpleasing life in the world.

Habit has rendered the man of business more cool in his desires, he finds less regret for past pleasures, and less solicitude for those to come. The life he now leads, though tainted in some measure with hope, is yet not afflicted so strongly with regret, and is less divided between short-lived rapture and lasting anguish. The pleasures he has enjoyed are not so vivid, and those he has to expect, cannot consequently create so much anxiety.

The philosopher, who extends his regard to all mankind, must have still a smaller concern for what has already affected, or may hereafter affect himself; the concerns of others make his whole study, and that study is his pleasure; and this pleasure is continuing in its nature, because it can be changed at will, leaving but few of these anxious intervals which are employed in remembrance or anticipation. The philosopher by this means leads a life of almost continued dissipation; and reflection, which makes the uneasiness and misery of others, serves as a companion and instructor to him.

In a word, positive happiness is constitutional, and incapable of increase; misery is artificial, and generally proceeds from our folly. Philosophy can add to our happiness in no other manner, but by diminishing our misery: it should not pretend to increase our present stock, but make us economists of what we are possessed of. The great source of calamity lies in regret or anticipation: he, therefore, is most wise who thinks of the present alone, regardless of the past or the future. This is impossible to the man of pleasure; it is difficult to the man of business; and is in some measure attainable by the philosopher. Happy were we all born philosophers, all born with a talent of thus dissipating our own cares, by spreading them upon all mankind! Adieu.

LETTER XLV.—*From Lien Chi Altangi, to Fum Hoam, first President of the Ceremonial Academy at Pekin, in China.*

THOUGH the frequent invitations I receive from men of distinction here might excite the vanity of some, I am quite mortified however when I consider the motives that inspire their civility. I am sent for not to be treated as a friend, but to satisfy curiosity; not to be entertained so much as wondered at; the same earnestness which excites them to see a Chinese, would have made them equally proud of a visit from the rhinoceros.

From the highest to the lowest, this people seem fond of sights and monsters. I am told of a person here who gets a very comfortable livelihood by making wonders, and then selling or shewing them to the people for money, no matter how insignificant they were in the beginning; by locking them up close, and shewing for money, they soon become prodigies! His first essay in this way was to exhibit himself as a wax-work figure behind a glass door at a puppet show. Thus keeping the spectators at a proper distance, and having his head adorned with a copper crown, he looked extremely *natural, and very like the life itself*. He continued this exhibition with success, till an involuntary fit of sneezing brought him to life before all the spectators, and consequently rendered him for that time as entirely useless, as the peaceable inhabitant of a catacomb.

Determined to act the statue no more, he next levied contributions under the figure of an Indian king; and by painting his face, and counterfeiting the savage howl, he frighted several ladies and children with amazing success: in this manner therefore he might have lived very comfortably, had he not been arrested for a debt that was contracted when he was the figure in wax-work: thus his face underwent an involuntary ablution, and he found himself reduced to his primitive complexion and indigence.

After some time, being freed from gaol, he was now grown wiser, and instead of making himself a wonder, was resolved only to make wonders. He learned the art of pasting up mummies: was never at a loss for an artificial *lusus naturæ*; nay, it has been reported, that he has sold seven petrified lobsters of his own manufacture to a noted collector of rarities; but this the learned Cracovius Putridus has undertaken to refute in a very elaborate dissertation.

His last wonder was nothing more than an halter, yet by this halter he gained more than by all his former exhibitions. The people, it seems, had got it in their heads, that a certain noble criminal was to be hanged with a silken rope. Now there was nothing they so much desired to see as this very rope; and he was resolved to gratify their curiosity: he therefore got one made, not only of silk, but to render it more striking, several threads of gold were intermixed. The people paid their money only to see silk, but were highly satisfied when they found it was mixed with gold into the bargain. It is scarce necessary to mention, that the projector sold his silken rope for almost what it had cost him, as soon as the criminal was known to be hanged in hempen materials.

By their fondness of sights, one would be apt to imagine, that instead of desiring to see things as they should be, they are rather solicitous of seeing them as they ought not to be. A cat with four legs is disregarded, though never so useful; but if it has but two, and is consequently incapable of catching mice, it is reckoned inestimable, and every man of taste is ready to raise the auction. A man, though in his person faultless as an aerial genius, might starve; but if stuck over with hideous warts like a porcupine, his fortune is made for ever, and he may propagate the breed with impunity and applause.

A good woman in my neighbourhood, who was bred an habit-maker, though she handled her needle tolerably well, could scarcely get employment. But being obliged by an accident to have both her hands cut off from the elbows, what would in another country have been her ruin, made her fortune here, she now was thought more fit for her trade than before: business flowed in a-pace, and all people paid for seeing the mantua-maker who wrought without hands.

A gentleman shewing me his collection of pictures, stopped at one with peculiar admiration; There, cries he, is an inestimable piece. I gazed at the picture for some time, but could see none of those graces with which he seemed enraptured; it appeared to me the most paltry piece of the whole collection: I therefore demanded where those beauties lay, of which I was yet insensible. Sir, cries he, the merit does not consist in the piece, but in the manner in which it was done. The painter drew the whole with his foot, and held the pencil between his toes: I bought it at a very great price; for peculiar merit should ever be rewarded.

But these people are not more fond of wonders than liberal in rewarding those who shew them. From the wonderful dog of knowledge at present under the patronage of the nobility, down to the man with the box, who professes to shew *the most imitation of Nature that was ever seen*; they all live in luxury. A singing woman shall collect subscriptions in her own coach and six; a fellow shall make a fortune by tossing a straw from his toe to his nose; one in particular has found that eating fire was the most ready way to live; and another who jingles several bells fixed to his cap, is the only man that I know of who has received emolument from the labours of his head.

A young author, a man of good-nature and learning, was complaining to me some nights ago of this misplaced generosity of the times. Here, says he, have I spent part of my youth in attempting to instruct and amuse my fellow creatures, and all my reward has been solitude, poverty, and reproach; while a fellow, possessed of even the smallest share of fiddling merit, or who has perhaps learned to whistle double, is rewarded, applauded, and caressed! Prythee, young man, says I to him, are you ignorant, that in so large a city as this, it is better to be an amusing than an useful member of society? Can you leap up, and touch your feet four times before you come to the ground? *No, Sir.* Can you pimp for a man of quality? *No, Sir.* Can you stand upon two horses at full speed? *No, Sir.* Can you swallow a pen-knife? *I can do none of these tricks.* Why then, cried I, there is no other prudent means of subsistence left but to apprise the town that you speedily intend to eat up your own nose, by subscription.

I have frequently regretted that none of our eastern posture masters or show men have ever ventured to England. I should be pleased to see the money circulate in Asia, which is now sent to Italy and France, in order to bring their vagabonds hither. Several of our tricks would undoubtedly give the English high satisfaction. Men of fashion would be greatly pleased with the postures as well as the condescension of our dancing girls: and ladies would equally admire the conductors of our fire-works. What an agreeable surprise would it be to see a huge fellow with whiskers flash a charged blunderbuss full in a lady's face, without singeing her hair, or melting her pomatum. Perhaps when the first surprise was over, she might then grow familiar with danger; and the ladies might vie with each other in standing fire with intrepidity.

But of all the wonders of the east, the most useful, and I should fancy, the most pleasing, would be the looking-glass of Lao, which reflects the mind as well as the body. It is said that the emperor Chusi used to make his concubines dress their heads and their hearts in one of these glasses every morning; while the lady was at her toilet, he would frequently look over her shoulder; and it is recorded, that among the three hundred which composed his seraglio, not one was found whose mind was not even more beautiful than her person.

I made no doubt but a glass in this country would have the very same effect. The English ladies, concubines and all, would undoubtedly cut very pretty figures in so faithful a monitor. There, should we happen to peep over a lady's shoulder while dressing, we might be able to see neither gaming nor ill-nature; neither pride, debauchery, nor a love of gadding. We should find her, if any sensible defect appeared in the mind, more careful in rectifying it, than plastering up the irreparable decays of the person; nay, I am even apt to fancy, that ladies would find more real pleasure in this utensil in private, than in any other bauble imported from China, though never so expensive, or amusing.

LETTER XLVI.—*To the same.*

UPON finishing my last letter I retired to rest, reflecting upon the wonders of the glass of Lao, wishing to be possessed of one here, and resolved in such a case to oblige every lady with a sight of it for nothing. What fortune denied me waking, fancy supplied in a dream; the glass, I know not how, was put into my possession, and I could perceive several ladies approaching, some voluntarily, others driven forward against their wills by a set of discontented genii, whom by intuition I knew were their husbands.

The apartment in which I was to shew away was filled with several gaming tables, as if just forsaken; the candles were burnt to the socket, and the hour was five o'clock in the morning. Placed at one end of the room, which was of prodigious length, I could more easily distinguish every female figure as she marched up from the door; but guess my surprise, when I could scarce perceive one blooming or agreeable face among the number. This, however, I attributed to the early hour, and kindly considered that the face of a lady just risen from bed ought always to find a compassionate advocate.

The first person who came up in order to view her intellectual face was a commoner's wife, who, as I afterwards found, being bred up during her virginity in a pawn-broker's shop, now attempted to make up the defects of breeding and sentiment by the magnificence of her dress, and the expensiveness of her amusements. 'Mr. Showman, cried she, approaching, I am told you *has* something to shew in *that there* sort of magic lanthorn, by which folks can see themselves on the inside; I protest, as my lord Beetle says, I am sure it will be vastly pretty, for I have never seen any thing like it before. But how; are we to strip off our clothes and be turned inside out; if so, as lord Beetle says, I absolutely declare off; for I would not strip for the world before a man's face, and so I *tells* his lordship almost every night of my life.' I informed the lady that I would dispense with the ceremony of stripping, and immediately presented my glass to her view.

As when a first-rate beauty, after having with difficulty escaped the small pox, revisits her favourite mirror, that mirror which had repeated the flattery of every lover, and even added force to the compliment; expecting to see what had so often given her pleasure, she no longer beholds the cherried lip, the polished forehead, and speaking blush, but an hateful phyz quilted into a thousand seams by the hand of deformity; grief, resentment, and rage fill her bosom by turns; she blames the fates and the stars, but most of all the unhappy glass feels her resentment. So it was with the lady in question; she had never seen her own mind before, and was now shocked at its deformity. One single look was sufficient to satisfy her curiosity; I held up the glass to her face, and she shut her eyes; no entreaties could prevail upon her to gaze once more! she was even going to snatch it from my hands, and break it in a thousand pieces. I found it was time therefore to dismiss her as incorrigible, and shew away to the next that offered.

This was an unmarried lady, who continued in a state of virginity till thirty-six, and then admitted a lover when she despaired of an husband. No woman was louder at a revel than she, perfectly free-hearted, and almost in every respect a man; she understood ridicule to perfection, and was once known even to sally out in order to beat the watch. 'Here, you my dear with the outlandish face (said she addressing me), let me take a single peep. Not that I care three damns what figure I may cut in the glass of such an old-fashioned creature; if I am allowed the beauties of the face by people of fashion, I know the world will be complaisant enough to toss me the beauties of the mind into the bargain.' I held my glass before her as she desired, and must confess, was shocked with the reflection. The lady, however, gazed for some time with the utmost complacency; and at last turning to me with the most satisfied smile said, she never could think she had been half to handsome.

Upon her dismission a lady of distinction was reluctantly hauled along to the glass by her husband; in bringing her forward, as he came first to the glass himself, his mind appeared tinctured with immoderate jealousy, and I was going to reproach him for using her with such severity; but when the lady came to present herself, I immediately retracted; for alas it was seen that he had but too much reason for his suspicions.

The next was a lady who usually teased all her acquaintance in desiring to be told of her faults, and then never mended any. Upon approaching the glass I could readily perceive vanity, affectation, and some other ill-looking blots on her mind: wherefore by my advice she immediately set about mending. But I could easily find she was not earnest in the work; for as she repaired them on one side, they generally broke out on another. Thus, after three or four attempts, she began to make the ordinary use of the glass in settling her hair.

The company now made room for a woman of learning, who approached with a slow pace and a solemn countenance, which for her own sake, I could wish had been cleaner. 'Sir, cried the lady, flourishing her hand, which held a pinch of snuff, I shall be enraptured by having presented to my view a mind with which I have so long studied to be acquainted: but, in order to give the sex a proper example, I must insist, that all the company may be permitted to look over my shoulder.' I bowed assent, and presenting the glass, showed the lady a mind by no means so fair as she had expected to see. Ill-nature, ill-placed pride, and spleen, were too legible to be mistaken. Nothing could be more amusing than the mirth of her female companions who had looked over. They had hated her from the beginning, and now the apartment echoed with an universal laugh. Nothing but a fortitude like her's could have withstood their raillery: she stood it however; and when the burst was exhausted, with great tranquillity she assured the company, that the whole was a *deceptio visus*, and that she was too well acquainted with her own mind to believe any false representations from another. Thus saying, she retired with a sullen satisfaction, resolved not to mend her faults, but to write a criticism on the mental reflector.

I must own, by this time I began myself to suspect the fidelity of my mirror; for as the ladies appeared at least to have the merit of rising early, since they were up at five, I was amazed to find nothing of this good quality pictured upon their minds in the reflection; I was resolved therefore to communicate my suspicions to a lady, whose intellectual countenance appeared more fair than any of the rest, not having above seventy-nine spots in all, besides slips and foibles. 'I own, young woman, said I, that there are some virtues upon that mind of your's; but there is still one which I do not see represented; I mean that of rising betimes in the morning; I fancy the glass false in that particular.' The young lady smiled at my simplicity; and, with a blush, confessed, that she and the whole company had been up all night gaming.

By this time all the ladies, except one, had seen themselves successively, and disliked the show, or scolded the show-man; I was resolved, however, that she who seemed to neglect herself, and was neglected by the rest, should take a view; and going up to a corner of the room, where she still continued sitting, I presented my glass full in her face. Here it was that I exulted in my success; no blot, no stain, appeared on any part of the faithful mirror. As when the large, unwritten page presents its snowy spotless bosom to the writer's hand; so appeared the glass to my view. Here, O ye daughters of English ancestors, cried I, turn hither, and behold an object worthy imitation: look upon the mirror now, and acknowledge its justice, and this woman's pre-eminence! The ladies obeying the summons, came up in a group, and looking on, acknowledged there was some truth in the picture, as the person now represented had been deaf, dumb, and a fool from her cradle.

Thus much of my dream I distinctly remember; the rest was filled with chimæras, enchanted castles, and flying dragons as usual. As you, my dear Fum Hoam, are particularly versed in the interpretation of those midnight warnings, what pleasure should I find in your explanation: but that our distance prevents; I make no doubt, however, but that from my description you will very much venerate the good qualities of the English ladies in general, since dreams, you know, go always by contraries. Adieu.

LETTER XLVII.—*From Lien Chi Altango to Hingpo, a slave in Persia.*[1]

YOUR last letters betray a mind seemingly fond of wisdom, yet tempested up by a thousand passions. You would fondly persuade me that my former lessons still influence your conduct, and yet your mind seems not less enslaved than your body. Knowledge, wisdom, erudition, arts and elegance, what are they, but the mere trappings of the mind, if they do not serve to encrease the happiness of the possessor? A mind rightly instituted in the school of philosophy, acquires at once the stability of the oak, and the flexibility of the osier. The truest manner of lessening our agonies, is to shrink from their pressure; is to confess that we feel them.

The fortitude of European sages is but a dream; for where lies the merit in being insensible to the strokes of fortune, or in dissembling our sensibility; if we are insensible, that arises only from an happy constitution; that is a blessing previously granted by heaven, and which no art can procure, no institutions improve. If we dissemble our feelings, we only artificially endeavour to persuade others that we enjoy privileges which we actually do not possess. Thus while we endeavour to appear happy, we

[1] This letter appears to be little more than a rhapsody of sentiments from Confucius. Vid. the Latin translation.

feel at once all the pangs of internal misery, and all the self-reproaching consciousness of endeavouring to deceive.

I know but of two sects of philosophers in the world that have endeavoured to inculcate that fortitude is but an imaginary virtue; I mean the followers of Confucius, and those who profess the doctrines of Christ. All other sects teach pride under misfortunes; they alone teach humility. Night, says our Chinese philosopher, not more surely follows day, than groans and tears grow out of pain; when misfortunes therefore oppress, when tyrants threaten, it is our interest, it is our duty, to fly even to dissipation for support, to seek redress from friendship, or seek redress from that best of friends who loved us into being.

Philosophers, my son, have long declaimed against the passions, as being the source of all our miseries; they are the source of all our misfortunes I own; but they are the source of our pleasures too: and every endeavour of our lives, and all the institutions of philosophy, should tend to this, not to dissemble an absence of passion, but to repel those which lead to vice, by those which direct to virtue.

The soul may be compared to a field of battle, where two armies are ready every moment to encounter; not a single vice but has a more powerful opponent; and not one virtue but may be overborne by a combination of vices. Reason guides the hands of either host, nor can it subdue one passion but by the assistance of another. Thus, as a bark, on every side beset with storms, enjoys a state of rest, so does the mind, when influenced by a just equipoise of the passions, enjoy tranquillity.

I have used such means as my little fortune would admit to procure your freedom. I have lately written to the Governor of Argun to pay your ransom, though at the expense of all the wealth I brought with me from China. If we become poor we shall at least have the pleasure of bearing poverty together; for what is fatigue or famine, when weighed against friendship and freedom. Adieu.

LETTER XLVIII.—*From Lien Chi Altangi to * * *, merchant in Amsterdam.*

HAPPENING some days ago to call at a painter's to amuse myself in examining some pictures (I had no design to buy) it surprised me to see a young prince in the working room, dressed in a painter's apron, and assiduously learning the trade. We instantly remembered to have seen each other; and, after the usual compliments, I stood by while he continued to paint on. As everything done by the rich is praised, as princes here, as well as in China, are never without followers, three or four persons, who had the appearance of gentlemen, were placed behind to comfort and applaud him at every stroke.

Need I tell, that it struck me with very disagreeable sensations *to see a youth who by his station in life, had it in his power to be useful to thousands, thus letting his mind run to waste upon canvas, at the same time fancying himself improving in taste, and filling his rank with proper decorum.*

As seeing an error, and attempting to redress it, are only one and the same with me, I took occasion, upon his lordship's desiring my opinion of a Chinese scroll, intended for the frame of a picture, to assure him, that a mandarine of China thought a minute acquaintance with such mechanical trifles below his dignity.

This reply raised the indignation of some, and the contempt of others: I could hear the names of Vandal, Goth, taste, polite arts, delicacy, and fire, repeated in tones of ridicule or resentment. But considering that it was in vain to argue against people who had so much to say, without contradicting them, I begged leave to repeat a fairy tale. This request redoubled their laughter; but not easily abashed at the raillery of boys, I persisted, observing that it would set the absurdity of placing our affections upon trifles in the strongest point of view, and adding that it was hoped the moral would compensate for its stupidity. For heaven's sake, cried the great man, washing his brush in water, let us have no morality at present; if we must have a story, let it be without any moral. I pretended not to hear, and while he handled the brush, proceeded as follows:

In the kingdom of Bonbobbin, which, by the Chinese annal, appears to have flourished twenty thousand years ago, there reigned a prince endowed with every accomplishment which generally distinguishes the sons of kings. His beauty was brighter than the sun. The sun, to which he was nearly related, would sometimes stop his course in order to look down and admire him.

His mind was not less perfect than his body; he knew all things without having ever read; philosophers, poets, and historians, submitted their works to his decision; and so penetrating was he, that he could tell the merit of a book by looking on the cover. He made epic poems, tragedies, and pastorals, with surprising facility; song, epigram, or rebus, was all one to him, though it is observed he could never finish an acrostic. In short, the fairy, who presided at his birth, had endowed him with almost every perfection, or what was just the same, his subjects were ready to acknowledge he possessed them all; and, for his own part, he knew nothing to the contrary. A prince so accomplished, received a name suitable to his merit; and he was called Bonbenin-bonbobbin-bonbobbinet, which signifies *Enlightener of the Sun*.

As he was very powerful, and yet unmarried, all the neighbouring kings earnestly sought his alliance. Each sent his daughter, dressed out in the most magnificent manner, and with the most sumptuous retinue imaginable, in order to allure the prince; so that at one time there were seen at his court not less than seven hundred foreign princesses of exquisite sentiment and beauty, each alone sufficient to make seven hundred ordinary men happy.

Distracted in such a variety, the generous Bonbenin, had he not been obliged by the laws of the empire to make choice of one, would very willingly have married them all, for none understood gallantry better. He spent numberless hours of solicitude in endeavouring to determine whom he should choose; one lady was possessed of every perfection, but he disliked her eyebrows; another was brighter than the morning star, but he disapproved her fong whang; a third did not lay white enough on her cheek; and a fourth did not sufficiently blacken her nails. At last, after numberless disappointments on one side and the other, he made choice of the incomparable Nanhoa, queen of the scarlet dragons.

The preparations for the royal nuptials, or the envy of the disappointed ladies, needs no description; both the one and the other were as great as they could be; the beautiful princess was conducted amidst admiring multitudes to the royal couch, where after being divested of every encumbering ornament, she was placed, in expectance of the youthful bridegroom, who did not keep her long in expectation. He came more chearful than the morning, and printing on her lips a burning kiss, the attendants took this as a proper signal to withdraw.

Perhaps I ought to have mentioned in the beginning that, among several other qualifications, the prince was fond of collecting and breeding mice, which being an harmless pastime, none of his councillors thought proper to dissuade him from: he therefore kept a variety of these pretty little animals in the most beautiful cages enriched with diamonds, rubies, emeralds, pearls, and other precious stones: thus he *innocently* spent four hours each day, in contemplating their innocent little pastimes.

But to proceed. The prince and princess were now in bed; one with all the love and expectation, the other with all the modesty and fear, which is natural to suppose, both willing, yet afraid to begin; when the prince happening to look towards the outside of the bed, perceived one of the most beautiful animals in the world, a white mouse with green eyes, playing about the floor, and performing an hundred pretty tricks. He was already master of blue mice, red mice, and even white mice with yellow eyes; but a white mouse with green eyes, was what he long endeavoured to possess: wherefore leaping from bed with the utmost impatience and agility, the youthful prince attempted to seize the little charmer, but it was fled in a moment; for alas! the mouse was sent by a discontented princess, and was itself a fairy.

It is impossible to describe the agony of the prince upon this occasion, he sought round and round every part of the room, even the bed where the princess lay was not exempt from the enquiry; he turned the princess on one side and t'other, stripped her quite naked, but no mouse was to be found; the princess herself was kind enough to assist, but still to no purpose.

Alas, cried the young prince in an agony, how unhappy am I to be thus disappointed; never sure was so beautiful an animal seen, I would give half my kingdom and my princess, to him that would find it. The princess, though not much pleased with the latter part of his offer, endeavoured to comfort him as well as she could; she let him know that he had an hundred mice already, which ought to be at least sufficient to satisfy any philosopher like him. Though none of them had green eyes, yet he should learn to thank heaven that they had eyes. She told him (for she was a profound moralist), that incurable evils must be borne, and that useless lamentations were vain, and that man was born to misfortunes; she even entreated him to return to bed, and she would endeavour to lull him on her bosom to repose; but still the prince continued inconsolable; and regarding her with a stern air, for which his family was remarkable, he vowed never to sleep in the royal palace, or indulge himself in the innocent pleasures of matrimony, till he had found the white mouse with the green eyes.

Prythee, Col. Leech, cried his Lordship, interrupting me, how do you like that nose; don't you think there is something of the manner of Rembrandt in it? A prince in all this agony for a white mouse, O ridiculous! Don't you think, Major Vampyre, that eyebrow stippled very prettily? but pray what are the green eyes to the purpose, except to amuse children? I would give a thousand guineas to lay on the colouring of this cheek more smoothly. But I ask pardon, pray, Sir, proceed.

LETTER XLIX.—*From the same.*

KINGS, continued I, at that time were different from what they are now; they then never engaged their word for any thing which they did not rigorously intend to perform. This was the case of Bonbenin, who continued all night to lament his misfortunes to the princess, who echoed groan for groan. When morning came, he published an edict, offering half his kingdom and his princess, to the person who should catch and bring him the white mouse with green eyes.

The edict was scarce published, when all the traps in the kingdom were baited with cheese; numberless mice were taken and destroyed; but still the much-wished-for mouse was not among the number. The privy council was assembled more than once to give their advice; but all their deliberations came to nothing; even though there were two complete vermin-killers and three professed rat-catchers of the number. Frequent addresses, as is usual on extraordinary occasions, were sent from all parts of the empire; but though these promised well, though in them he received an assurance, that his faithful subjects would assist in his search with their lives and fortunes, yet, with all their loyalty, they failed when the time came that the mouse was to be caught.

The prince therefore was resolved to go himself in search, determined never to lie two nights in one place till he had found what he sought for. Thus quitting his place without attendants, he set out upon his journey, and travelled through many a desert, and crossed many a river, high over hills, and down along vales, still restless, still enquiring wherever he came; but no white mouse was to be found.

As one day, fatigued with his journey, he was shading himself from the heat of the mid-day sun, under the arching branches of a banana tree, meditating on the object of his pursuit, he perceived an old woman, hideously deformed, approaching him; by her stoop, and the wrinkles of her visage, she seemed at least five hundred years old; and the spotted toad was not more freckled than was her skin. Ah! prince Bonbenin-bonbobbin-bonbobbinet, cried the creature, what has led you so many thousand miles from your own kingdom; what is it you look for, and what induces you to travel into the kingdom of Emmets? The prince, who was excessively complaisant, told her the whole story three times over; for she was hard of hearing. Well, says the old fairy, for such she was, I promise to put you in possession of the white mouse with green eyes, and that immediately too upon one condition. One condition, cried the prince in a rapture, name a thousand: I shall undergo them all with pleasure. Nay, interrupted the old fairy, I ask but one, and that not very mortifying neither; it is only that you instantly consent to marry me.

It is impossible to express the prince's confusion at this demand; he loved the mouse, but he detested the bride; he hesitated; he desired time to think upon the proposal; he would have been glad to consult his friends on such an occasion. Nay, nay, cried the odious fairy, if you demur, I retract my promise; I do not desire to force my favours on any man. Here, you my attendants, cried she, stamping with her foot, let my machine be driven up; Barbacela, Queen of Emmets, is not used to contemptuous treatment. She had no sooner spoken than her fiery chariot appeared in the air, drawn by two snails; and she was just going to step in, when the prince reflected, that now or never was the time to be possessed of the white mouse; and quite forgetting his lawful princess Nanhoa, falling on his knees, he implored forgiveness for having rashly rejected so much beauty. This well-timed compliment instantly appeased the angry fairy. She affected an hideous leer of approbation, and, taking the young prince by the hand, conducted him to a neighbouring church, where they were married together in a moment. As soon as the ceremony was performed, the prince, who was to the last degree desirous of seeing his favourite mouse, reminded the bride of her promise. To confess a truth, my prince, cried she, I myself am that very white mouse you saw on your wedding night in the royal apartment. I now therefore give you the choice, whether you would have me a mouse by day and a woman by night, or a mouse by night and a woman by day. Though the prince was an excellent casuist, he was quite at a loss how to determine, but at last thought it most prudent to have recourse to a blue cat that had followed him from his own dominions, and frequently amused him with its conversation, and assisted him with its advice; in fact this cat was no other than the faithful princess Nanhoa herself, who had shared with him all his hardships in this disguise.

By her instructions he was determined in his choice, and returning to the old fairy, prudently observed that as she must have been sensible he had married her *only for the sake of what she had*, and not for her personal qualifications, he thought it would for several reasons be most convenient if she continued a woman by day and appeared a mouse by night.

The old fairy was a good deal mortified at her husband's want of gallantry, though she was reluctantly obliged to comply; the day was therefore spent in the most polite amusements, the gentlemen talked smut, the ladies laughed, and were angry. At last the happy night drew near, the blue cat still stuck by the side of its master, and even followed him to the bridal apartment. Barbacela entered the chamber, wearing a train fifteen yards long, supported by porcupines, and all over beset with jewels, which served to render her more detestable. She was just stepping into bed to the prince, forgetting her promise, when he insisted upon seeing her in the shape of a mouse. She had promised, and no fairy can break her word; wherefore assuming the figure of the most beautiful mouse in the world, she skipped and played about with an infinity of amusement. The prince in an agony of rapture, was desirous of seeing his pretty playfellow move a slow dance about the floor to his own singing; he began to sing, and the mouse immediately to perform with the most perfect knowledge of time, and the finest grace and greatest gravity imaginable; it only began, for Nanhoa, who had long waited for the opportunity in the shape of a cat, flew upon it instantly without remorse, and eating it up in the hundredth part of a moment, broke the charm, and then resumed her natural figure.

The prince now found that he had all along been under the power of enchantment, that his passion for the white mouse was entirely fictitious, and not the genuine complexion of his soul; he now saw that his earnestness after mice was an illiberal amusement, and much more becoming a ratcatcher than a prince. All his meannesses now stared him in the face, he begged the discreet princess's pardon an hundred times. The princess very readily forgave him; and both returning to their palace in Bonbobbin lived very happily together, and reigned many years with all that wisdom, which, by the story, they appear to have been possessed of; perfectly convinced by their former adventures that *they who place their affections on trifles at first for amusement, will find those trifles at last become their most serious concern*. Adieu.

LETTER L.—*From Lien Chi Altangi, to Fum Hoam, first President of the Ceremonial Academy at Pekin, in China.*

ASK an Englishman what nation in the world enjoys most freedom, and he immediately answers, his own. Ask him in what that freedom principally consists, and he is instantly silent. This happy pre-eminence does not arise from the people's enjoying a larger share in legislation than elsewhere; for in this particular, several states in Europe excel them; nor does it arise from a greater exemption from taxes, for few countries pay more; it does not proceed from their being restrained by fewer laws, for no people are burthened with so many; nor does it particularly consist in the security of their property, for property is pretty well secured in every polite state of Europe.

How then are the English more free (for more free they certainly are) than the people of any other country, or under any other form of government whatever? Their freedom consists in their enjoying all the advantages of democracy with this superior prerogative borrowed from monarchy, that *the severity of their laws may be relaxed without endangering the constitution.*

In a monarchical state, in which the constitution is strongest, the laws may be relaxed without danger; for though the people should be unanimous in the breach of any one in particular, yet still there is an *effective* power superior to the people, capable of enforcing obedience, whenever it may be proper to inculcate the law either towards the support or welfare of the community.

But in all those governments, where laws derive their sanction from the *people alone*, transgressions cannot be overlooked without bringing the constitution into danger. They who transgress the law in such a case, are those who prescribe it, by which means it loses not only its influence but its sanction. In every republic the laws must be strong, because the constitution is feeble, they must resemble an Asiatic husband who is justly jealous, because he knows himself impotent. Thus in Holland, Switzerland, and Genoa, new laws are not frequently enacted, but the old ones are observed with unremitting severity. In such republics therefore the people are slaves to laws of their own making, little less than in unmixed monarchies where they are slaves to the will of one subject to frailties like themselves.

In England, from a variety of happy accidents, their constitution is just strong enough, or if you will, monarchical enough, to permit a relaxation of the severity of laws, and yet those laws still to remain sufficiently strong to govern the people. This is the most perfect state of civil liberty, of which we can form any idea; here we see a greater number of laws than in any other country, while the people at the same time obey only such as are *immediately* conducive to the interests of society; several are unnoticed, many unknown; some kept to be revived and enforced upon proper occasions, others left to grow obsolete, even without the necessity of abrogation.

Scarce an Englishman who does not almost every day of his life offend with impunity against some express law, and for which in a certain conjuncture of circumstances he would not receive punishment. Gaming houses, preaching at prohibited places, assembled crowds, nocturnal amusements, public shows, and an hundred other instances are forbid and frequented. These prohibitions are useful; though it be prudent in their magistrates, and happy for their people, that they are not enforced, and none but the venal or mercenary attempt to enforce them.

The law in this case, like an indulgent parent, still keeps the rod, though the child is seldom corrected. Were those pardoned offences to rise into enormity, were they likely to obstruct the happiness of society, or endanger the state, it is then that justice would resume her terrors, and punish those faults which she had so often overlooked with indulgence. It is to this ductility of the laws that an Englishman owes the freedom he enjoys superior to others in a more popular government; every step therefore the constitution takes towards a democratic form, every diminution of the legal authority is, in fact, a diminution of the subjects' freedom; but every attempt to render the government more popular, not only impairs natural liberty, but even will at last, dissolve the political constitution.

Every popular government seems calculated to last only for a time, it grows rigid with age, new laws are multiplying, and the old continue in force, the subjects are oppressed, burdened with a multiplicity of legal injunctions, there are none from whom to expect redress, and nothing but a strong convulsion in the state can vindicate them into former liberty: thus the people of Rome, a few great ones excepted, found more real freedom under their emperors though tyrants, than they had experienced in the old age of the commonwealth, in which their laws were become numerous and painful, in which new laws were every day enacting and the old ones executed with rigour. They even refused to be reinstated in their former prerogatives, upon an offer made them to this purpose; for they actually found emperors the only means of softening the rigours of their constitution.

The constitution of England is at present possessed of the strength of its native oak, and the flexibility of the bending tamarisk; but should the people at any time, with a mistaken zeal, pant after an imaginary freedom, and fancy that abridging monarchy was encreasing their privileges, they would be very much mistaken, since every jewel plucked from the crown of majesty would only be made use of as a bribe to corruption; it might enrich the few who shared it among them, but would in fact impoverish the public.

As the Roman senators by slow and imperceptible degrees became masters of the people, yet still flattered them with a shew of freedom, while themselves only were free; so is it possible for a body of men, while they stand up for privileges, to grow into an exuberance of power themselves, and the public become actually dependent, while some of its individuals only governed.

If then, my friend, there should in this country, ever be on the throne a king who through good-nature or age, should give up the smallest part of his prerogative to the people, if there should come a minister of merit and popularity—But I have room for no more. Adieu.

LETTER LI.—*To the same.*

As I was yesterday seated at breakfast over a pensive dish of tea, my meditations were interrupted by my old friend and companion, who introduced a stranger, dressed pretty much like himself. The gentleman made several apologies for his visit, begged of me to impute his intrusion to the sincerity of his respect, and the warmth of his curiosity.

As I am very suspicious of my company, when I find them very civil without any apparent reason, I answered the stranger's caresses at first with reserve; which my friend perceiving, instantly let me into my visitor's trade and character, asking Mr. Fudge, whether he had lately published any thing new? I now conjectured that my guest was no other than a bookseller, and his answer confirmed my suspicions.

'Excuse me, Sir, says he, it is not the season; books have their time as well as cucumbers. I would no more bring out a new work in summer, than I would sell pork in the dog-days. Nothing in my way goes off in summer, except very light goods indeed. A review, a magazine, or a sessions paper, may amuse a summer reader; but all our stock of value we reserve for a spring and winter trade.' *I must confess, Sir, says I, a curiosity to know what you call a valuable stock, which can only bear a winter perusal.* 'Sir, replied the bookseller, it is not my way to cry up my own goods; but without exaggeration I will venture to shew with any of the trade; my books at least have the peculiar advantage of being always new; and it is my way to clear off my old to the trunkmakers every season. I have ten new title pages now about me, which only want books to be added to make them the finest things in Nature. Others may pretend to direct the vulgar; but that is not my way; I always let the vulgar direct me; wherever popular clamour arises, I always echo the million. For instance, should the people in general say that such a man is a rogue, I instantly give orders to set him down in print a villain; thus every man buys the book, not to learn new sentiments, but to have the pleasure of seeing his own reflected.' *But Sir, interrupted I, you speak as if you yourself wrote the books you publish; may I be so bold as to ask a sight of some of those intended publications which are shortly to surprise the world?* 'As to that, Sir, replied the talkative bookseller, I only draw out the plans myself; and though I am very cautious of communicating them to any, yet, as in the end, I have a favour to ask, you shall see a few of them. Here, Sir, here they are, diamonds of the first water, I assure you. Imprimis, a translation of several medical precepts for the use of such physicians as do not understand Latin. Item, the young clergyman's art of placing patches regularly, with a dissertation on the different manner of smiling without distorting the face. Item, the whole art of love made perfectly easy by a broker of 'Change Alley. Item, the proper manner of cutting blacklead pencils, and making crayons; by the Right Hon. the Earl of * * *. Item, the muster-master-general, or the review of reviews—' *Sir, cried I, interrupting him, my curiosity with regard to title pages is satisfied, I should be glad to see some longer manuscript, an history, or an epic poem.*—'Bless me, cries the man of industry, now you speak of an epic poem, you shall see an excellent farce. Here it is; dip into it where you will, it will be found replete with true modern humour. Strokes, Sir; it is filled with strokes of wit and satire in every line.' *Do you call these dashes of the pen strokes, replied I, for I must confess I can see no other?* 'And pray, Sir, returned he, what do you call them? Do you see any thing good now-a-days that is

not filled with strokes—and dashes?——Sir, a well placed
dash makes half the wit of our writers of modern humour.
I bought last season a piece that had no other merit upon earth
than nine hundred and ninety-five breaks, seventy-two ha ha's,
three good things, and a garter. And yet it played off, and
bounced, and cracked, and made more sport than a fine work.'
I fancy then, Sir, you were a considerable gainer? 'It must be
owned the piece did pay; but upon the whole I cannot much
boast of last winter's success; I gained by two murders, but
then I lost by an ill-timed charity sermon. I was a considerable sufferer by my Direct Road to an Estate, but the Infernal
Guide brought me up again. Ah, Sir, that was a piece touched
off by the hands of a master, filled with good things from one
end to the other. The author had nothing but the jest in view;
no dull moral lurking beneath, nor ill-natured satire to sour the
reader's good humour; he wisely considered that moral and
humour at the same time were quite overdoing the business.'
To what purpose was the book then published? cried I. 'Sir, the
book was published in order to be sold; and no book sold better,
except the criticisms upon it, which came out soon after. Of
all kinds of writings that goes off best at present; and I generally
fasten a criticism upon every selling book that is published.

'I once had an author who never left the least opening for the
critics; close was the word, always very right, and very dull,
ever on the safe side of an argument; yet, with all his qualifications, incapable of coming into favour. I soon perceived that
his bent was for criticism; and as he was good for nothing else,
supplied him with pens and paper, and planted him at the
beginning of every month as a censor on the works of others.
In short, I found him a treasure, no merit could escape him:
but what is most remarkable of all, he ever wrote best and
bitterest when drunk.' *But are there not some works*, interrupted
I, *that from the very manner of their compilation must be exempt
from criticism; particularly such as profess to disregard its laws?*
'There is no work whatsoever but he can criticise, replied the
bookseller; even though you wrote in Chinese he would have a
pluck at you. Suppose you should take it into your head to
publish a book, let it be a volume of Chinese letters for instance;
write how you will, he shall shew the world you could have
written better. Should you, with the most local exactness,
stick to the manners and customs of the country from whence
you come; should you confine yourself to the narrow limits
of eastern knowledge, and be perfectly simple, and perfectly

natural, he has then the strongest reason to exclaim. He may with a sneer send you back to China for readers. He may observe, that after the first or second letter the iteration of the same simplicity is insupportably tedious; but the worst of all is, the public in such a case will anticipate his censures, and leave you with all your uninstructive simplicity to be mauled at discretion.'

Yes, cried I, *but, in order to avoid his indignation, and what I should fear more, that of the public, I would in such a case write with all the knowledge I was master of. As I am not possessed of much learning, at least I would not suppress what little I had; nor would I appear more stupid than Nature made me.* 'Here then, cries the bookseller, we should have you entirely in our power; unnatural, uneastern; quite out of character; erroneously sensible would be the whole cry; Sir, we should then hunt you down like a rat.' *Head of my father!* said I, *sure there are but the two ways; the door must either be shut, or it must be open. I must either be natural or unnatural.* 'Be what you will, we shall criticise you, returned the bookseller, and prove you a dunce in spite of your teeth. But, Sir, it is time that I should come to business. I have just now in the press an history of China; but if you will but put your name to it as the author, I shall repay the obligation with gratitude.' *What, Sir*, replied I, *put my name to a work which I have not written! Never while I retain a proper respect for the public and myself.* The bluntness of my reply quite abated the ardour of the bookseller's conversation; and, after about half an hour's disagreeable reserve, he with some ceremony took his leave and withdrew. Adieu.

LETTER LII.—*To the same.*

In all other countries, my dear Fum Hoam, the rich are distinguished by their dress. In Persia, China, and most parts of Europe, those who are possessed of much gold or silver, put some of it upon their clothes; but in England, those who carry much upon their clothes, are remarked for having but little in their pockets. A tawdry outside is regarded as a badge of poverty, and those who can sit at home, and gloat over their thousands in silent satisfaction, are generally found to do it in plain clothes.

This diversity of thinking from the rest of the world which prevails here, I was first at a loss to account for; but since am informed that it was introduced by an intercourse between them and their neighbours the French; who, whenever they came in order to pay those islanders a visit, were generally very well dressed, and very poor, daubed with lace, but all the gilding on the outside. By this means laced clothes have been brought so much into contempt, that at present even their mandarines are ashamed of finery.

I must own myself a convert to English simplicity; I am no more for ostentation of wealth than of learning; the person who in company should pretend to be wiser than others, I am apt to regard as illiterate and ill bred; the person whose clothes are extremely fine, I am too apt to consider as not being possessed of any superiority of fortune, but resembling those Indians who are found to wear all the gold they have in the world in a bob at the nose.

I was lately introduced into a company of the best dressed men I have seen since my arrival. Upon entering the room, I was struck with awe at the grandeur of the different dresses. That personage, thought I, in blue and gold, must be some emperor's son; that, in green and silver, a prince of the blood; he, in embroidered scarlet, a prime minister, all first rate noblemen, I suppose, and well-looking noblemen too. I sat for some time with that uneasiness which conscious inferiority produces in the ingenuous mind, all attention to their discourse. However, I found their conversation more vulgar than I could have expected from personages of such distinction: if these, thought I to myself, be princes, they are the most stupid princes I have ever conversed with: yet still I continued to venerate their dress; for dress has a kind of mechanical influence on the mind.

My friend in black indeed did not behave with the same deference, but contradicted the finest of them all in the most peremptory tones of contempt. But I had scarce time to wonder at the imprudence of his conduct, when I found occasion to be equally surprised at the absurdity of theirs; for upon the entry of a middle-aged man, dressed in a cap, dirty shirt and boots, the whole circle seemed diminished of their former importance, and contended who should be the first to pay their obeisance to the stranger. They somewhat resembled a circle of Kalmucs offering incense to a bear.

Eager to know the cause of so much seeming contradiction, I whispered my friend out of the room, and found that the august company consisted of no other than a dancing master, two fiddlers, and a third rate actor, all assembled in order to make a set at country dances; as the middle-aged gentleman whom I saw enter was a squire from the country, and desirous of learning the new manner of footing, and smoothing up the rudiments of his rural minuet.

I was no longer surprised at the authority which my friend assumed among them, nay, was even displeased (pardon my eastern education) that he had not kicked every creature of them down stairs. 'What, said I, shall a set of such paltry fellows dress themselves up like sons of kings, and claim even the transitory respect of half an hour! There should be some law to restrain so manifest a breach of privilege; they should go from house to house, as in China, with the instruments of their profession strung round their necks; by this means we might be able to distinguish and treat them in a style of becoming contempt.' 'Hold, my friend, replied my companion, were your reformation to take place, as dancing masters and fiddlers now mimic gentlemen in appearance, we should then find our fine gentlemen conforming to theirs. A beau might be introduced to a lady of fashion with a fiddle case hanging at his neck by a red ribbon; and, instead of a cane, might carry a fiddle stick. Though to be as dull as a first rate dancing master might be used with proverbial justice; yet, dull as he is, many a fine gentleman sets him up as the proper standard of politeness, copies not only the pert vivacity of his air, but the flat insipidity of his conversation. In short, if you make a law against dancing masters imitating the fine gentleman, you should with as much reason enact, That no fine gentleman shall imitate the dancing master.'

After I had left my friend, I made towards home, reflecting as I went upon the difficulty of distinguishing men by their appearance. Invited, however, by the freshness of the evening, I did not return directly, but went to ruminate on what had passed in a public garden belonging to the city. Here, as I sat upon one of the benches, and felt the pleasing sympathy which Nature in bloom inspires, a disconsolate figure, who sat on the other end of the seat, seemed in no way to enjoy the serenity of the season.

His dress was miserable beyond description; a thread-bare coat of the rudest materials; a shirt, though clean, yet extremely coarse; hair that seemed to have been long unconscious of the comb; and all the rest of his equipage impressed with the marks of genuine poverty.

As he continued to sigh, and testify every symptom of despair,

I was naturally led, from a motive of humanity, to offer comfort and assistance You know my heart; and that all who are miserable may claim a place there. The pensive stranger at first declined any conversation; but at last perceiving a peculiarity in my accent and manner of thinking, he began to unfold himself by degrees.

I now found that he was not so very miserable as he at first appeared; upon my offering him a small piece of money, he refused my favour, yet without appearing displeased at my intended generosity. It is true he sometimes interrupted the conversation with a sigh, and talked pathetically of neglected merit; still I could perceive a serenity in his countenance, that upon a closer inspection bespoke inward content.

Upon a pause in the conversation I was going to take my leave, when he begged I would favour him with my company home to supper. I was surprised at such a demand from a person of his appearance, but willing to indulge curiosity, I accepted his invitation; and though I felt some repugnance at being seen with one who appeared so very wretched, went along with seeming alacrity.

Still as he approached nearer home, his good humour proportionately seemed to increase. At last he stopped, not at the gate of an hovel, but of a magnificent palace! When I cast my eyes upon all the sumptuous elegance which every where presented upon entering, and then when I looked at my seeming miserable conductor, I could scarce think that all this finery belonged to him; yet in fact it did. Numerous servants ran through the apartments with silent assiduity; several ladies of beauty and magnificently dressed came to welcome his return; a most elegant supper was provided; in short, I found the person, whom a little before I had sincerely pitied, to be in reality a most refined epicure; *one who courted contempt abroad, in order to feel with keener gust the pleasure of pre-eminence at home.* Adieu.

LETTER LIII.—*From the same.*

How often have we admired the eloquence of Europe! That strength of thinking, that delicacy of imagination, even beyond the efforts of the Chinese themselves. How were we enraptured with those bold figures which sent every sentiment with force to the heart! How have we spent whole days together in learning those arts by which European writers got within the passions, and led the reader as if by enchantment!

But though we have learned most of the rhetorical figures of the last age, yet there seems to be one or two of great use here, which have not yet travelled to China.   The figures I mean are called *Bawdy* and *Pertness*; none are more fashionable; none so sure of admirers; they are of such a nature, that the merest blockhead, by a proper use of them, shall have the reputation of a wit; they lie level to the meanest capacities, and address those passions which all have, or would be ashamed to disown.

It has been observed, and I believe with some truth, that it is very difficult for a dunce to obtain the reputation of a wit; yet by the assistance of the figure *Bawdy*, this may be easily effected, and a bawdy blockhead often passes for a fellow of smart parts and pretensions.   Every object in Nature helps the jokes forward, without scarce any effort of the imagination.   If a lady stands, something very good may be said upon that; if she happens to fall, with the help of a little fashionable pruriency, there are forty sly things ready on the occasion.   But a prurient jest has always been found to give most pleasure to a few very old gentlemen, who being in some measure dead to other sensations, feel the force of the allusion with the double violence on the organs of risibility.

An author who writes in this manner is generally sure therefore of having the very old and the impotent among his admirers; for these he may properly be said to write, and from these he ought to expect his reward, his works being often a very proper succedaneum to cantharides, or an assafœtida pill.   His pen should be considered in the same light as the squirt of an apothecary, both being directed at the same generous end.

But though this manner of writing be perfectly adapted to the taste of gentlemen and ladies of fashion here, yet still it deserves greater praise in being equally suited to the most vulgar apprehensions.   The very ladies and gentlemen of Benin or Caffraria, are in this respect tolerably polite, and might relish a prurient joke of this kind with critical propriety; probably, too, with higher gust, as they wear neither breeches nor petticoats to intercept the application.

It is certain I never could have expected the ladies here, biassed as they are by education, capable at once of bravely throwing off their prejudices, and not only applauding books in which this figure makes the only merit, but even adopting it in their own conversation.   Yet so it is, the pretty innocents now carry these books openly in their hands, which formerly were hid under the cushion; they now lisp their double meanings with so much grace, and talk over the raptures they bestow with such little reserve, that I am sometimes reminded of a custom among the entertainers in China, who think it a piece of necessary breeding to whet the appetites of their guests, by letting them smell dinner in the kitchen before it is served up to table.

The veneration we have for many things, entirely proceeds from their being carefully concealed. Were the idolatrous Tartar permitted to lift the veil which keeps his idol from view, it might be a certain method to cure his future superstition; with what a noble spirit of freedom therefore must that writer be possessed, who bravely paints things as they are, who lifts the veil of modesty, who displays the most hidden recesses of the temple, and shews the erring people that the object of their vows is either, perhaps a mouse, or a monkey.

However, though this figure be at present so much in fashion; though the professors of it are so much caressed by the great, those perfect judges of literary excellence; yet it is confessed to be only a revival of what was once fashionable here before. There was a time, when by this very manner of writing, the gentle Tom Durfey, as I read in English authors, acquired his great reputation, and became the favourite of a king.

The works of this original genius, though they never travelled abroad in China, and scarce have reached posterity at home, were once found upon every fashionable toilet, and made the subject of polite, I mean very polite conversation. 'Has your Grace seen Mr. Durfey's last new thing, the Oylet Hole? A most facetious piece! Sure, my lord, all the world must have seen it; Durfey is certainly the most comical creature alive. It is impossible to read his things and live. Was there ever any thing so natural and pretty, as when the Squire and Bridget meet in the cellar? And then the difficulties they both find in broaching the beer barrel are so arch and so ingenious! We have certainly nothing of this kind in the language.'

In this manner they spoke then, and in this manner they speak now; for though the successor of Durfey does not excel him in wit, the world must confess he outdoes him in obscenity.

There are several very dull fellows, who, by a few mechanical helps, sometimes learn to become extremely brilliant and pleasing; with a little dexterity in the management of the eyebrows, fingers, and nose. By imitating a cat, a sow and pigs; by a loud laugh, and a slap on the shoulder, the most ignorant are furnished out for conversation. But the writer finds it impossible to throw his winks, his shrugs, or his attitudes upon paper; he may borrow some assistance indeed, by printing his face at the title page; but without wit to pass for a man of ingenuity, no other mechanical help but downright obscenity will suffice. By speaking to some peculiar sensations, we are always sure of exciting laughter, for the jest does not lie in the writer, but in the subject.

But Bawdy is often helped on by another figure, called Pertness; and few indeed are found to excel in one that are not possessed of the other.

As in common conversation the best way to make the audience laugh is by first laughing yourself; so in writing, the properest manner is to shew an attempt at humour, which will pass upon most for humour in reality. To effect this, readers must be treated with the most perfect familiarity: in one page the author is to make them a low bow, and in the next to pull them by the nose: he must talk in riddles, and then send them to bed in order to dream for the solution. He must speak of himself and his chapters, and his manner, and what he would be at, and his own importance, and his mother's importance with the most unpitying prolixity: now and then testifying his contempt for all but himself, smiling without a jest, and without wit possessing vivacity. Adieu.

LETTER LIV.—*From the same.*

THOUGH naturally pensive, yet I am fond of gay company, and take every opportunity of thus dismissing the mind from duty. From this motive I am often found in the centre of a crowd; and wherever pleasure is to be sold, am always a purchaser. In those places, without being remarked by any, I join in whatever goes forward, work my passions into a similitude of frivolous earnestness, shout as they shout, and condemn as they happen to disapprove. A mind thus sunk for a while below its natural standard, is qualified for stronger flights, as those first retire who would spring forward with greater vigour.

Attracted by the serenity of the evening, my friend and I lately went to gaze upon the company in one of the public walks near the city. Here we sauntered together for some time, either praising the beauty of such as were handsome, or the dresses of such as had nothing else to recommend them. We had gone thus deliberately forward for some time, when stopping on a sudden, my friend caught me by the elbow, and led me out of the public walk; I could perceive by the quickness of his pace, and by his frequently looking behind, that he was attempting to avoid somebody who followed; we now turned to the right, then to the left; as we went forward he still went faster, but in vain; the person whom he attempted to escape, hunted us through every doubling, and gained upon us each moment; so that at last we fairly stood still, resolving to face what we could not avoid.

Our pursuer soon came up, and joined us with all the familiarity of an old acquaintance. *My dear Drybone*, cries he, shaking my friend's hand, *where have you been hiding this half a century? Positively I had fancied you were gone down to cultivate matrimony and your estate in the country.* During the reply, I had an opportunity of surveying the appearance of our new companion; his hat was pinched up with peculiar smartness; his looks were pale, thin, and sharp; round his neck he wore a broad black ribbon, and in his bosom a buckle studded with glass; his coat was trimmed with tarnished twist; he wore by his side a sword with a black hilt, and his stockings of silk, though newly washed, were grown yellow by long service. I was so much engaged with the peculiarity of his dress, that I attended only to the latter part of my friend's reply, in which he complimented Mr. Tibbs on the taste of his clothes, and the bloom in his countenance. *Psha, psha, Will*, cried the figure, *no more of that if you love me, you know I hate flattery, on my soul I do; and yet to be sure an intimacy with the great will improve one's appearance, and a course of venison will fatten; and yet faith I despise the great as much as you do; but there are a great many damn'd honest fellows among them; and we must not quarrel with one half, because the other wants weeding. If they were all such as my lord Mudler, one of the most good-natured creatures that ever squeezed a lemon, I should myself be among the number of their admirers. I was yesterday to dine at the Duchess of Piccadilly's, my lord was there. Ned, says he to me, Ned, says he, I'll hold gold to silver I can tell where you were poaching last night. Poaching, my lord, says I; faith you have missed already; for I staid at home, and let the girls poach for me. That's my way; I take a fine woman as some animals do their prey; stand still, and swoop, they fall into my mouth.*

Ah, Tibbs, thou art an happy fellow, cried my companion with looks of infinite pity, I hope your fortune is as much improved as your understanding in such company? *Improved*, replied the other; *You shall know,——but let it go no further,——a great secret——five hundred a year to begin with.——My lord's word of honour for it——His lordship took me down in his own chariot yesterday, and we had a tête-à-tête dinner in the country; where we talked of nothing else.* I fancy you forget, sir, cried I, you told us but this moment of your dining yesterday in town! *Did I say so, replied he coolly, to be sure if I said so, it was so——Dined in town: egad now I do remember, I did dine in town; but I dined in the country too; for you must know, my boys, I eat two dinners. By the bye, I am grown as nice as the Devil in my eating. I'll tell you a pleasant affair about that: We were a select party of us to dine at Lady Grogram's, an affected piece, but let it go no further; a secret: well, there happened to be no assafœtida in the sauce to a turkey, upon which says I, I'll hold a thousand guineas, and say done first, that——But dear Drybone, you are an honest creature, lend me half-a-crown for a minute or two, or so, just till——But hearkee, ask me for it the next time we meet, or it may be twenty to one but I forget to pay you.*

When he left us, our conversation naturally turned upon so extraordinary a character. His very dress, cried my friend, is not less extraordinary than his conduct. If you meet him this day you find him in rags, if the next in embroidery. With those persons of distinction, of whom he talks so familiarly, he has scarce a coffee-house acquaintance. However, both for interests of society, and perhaps for his own, heaven has made him poor, and while all the world perceive his wants, he fancies them concealed from every eye. An agreeable companion because he understands flattery, and all must be pleased with the first part of his conversation, though all are sure of its ending with a demand on their purse. While his youth countenances the levity of his conduct, he may thus earn a precarious subsistence, but when age comes on, the gravity of which is incompatible with buffoonery, then will he find himself forsaken by all; condemned in the decline of life to hang upon some rich family whom he once despised, there to undergo all the ingenuity of studied contempt, to be employed only as a spy upon the servants, or a bugbear to fight the children into obedience. Adieu.

LETTER LV.—*To the same.*

I AM apt to fancy I have contracted a new acquaintance whom it will be no easy matter to shake off. My little beau yesterday overtook me again in one of the public walks, and slapping me on the shoulder, saluted me with an air of the most perfect familiarity. His dress was the same as usual, except that he had more powder in his hair, wore a dirtier shirt, a pair of temple spectacles, and his hat under his arm.

As I knew him to be an harmless amusing little thing, I could not return his smiles with any degree of severity; so we walked forward on terms of the utmost intimacy, and in a few minutes discussed all the usual topics preliminary to particular conversation.

The oddities that marked his character, however, soon began to appear; he bowed to several well dressed persons, who, by their manner of returning the compliment, appeared perfect strangers. At intervals he drew out a pocket book, seeming to take memorandums before all the company, with much importance and assiduity. In this manner he led me through the length of the whole walk, fretting at his absurdities, and fancying myself laughed at not less than him by every spectator.

When we were got to the end of our procession, *Blast me*, cries he, with an air of vivacity, *I never saw the park so thin in my life before; there's no company at all to-day. Not a single face to be seen.* No company, interrupted I peevishly; no company where there is such a crowd; why man, there's too much. What are the thousands that have been laughing at us but company! *Lard, my dear*, returned he, with the utmost good humour, *you seem immensely chagrined; but blast me, when the world laughs at me, I laugh at all the world, and so we are even. My lord Trip, Bill Squash the Creolian, and I, sometimes make a party at being ridiculous; and so we say and do a thousand things for the joke sake. But I see you are grave, and if you are for a fine grave sentimental companion, you shall dine with me and my wife to day, I must insist on't; I'll introduce you to Mrs. Tibbs, a Lady of as elegant qualifications as any in Nature; she was bred, but that's between ourselves, under the inspection of the Countess of All-night. A charming body of voice, but no more of that, she will give us a song. You shall see my little girl too, Carolina Wilhelmina Amelia Tibbs, a sweet pretty creature; I design her for my Lord Drumstick's eldest son, but that's in friendship, let it go no further; she's but six years old, and yet she walks a minuet, and plays on the guitar immensely already. I intend she shall be as perfect as possible in every accomplishment. In the first place I'll make her a scholar; I'll teach her Greek myself, and learn that language purposely to instruct her; but let that be a secret.*

Thus saying, without waiting for a reply, he took me by the

arm and hauled me along. We passed through many dark alleys and winding ways; for, from some motives to me unknown, he seemed to have a particular aversion to every frequented street; at last, however, we got to the door of a dismal looking house in the outlets of the town, where he informed me he chose to reside for the benefit of the air.

We entered the lower door, which ever seemed to lie most hospitably open; and I began to ascend an old and creaking stair-case, when, as he mounted to shew me the way, he demanded, whether I delighted in prospects, to which answering in the affirmative, *Then*, says he, *I shall shew you one of the most charming in the world out of my windows; we shall see the ships sailing, and the whole country for twenty miles round, tip top, quite high. My Lord Swamp would give ten thousand guineas for such a one; but as I sometimes pleasantly tell him, I always love to keep my prospects at home, that my friends may see me the oftener.*

By this time we were arrived as high as the stairs would permit us to ascend, till we came to what he was facetiously pleased to call the first floor down the chimney; and knocking at the door, a voice from within demanded, Who's there? My conductor answered, that it was him. But this not satisfying the querist, the voice again repeated the demand: to which he answered louder than before; and now the door was opened by an old woman with cautious reluctance.

When we were got in, he welcomed me to his house with great ceremony, and turning to the old woman, asked where was her lady? 'Good troth, replied she, in a peculiar dialect, she's washing your two shirts at the next door, because they have taken an oath against lending out the tub any longer.' *My two shirts*, cries he in a tone that faltered with confusion, *what does the idiot mean!* 'I ken what I mean well enough, replied the other, she's washing your twa shirts at the next door, because——' *Fire and fury, no more of thy stupid explanations*, cried he,—*Go and inform her we have got company. Were that Scotch hag to be for ever in the family, she would never learn politeness, nor forget that absurd poisonous accent of hers, or testify the smallest specimen of breeding or high life; and yet it is very surprising too, as I had her from a parliament man, a friend of mine, from the highlands, one of the politest men in the world; but that's a secret.*

We waited some time for Mrs. Tibbs' arrival, during which interval I had a full opportunity of surveying the chamber and all its furniture; which consisted of four chairs with old wrought bottoms, that he assured me were his wife's embroidery; a square table that had been once japanned, a cradle, in one corner, a lumbering cabinet in the other; a broken shepherdess, and a mandarine without a head, were stuck over the chimney; and round the wall several paltry, unframed pictures, which he observed, were all his own drawing: *What do you think, Sir, of that head in a corner, done in the manner of Grisoni? there's the true keeping in it; it's my own face, and though there happens to be no likeness, a countess offered me an hundred for its fellow: I refused her, for, hang it, that would be mechanical, you know.*

The wife at last made her appearance, at once a slattern and a coquet; much emaciated, but still carrying the remains of beauty. She made twenty apologies for being seen in such odious dishabille, but hoped to be excused, as she had staid out all night at the gardens with the countess, who was excessively fond of the *horns.* 'And, indeed, my dear, added she, turning to her huband, his lordship drank your health in a bumper.' *Poor Jack,* cries he, *a dear good-natured creature, I know he loves me; but I hope, my dear, you have given orders for dinner; you need make no great preparations neither, there are but three of us, something elegant, and little will do; a turbot, an ortolan, or a——. Or what do you think my dear,* interrupts the wife, *of a nice, pretty bit of ox cheek, piping hot, and dressed with a little of my own sauce—The very thing,* replies he, *it will eat best with some smart bottled beer; but be sure to let's have the sauce his grace was so fond of. I hate your immense loads of meat, that is country all over; extreme disgusting to those who are in the least acquainted with high life.*

By this time my curiosity began to abate, and my appetite to increase; the company of fools may at first make us smile, but at last never fails of rendering us melancholy. I therefore pretended to recollect a prior engagement, and after having shewn my respects to the house, according to the fashion of the English, by giving the old servant a piece of money at the door, I took my leave; Mr. Tibbs assuring me that dinner, if I staid, would be ready at least in less than two hours.

LETTER LVI.—*From Fum Hoam to Altangi, the discontented wanderer.*

THE distant sounds of music that catch new sweetness as they vibrate through the long drawn valley, are not more pleasing to the ear than the tidings of a far distant friend.

I have just received two hundred of thy letters by the Russian caravan, descriptive of the manners of Europe. You have left it to geographers to determine the size of their mountains, and extent of their lakes, seeming only employed in discovering the genius, the government, and disposition of the people.

In those letters I perceive a journal of the operations of your mind upon whatever occurs, rather than a detail of your travels from one building to another; of your taking a draught of this ruin, or that obelisk; of paying so many Tomans for this commodity, or laying up a proper store for the passage of some new wilderness.

From your accounts of Russia I learn, that this nation is again relaxing into pristine barbarity, that its great emperor wanted a life of an hundred years more to bring about his vast design. A savage people may be resembled to their own forests; a few years are sufficient to clear away the obstructions to agriculture; but it requires many ere the ground acquires a proper degree of fertility; the Russians, attached to their ancient prejudices, again renew their hatred to strangers, and indulge every former brutal excess. So true it is, that the revolutions of wisdom are slow and difficult, the revolutions of folly or ambition precipitate and easy. *We are not to be astonished*, says Confucius,[1] *that the wise walk more slowly in their road to virtue, than fools in their passage to vice; since passion drags us along, while wisdom only points out the way.*

The German empire, that remnant of the majesty of ancient Rome, appears from your account on the eve of dissolution. The members of its vast body want every tie of government to unite them, and seem feebly held together only by their respect for ancient institutions. The very name of country and countrymen, which in other nations make one of the strongest bonds of government, has been here for some time laid aside, each of its inhabitants seeming more proud of being called from the petty state which gives him birth, than by the more well known title of German.

This government may be regarded in the light of a severe master, and a feeble opponent. The states which are now subject to the laws of the empire, are only watching a proper occasion to fling off the yoke, and those which are become too powerful to be compelled to obedience, now begin to think of

---

[1] Though this fine maxim be not found in the Latin edition of the Morals of Confucius, yet we find it ascribed to him by Le Comte, Etat présent de la Chine, vol. i, p. 342.

dictating in their turn. The struggles in this state are therefore not in order to preserve but to destroy the ancient constitution; if one side succeeds, the government must become despotic, if the other, several states will subsist without nominal subordination, but in either case the Germanic constitution will be no more.

Sweden, on the contrary, though now seemingly a strenuous assertor of its liberties, is probably only hastening on to despotism. Their senators, while they pretend to vindicate the freedom of the people, are only establishing their own independence. The deluded people will however at last perceive the miseries of an aristocratical government; they will perceive that the administration of a society of men is ever more painful than that of one only. They will fly from this most oppressive of all forms, where one single member is capable of controlling the whole, to take refuge under the throne which will ever be attentive to their complaints. No people long endure an aristocratical government, when they could apply elsewhere for redress. The lower orders of people may be enslaved for a time by a number of tyrants, but upon the first opportunity they will ever take a refuge in despotism or democracy.

As the Swedes are making concealed approaches to despotism, the French, on the other hand, are imperceptibly vindicating themselves into freedom. When I consider that those parliaments (the members of which are all created by the court, the presidents of which can act only by immediate direction) presume even to mention privileges and freedom, who, till of late, received directions from the throne with implicit humility; when this is considered, I cannot help fancying that the genius of freedom has entered that kingdom in disguise. If they have but three weak monarchs more, successively on the throne, the mask will be laid aside, and the country will certainly once more be free.

When I compare the figure which the Dutch make in Europe with that they assume in Asia, I am struck with surprise. In Asia, I find them the great Lords of all the Indian seas; in Europe the timid inhabitants of a paltry state. No longer the sons of freedom, but of avarice; no longer assertors of their rights by courage, but by negotiations; fawning on those who insult them, and crouching under the rod of every neighbouring power. Without a friend to save them in distress, and without virtue to save themselves; their government is poor, and their private wealth will serve to invite some neighbouring invader.

I long with impatience for your letters from England,

Denmark, Holland, and Italy; yet why wish for relations which only describe new calamities, which shew that ambition and avarice are equally terrible in every region.   Adieu.

LETTER LVII.—*From Lien Chi Altangi, to Fum Hoam, first President of the Ceremonial Academy at Pekin, in China.*

I HAVE frequently admired the manner of criticising in China, where the learned are assembled in a body to judge of every new publication; to examine the merits of the work without knowing the circumstances of the author, and then to usher it into the world with proper marks of respect or reprobation.

In England there are no such tribunals erected; but if a man thinks proper to be a judge of genius, few will be at the pains to contradict his pretensions. If any choose to be critics, it is but saying they are critics; and from that time forward they become invested with full power and authority over every caitiff who aims at their instruction or entertainment.

As almost every member of society has by this means a vote in literary transactions, it is no way surprising to find the rich leading the way here as in other common concerns of life, to see them either bribing the numerous herd of voters by their interest, or brow-beating them by their authority.

A great man says, at his table, that such a book *is no bad thing*. Immediately the praise is carried off by five flatterers to be dispersed at twelve different coffee-houses, from whence it circulates, still improving as it proceeds, through forty-five houses, where cheaper liquors are sold; from thence it is carried away by the honest tradesman to his own fire-side, where the applause is eagerly caught up by his wife and children who have been long taught to regard his judgment as the standard of perfection. Thus when we have traced a wide extended literary reputation up to its original source, we shall find it derived from some great man, who has, perhaps, received all his education and English from a tutor of Berne, or a dancing-master of Picardy.

The English are a people of good sense; and I am the more surprised to find them swayed in their opinions, by men who often from their very education are incompetent judges. Men who, being always bred in affluence, see the world only on one side, are surely improper judges of human nature; they may indeed describe a ceremony, a pageant or a ball; but how can they pretend to dive into the secrets of the human heart, who have been nursed up only in forms, and daily behold nothing but the same insipid adulation smiling upon every face. Few of them have been bred in that best of schools, the school of adversity; and by what I can learn, fewer still have been bred in any school at all.

From such a description one would think, that a droning duke, or a dowager duchess, was not possessed of more just pretensions to taste than persons of less quality; and yet whatever the one or the other may write or praise, shall pass for perfection, without farther examination. A nobleman has but to take a pen, ink, and paper, write away through three large volumes, and then sign his name to the title page, though the whole might have been before more disgusting than his own rent-roll, yet signing his name and title gives value to the deed; title being alone equivalent to taste, imagination, and genius.

As soon as a piece therefore is published the first questions are, Who is the author? Does he keep a coach? Where lies his estate? What sort of a table does he keep? If he happens to be poor and unqualified for such a scrutiny, he and his works sink into irremediable obscurity; and too late he finds, that having fed upon turtle is a more ready way to fame than having digested Tully.

The poor devil, against whom fashion has set its face, vainly alleges, that he has been bred in every part of Europe where knowledge was to be sold; that he has grown pale in the study of Nature and himself; his works may please upon the perusal, but his pretensions to fame are entirely disregarded; he is treated like a fiddler, whose music, though liked, is not much praised, because he lives by it; while a gentleman performer, though the most wretched scraper alive, throws the audience into raptures. The fiddler indeed may in such a case console himself by thinking, that while the other goes off with all the praise, he runs away with all the money: but here the parallel drops; for while the nobleman triumphs in unmerited applause, the author by profession, steals off with—*Nothing*.

The poor, therefore, here, who draw their pens auxiliary to the laws of their country, must think themselves very happy if they find, not fame but forgiveness; and yet they are hardly treated; for as every country grows more polite, the press becomes more useful; and writers become more necessary, as readers are supposed to increase. In a polished society, that man, though in rags, who has the power of enforcing virtue from the press, is of more real use than forty stupid brachmans or bonzes, or guebres, though they preached never so often, never so loud, or never so long. That man, though in rags, who is capable of deceiving even indolence into wisdom, and who professes amusement while he aims at reformation, is more useful in refined society than twenty cardinals with all their scarlet, and tricked out in all the fopperies of scholastic finery.

LETTER LVIII.—*To the same.*

As the man in black takes every opportunity of introducing me to such company as may serve to indulge my speculative temper, or gratify my curiosity, I was by his influence lately invited to a *visitation* dinner. To understand this term, you must know, that it was formerly the custom here for the principal priests to go about the country once a year, and examine upon the spot whether those of subordinate orders did their duty, or were qualified for the task; whether their temples were kept in proper repair, or the laity pleased with their administration.

Though a visitation of this nature was very useful, yet it was found to be extremely troublesome, and for many reasons utterly inconvenient; for as the principal priests were obliged to attend at court, in order to solicit preferment, it was impossible they could at the same time attend in the country, which was quite out of the road to promotion: if we add to this the gout, which has been time immemorial a clerical disorder here, together with the bad wine, and ill dressed provisions that must infallibly be served up by the way, it was not strange that the custom has been long discontinued. At present, therefore, every head of the church, instead of going about to visit his priests, is satisfied if his priests come in a body once a year to visit him; by this means the duty of half a year is despatched in a day. When assembled, he asks each in his turn how they have behaved, and are liked; upon which, those who have neglected their duty, or are disagreeable to their congregation, no doubt accuse themselves, and tell him all their faults; for which, he reprimands them most severely.

The thoughts of being introduced into a company of philosophers and learned men (for such I conceived them) gave me no small pleasure; I expected our entertainment would resemble those sentimental banquets so finely described by Xenophon and Plato; I was hoping some Socrates would be brought in from the door, in order to harangue upon divine love; but as for eating and drinking I had prepared myself to be disappointed in that particular. I was apprised, that fasting and temperance were tenets strongly recommended to the professors of Christianity; and I had seen the frugality and mortification of the priests of the east; so that I expected an entertainment where we should have much reasoning, and little meat.

Upon being introduced, I confess I found no great signs of mortification in the faces or persons of the company. However, I imputed their florid looks to temperance, and their corpulency to a sedentary way of living. I saw several preparations indeed for dinner, but none for philosophy. The company seemed to gaze upon the table with silent expectation; but this I easily excused. Men of wisdom, thought I, are ever slow of speech; they deliver nothing unadvisedly. *Silence*, says Confucius, *is a friend that will never betray*. They are now probably inventing maxims, or hard sayings, for their mutual instruction, when some one shall think proper to begin.

My curiosity was now wrought up to the highest pitch, I impatiently looked round to see if any were going to interrupt the mighty pause; when, at last, one of the company declared, that there was a sow in his neighbourhood that farrowed fifteen pigs at a litter. This I thought a very preposterous beginning: but just as another was going to second the remark, dinner was served, which interrupted the conversation for that time.

The appearance of dinner, which consisted of a variety of dishes, seemed to diffuse new cheerfulness upon every face; so that I now expected the philosophical conversation to begin, as they improved in good humour. The principal priest, however, opened his mouth, with only observing, that the venison had not been kept enough, though he had given strict orders for having it killed ten days before. *I fear*, continued he, *it will be found to want the true heathy flavour; you will find nothing of the original wildness in it.* A priest, who sat next him, having smelt it and wiped his nose: 'Ah, my good lord, cries he, you are too modest, it is perfectly fine; everybody knows that no body understands keeping venison with your lordship.' 'Ay, and partridges, too interrupted another; I never find them right anywhere else.' His lordship was going to reply, when a third took off the attention of the company, by recommending the pig as inimitable. 'I fancy, my lord, continues he, it has been smothered in its own blood.' 'If it has been smothered in its blood, cried a facetious member, helping himself, we 'll now smother it in egg sauce.' This poignant piece of humour produced a long loud laugh, which the facetious brother observing, and now that he was in luck, willing to second his blow, assured the company he would tell them a good story about that: 'As good a story, cries he, bursting into a violent fit of laughter himself, as ever you heard in your lives; there was a farmer of my parish, who used to sup upon wild ducks and flummery; so this farmer—*Doctor Marrowfat*, cries his lordship, interrupting him, *give me leave to drink your health*—so being fond of wild ducks and flummery—*Doctor*, adds a gentleman who sate next him, *let me advise to a wing of this turkey;*—so this farmer being fond—*Hob, nob, Doctor, which do you choose, white or red?*—So being fond of wild ducks and flummery—*Take care of your hand, Sir, it may dip in the gravy*. The doctor, now looking round, found not a single *eye* disposed to listen; wherefore calling for a glass of wine, he gulped down the disappointment and the tale in a bumper.

The conversation now began to be little more than a rhapsody of exclamations; as each had pretty well satisfied his own appetite, he now found sufficient time to press others. *Excellent, the very thing; let me recommend the pig, do but taste the bacon; never eat a better thing in my life; exquisite, delicious*. This edifying discourse continued through three courses, which lasted as many hours, till every one of the company were unable to swallow or utter any thing more.

It is very natural for men who are abridged in one excess, to break into some other. The clergy here, particularly those who are advanced in years, think if they are abstemious with regard to women and wine, they may indulge their other appetites without censure. Thus some are found to rise in the morning only to a consultation with their cook about dinner, and when that has been swallowed, make no other use of their faculties (if they have any) but to ruminate on the succeeding meal.

A debauch in wine is even more pardonable than this, since one glass insensibly leads on to another, and instead of sating whets the appetite. The progressive steps to it are cheerful and seducing; the grave are animated, the melancholy relieved, and there is even classic authority to countenance the excess. But in eating after Nature is once satisfied every additional morsel brings stupidity and distempers with it, and as one of their own poets expresses it,

> The soul subsides, and wickedly inclines,
> To seem but mortal, even in sound divines.

Let me suppose, after such a meal as this I have been describing, while all the company are sitting in lethargic silence round the table, grunting under a load of soup, pig, pork, and bacon; let me suppose, I say, some hungry beggar, with looks of want, peeping through one of the windows, and thus addressing the assembly, *Prythee, pluck those napkins from your chins; after Nature is satisfied all that you eat extraordinary is my property, and I claim it as mine. It was given you in order to relieve me, and not to oppress yourselves. How can they comfort or instruct others who can scarce feel their own existence, except from the unsavoury returns of an ill digested meal? But though neither you nor the cushions you sit upon will hear me, yet the world regards the excesses of its teachers with a prying eye, and notes their conduct with double severity.* I know no other answer any one of the company could make to such an expostulation, but this: 'Friend, you talk of our losing a character, and being disliked by the world; well, and supposing all this to be true, what then! who cares for the world? We'll preach for the world, and the world shall pay us for preaching, whether we like each other or not.'

LETTER LIX.—*From Hingpo to Lien Chi Altangi, by the way of Moscow.*

YOU will probably be pleased to see my letter dated from Terki, a city which lies beyond the bound of the Persian empire; here, blessed with security, with all that is dear, I double my raptures, by communicating them to you; the mind sympathizing with the freedom of the body, my whole soul is dilated in gratitude, love, and praise.

Yet were my own happiness all that inspired my present joy, my raptures might justly merit the imputation of self-interest; but when I think that the beautiful Zelis is also free, forgive my triumph when I boast of having rescued from captivity the most deserving object upon earth.

You remember the reluctance she testified at being obliged to marry the tyrant she hated. Her compliance at last was only feigned, in order to gain time to try some future means of escape. During the interval between her promise and the intended performance of it, she came undiscovered one evening to the place where I generally retired after the fatigues of the day; her appearance was like that of an aerial genius, when it descends to minister comfort to undeserved distress; the mild lustre of her eye served to banish my timidity; her accents were sweeter than the echo of some distant symphony. 'Unhappy stranger, said she, in the Persian language, you here perceive one more wretched than thyself; all this solemnity of preparation, this elegance of dress, and the number of my attendants, serve but to encrease my miseries; if you have courage to rescue an unhappy woman from approaching ruin, and our detested tyrant, you may depend upon my future gratitude.' I bowed to the ground, and she left me, filled with rapture and astonishment. Night brought me no rest, nor could the ensuing morning calm the anxieties of my mind. I projected a thousand methods or her delivery; but each, when strictly examined, appeared mpracticable; in this uncertainty the evening again arrived, and I placed myself on my former station in hopes of a repeated visit. After some short expectation, the bright perfection again appeared; I bowed, as before, to the ground; when raising me up she observed that the time was not to be spent in useless ceremony; she observed that the day following was appointed for the celebration of her nuptials, and that something was to be done that very night for our mutual deliverance. I offered with the utmost humility to pursue whatever scheme she should direct; upon which she proposed that instant to scale the garden wall, adding, that she had prevailed upon a female slave, who was now waiting at the appointed place, to assist her with a ladder.

Pursuant to this information I led her trembling to the place appointed; but instead of the slave we expected to see, Mostadad himself was there awaiting our arrival; the wretch in whom we confided, it seems, had betrayed our design to her master, and he now saw the most convincing proofs of her information. He was just going to draw his sabre, when a principle of avarice repressed his fury, and he resolved, after a severe chastisement, to dispose of me to another master, in the mean time ordering me to be confined in the strictest manner, and the next day to receive an hundred blows on the soles of my feet.

When the morning came I was led out in order to receive the punishment, which, from the severity with which it is generally inflicted upon slaves, is worse even than death.

A trumpet was to be a signal for the solemnisation of the nuptials of Zelis, and for the infliction of my punishment. Each ceremony to me equally dreadful were just going to begin, when we were informed that a large party of Circassian Tartars had invaded the town, and were laying all in ruin. Every person now thought only of saving himself; I instantly unloosed the cords with which I was bound, and seizing a scymetar from one of the slaves who had not courage to resist me, flew to the women's apartment where Zelis was confined, dressed out for the intended nuptials. I bade her follow me without delay; and going forward, cut my way through the eunuchs, who made but a faint resistance. The whole city was now a scene of conflagration and terror; every person was willing to save himself, unmindful of others. In this confusion seizing upon two of the fleetest coursers in the stables of Mostadad, we fled northward towards the kingdom of Circassia. As there were several others flying in the same manner, we passed without notice, and in three days arrived at Terki, a city that lies in a valley within the bosom of the frowning mountains of Caucasus.

Here, free from every apprehension of danger, we enjoy all those satisfactions which are consistent with virtue; though I find my heart at intervals give way to unusual passions, yet such is my admiration for my fair companion, that I lose even tenderness in distant respect. Though her person demands particular regard even among the beauties of Circassia, yet is her mind far more lovely. How very different is a woman who thus has cultivated her understanding, and been refined into delicacy of sentiment, from the daughter of the East, whose education is only formed to improve the person, and make them more tempting objects of prostitution! Adieu.

LETTER LX.—*From Hingpo to Lien Chi Altangi, by the way of Moscow.*

WHEN sufficiently refreshed after the fatigues of our precipitate flight, my curiosity, which had been restrained by the appearance of immediate danger, now began to revive: I longed to know by what distressful accidents my fair fugitive became a captive, and could not avoid testifying a surprise how so much beauty could be involved in the calamities from whence she had been so lately rescued.

Talk not of personal charms, cried she with emotion, since

to them I owe every misfortune: look round on the numberless beauties of the country where we are; and see how Nature has poured its charms upon every face, and yet by this profusion heaven would seem to shew how little it regards such a blessing, since the gift is lavished upon a nation of prostitutes.

I perceive you desire to know my story, and your curiosity is not so great as my impatience to gratify it: I find a pleasure in telling past misfortunes to any, but when my deliverer is pleased with the relation, my pleasure is prompted by duty.

'I [1] was born in a country far to the west, where the men are braver, and the women more fair than those of Circassia; where the valour of the hero is guided by wisdom, and where delicacy of sentiment points the shafts of female beauty. I was the only daughter of an officer in the army, the child of his age, and as he used fondly to express it, the only chain that bound him to the world, or made his life pleasing. His station procured him an acquaintance with men of greater rank or fortune than himself, and his regard for me induced him to bring me into every family where he was acquainted. Thus I was early taught all the elegancies and fashionable foibles of such as the world calls polite, and though without fortune myself, was taught to despise those who lived as if they were poor.

'My intercourse with the great, and my affectation of grandeur procured me many lovers: but want of fortune deterred them all from any other views than those of passing the present moment agreeably, or of meditating my future ruin. In every company I found myself addressed in a warmer strain of passion than other ladies who were superior in point of rank and beauty; and this I imputed to an excess of respect, which in reality proceeded from very different motives.

'Among the number of such as paid me their addresses, was a gentleman, a friend of my father, rather in the decline of life, with nothing remarkable either in his person or address to recommend him. His age which was about forty, his fortune which was moderate, and barely sufficient to support him, served to throw me off my guard, so that I considered him as the only sincere admirer I had.

'Designing lovers in the decline of life are ever most dangerous. Skilled in all the weaknesses of the sex, they seize each favourable opportunity, and by having less passion than youthful

---

[1] This story bears a striking similitude to the real history of Miss S——d who accompanied Lady W——e, in her retreat near Florence, and which the editor had from her own mouth.

admirers, have less real respect, and therefore less timidity. This insidious wretch used a thousand arts to succeed in his base designs, all which I saw, but imputed to different views, because I thought it absurd to believe the real motives.

'As he continued to frequent my father's, the friendship between them became every day greater; and at last, from the intimacy with which he was received, I was taught to look upon him as a guardian and a friend. Though I never loved, yet I esteemed him; and this was enough to make me wish for an union, for which he seemed desirous, but to which he feigned several delays; while in the mean time, from a false report of our being married, every other admirer forsook me.

'I was at last however awakened from the delusion, by an account of his being just married to another young lady with a considerable fortune. This was no great mortification to me, as I had always regarded him merely from prudential motives; but it had a very different effect upon my father, who, rash and passionate by Nature, and besides, stimulated by a mistaken notion of military honour, upbraided his friend in such terms, that a challenge was soon given and accepted.

'It was about midnight when I was awakened by a message from my father, who desired to see me that moment. I rose with some surprise, and following the messenger, attended only by another servant, came to a field not far from the house, where I found him, the assertor of my honour, my only friend and supporter, the tutor and companion of my youth, lying on one side covered over with blood, and just expiring. No tears streamed down my cheeks, nor sigh escaped from my breast, at an object of such terror. I sat down, and supporting his aged head in my lap, gazed upon the ghastly visage with an agony more poignant even than despairing madness. The servants were gone for more assistance. In this gloomy stillness of the night no sounds were heard but his agonising respirations; no object was presented but this wounds, which still continued to stream. With silent anguish I hung over his dear face, and with my hands strove to stop the blood as it flowed from his wounds; he seemed at first insensible, but at last turning his dying eyes upon me, *My dear, dear child, cried he, dear, though you have forgotten your own honour and stained mine, I will yet forgive you; by abandoning virtue you have undone me and yourself, yet take my forgiveness with the same compassion I wish heaven may pity me.* He expired. All my succeeding happiness fled with him. Reflecting that I was the cause of his death whom only I loved upon earth, accused of betraying the honour of his family with his latest breath: conscious of my own innocence, yet without even a possibility of vindicating it; without fortune or friends to believe or pity me, abandoned to infamy and the wide censuring world, I called out upon the dead body that lay stretched before me, and in the agony of my heart asked why he could have left me thus? Why, my dear, my only papa, why could you ruin me thus and yourself for ever! O pity, and return, since there is none but you to comfort me.

'I soon found that I had real cause for sorrow; that I was to expect no compassion from my own sex, nor assistance from the other; and that reputation was much more useful in our commerce with mankind than really to deserve it. Wherever I came, I perceived myself received either with contempt or detestation; or whenever I was civilly treated, it was from the most base and ungenerous motives.

'Thus driven from the society of the virtuous, I was at last, in order to dispel the anxieties of insupportable solitude, obliged to take up with the company of those whose characters were blasted like my own; but who perhaps deserved their infamy. Among this number was a lady of the first distinction, whose character the public thought proper to brand even with greater infamy than mine. A similitude of distress soon united us; I knew that general reproach had made her miserable; and I had learned to regard misery as an excuse for guilt. Though this lady had not virtue enough to avoid reproach, yet she had too much delicate sensibility not to feel it. She therefore proposed our leaving the country where we were born, and going to live in Italy, where our characters and misfortunes would be unknown. With this I eagerly complied, and we soon found ourselves in one of the most charming retreats in the most beautiful province of that enchanting country.

'Had my companion chosen this as a retreat for injured virtue, an harbour where we might look with tranquillity on the distant angry world, I should have been happy; but very different was her design; she had pitched upon this situation only to enjoy those pleasures in private, which she had not sufficient effrontery to satisfy in a more open manner. A nearer acquaintance soon shewed me the vicious part of her character; her mind as well as her body seemed formed only for pleasure; she was sentimental only as it served to protract the immediate enjoyment. Formed for society alone, she spoke infinitely better than she wrote, and wrote infinitely better than she lived. A person devoted to pleasure often leads the most miserable life imaginable; such was her case; she considered the natural moments of languor as insupportable, passed all her hours between rapture and anxiety; ever in an extreme of agony or of bliss. She felt a pain as sincere for want of appetite, as the starving wretch who wants a meal. In those intervals she usually kept her bed, and rose only when in expectation of some new enjoyment. The luxuriant air òf the country, the romantic situation of her palace, and the genius of a people whose only happiness lies in sensual refinement, all contributed to banish the remembrance of her native country.

'But though such a life gave her pleasure, it had a very different effect upon me; I grew every day more pensive, and my melancholy was regarded as an insult upon her good humour; I now perceived myself entirely unfit for all society; discarded from the good, and detesting the infamous; I seemed in a state of war with every rank of people; that virtue which should have been my protection in the world, was here my crime: in short, detesting life, I was determined to become a recluse, to leave a world where I found no pleasure that could allure me to stay. Thus determined, I embarked in order to go by sea to Rome, where I intended to take the veil; but even in so short a passage my hard fortune still attended me; our ship was taken by a Barbary corsair; the whole crew, and I among the number, being made slaves. It carries too much the air of romance to inform you of my distresses or obstinacy in this miserable state; it is enough to observe that I have been bought by several masters, each of whom perceiving my reluctance, rather than use violence, sold me to another, till it was my happiness to be at last rescued by you.'

Thus ended her relation, which I have abridged, but as soon as we are arrived at Moscow, for which we intend to set out shortly, you shall be informed of all more particularly. In the mean time, the greatest addition of my happiness will be to hear of yours. Adieu.

LETTER LXI.—*From Lien Chi Altangi to Hingpo*.

THE news of your freedom lifts the load of former anxiety from my mind; I can now think of my son without regret, applaud his resignation under calamities, and his conduct in extricating himself from it.

You are now free, just let loose from the bondage of an hard master: this is the crisis of your fate; and as you now manage fortune, succeeding life will be marked with happiness or misery; a few years' perseverance in prudence, which at your age is but another name for virtue, will ensure comfort, pleasure, tranquillity, esteem; too eager an enjoyment of every good that now offers, will reverse the medal, and present you with poverty, anxiety, remorse, contempt.

As it has been observed that none are better qualified to give others advice, than those who have taken the least of it themselves; so in this respect I find myself perfectly authorised to offer mine, even though I should waive my paternal authority upon this occasion.

The most usual way among young men who have no resolution of their own, is first to ask one friend's advice and follow it for some time; then to ask advice of another, and turn to that; so of a third, still unsteady, always changing. However, be assured that every change of this nature is for the worse; people may tell you of your being unfit for some peculiar occupations in life; but heed them not; whatever employment you follow with perseverance and assiduity will be found fit for you; it will be your support in youth, and comfort in age. In learning the useful part of every profession, very moderate abilities will suffice; even if the mind be a little balanced with stupidity, it may in this case be useful. Great abilities have always been less serviceable to the possessors than moderate ones. Life has been compared to a race, but the allusion still improves, by observing that the most swift are ever the least manageable.

To know one profession only, is enough for one man to know; and this (whatever the professors may tell you to the contrary) is soon learned. Be contented therefore with one good employment; for if you understand two at a time, people will give you business in neither.

A conjurer and a tailor once happened to converse together. Alas, cries the tailor, what an unhappy poor creature am I; if people should ever take it in their heads to live without clothes I am undone; I have no other trade to have recourse to. Indeed, friend, I pity you sincerely, replies the conjuror; but thank heaven, things are not quite so bad with me; if one trick should fail, I have a hundred tricks more for them yet. However, if at any time you are reduced to beggary, apply to me and I will relieve you. A famine overspread the land; the tailor made a shift to live, because his customers could not be without clothes; but the poor conjurer, with all his hundred tricks, could find none that had money to throw away: it was in vain that he promised to eat fire, or to vomit pins; no single creature would relieve him, till he was at last obliged to beg from the very tailor whose calling he had formerly despised.

There are no obstructions more fatal to fortune than pride and resentment. If you must resent injuries at all, at least suppress your indignation until you become rich, and then shew away; the resentment of a poor man is like the efforts of a harmless insect to sting; it may get him crushed, but cannot defend him. Who values that anger which is consumed only in empty menaces?

Once upon a time a goose fed its young by a pond side; and a goose in such circumstances is always extremely proud, and excessively punctilious. If any other animal, without the least design to offend, happened to pass that way, the goose was immedately at him. The pond, she said, was hers, and she would maintain a right in it, and support her honour, while she had a bill to hiss, or a wing to flutter. In this manner she drove away ducks, pigs, and chickens; nay, even the insidious cat was seen to scamper. A lounging mastiff, however, happened to pass by, and thought it no harm if he should lap a little of the water, as he was thirsty. The guardian goose flew at him like a fury, pecked at him with her beak, and flapped him with her feathers. The dog grew angry, had twenty times a good mind to give her a sly snap; but suppressing his indignation, because his master was nigh, *A pox take thee*, cries he, *for a fool, sure those who have neither strength nor weapons to fight, at least should be civil; that fluttering and hissing of thine may one day get thine head snapt off, but it can neither injure thine enemies, or ever protect thee*. So saying, he went forward to the pond, quenched his thirst, in spite of the goose, and followed his master.

Another obstruction to the fortune of youth is, that while they are willing to take offence from none, they are also equally desirous of giving none offence. From hence they endeavour to please all, comply with every request, attempt to suit themselves to every company; have no will of their own, but like wax catch every contiguous impression. By thus attempting to give universal satisfaction, they at last find themselves miserably disappointed; to bring the generality of admirers on our side, it is sufficient to attempt pleasing a very few.

A painter of eminence was once resolved to finish a piece which should please the whole world. When, therefore, he had drawn a picture, in which his utmost skill was exhausted, it was exposed in the public market-place, with directions at the bottom for every spectator to mark with a brush, which lay by, every limb, and feature, which seemed erroneous. The spectators came, and in general applauded; but each, willing to show his talent at criticism, marked whatever he thought proper. At evening, when the painter came he was mortified to find the whole picture one universal blot; not a single stroke that was not stigmatised with marks of disapprobation: not satisfied with this trial, the next day he was resolved to try them in a different manner, and exposing his picture as before, desired that every spectator would mark those beauties he approved or admired. The people complied, and the artist returning, found his picture replete with the marks of beauty; every stroke that had been yesterday condemned now received the character of approbation. *Well*, cries the painter, *I now find that the best way to please one half of the world, is not to mind what the other half says; since what are faults in the eyes of these, shall be by those regarded as beauties*. Adieu.

LETTER LXII. *From the same.*

A CHARACTER such as you have represented that of your fair companion, which continues virtuous, though loaded with infamy, is truly great. Many regard virtue because it is attended with applause; your favourite only for the internal pleasure it confers. I have often wished that ladies like her were proposed as models for female imitation, and not such as have acquired fame by qualities repugnant to the natural softness of the sex.

Women famed for their valour, their skill in politics, or their learning, leave the duties of their own sex, in order to invade the privileges of ours. I can no more pardon a fair one for endeavouring to wield the club of Hercules, than I could him for attempting to twirl her distaff.

The modest virgin, the prudent wife, or the careful matron are much more serviceable in life than petticoated philosophers, blustering heroines, or virago queens. She who makes her husband and her children happy, who reclaims the one from vice, and trains up the other to virtue, is a much greater character than ladies described in romance, whose whole occupation is to murder mankind with shafts from their quiver or their eyes.

Women, it has been observed, are not naturally formed for great cares themselves, but to soften ours. Their tenderness is the proper reward for the dangers we undergo for their preservation; and the ease and cheerfulness of their conversation, our desirable retreat from the fatigues of intense application. They are confined within the narrow limits of domestic assiduity; and when they stray beyond them, they move beyond their sphere, and consequently without grace.

Fame therefore has been very unjustly dispensed among the female sex. Those who least deserved to be remembered, meet our admiration and applause; while many, who have been an honour to humanity, are passed over in silence. Perhaps no age has produced a stronger instance of misplaced fame than the present: the Semiramis and the Thalestris of antiquity are talked of, while a modern character, infinitely greater than either, is unnoticed and unknown.

Catherina Alexowna,[1] born near Dorpat, a little city in Livonia, was heir to no other inheritance than the virtues and frugality of her parents. Her father being dead, she lived with her aged mother, in their cottage covered with straw; and both, though very poor, were very contented. Here, retired from the gaze of the world, by the labour of her hands, she supported her parent, who was now incapable of supporting herself. While Catherina spun, the old woman would sit by, and read some book of devotion; thus when the fatigues of the day were over, both would sit down contentedly by their fireside, and enjoy the frugal meal with vacant festivity.

Though her face and person were models of perfection, yet her whole attention seemed bestowed upon her mind; her mother taught her to read, and an old Lutheran minister instructed her in the maxims and duties of religion. Nature had furnished her not only with a ready but a solid turn of thought, not only with a strong but a right understanding. Such truly female accomplishments procured her several solicitations of marriage from the peasants of the country; but their offers were refused: for she loved her mother too tenderly to think of separation.

Catherina was fifteen when her mother died; she now therefore left her cottage, and went to live with the Lutheran minister, by whom she had been instructed from her childhood. In his house she resided, in quality of governess to his children; at once reconciling in her character unerring prudence with surprising vivacity.

[1] This account seems taken from the manuscript memoirs of H. Spilman, Esq.

The old man, who regarded her as one of his own children, had her instructed in dancing and music by the masters who attended the rest of his family; thus she continued to improve till he died, by which accident she was once more reduced to pristine poverty. The country of Livonia was at this time wasted by war, and lay in a most miserable state of desolation. Those calamities are ever most heavy upon the poor; wherefore Catherina, though possessed of so many accomplishments, experienced all the miseries of hopeless indigence. Provisions becoming every day more scarce, and her private stock being entirely exhausted, she resolved at last to travel to Marienburgh, a city of greater plenty.

With her scanty wardrobe, packed up in a wallet, she set out on her journey on foot: she was to walk through a region miserable by nature, but rendered still more hideous by the Swedes and Russians, who, as each happened to become masters, plundered it at discretion: but hunger had taught her to despise the dangers and fatigues of the way.

One evening, upon her journey, as she had entered a cottage by the way side, to take up her lodging for the night, she was insulted by two Swedish soldiers, who insisted upon qualifying her, as they termed it, *to follow the camp*. They might probably have carried their insults into violence, had not a subaltern officer, accidentally passing by, come in to her assistance: upon his appearing, the soldiers immediately desisted; but her thankfulness was hardly greater than her surprise, when she instantly recollected in her deliverer, the son of the Lutheran minister, her former instructor, benefactor, and friend.

This was an happy interview for Catherina: the little stock of money she had brought from home was by this time quite exhausted; her clothes were gone, piece by piece, in order to satisfy those who had entertained her in their houses; her generous countryman, therefore, parted with what he could spare, to buy her clothes, furnished her with an horse, and gave her letters of recommendation to Mr. Gluck, a faithful friend of his father's, and Superintendent of Marienburgh.

Our beautiful stranger had only to appear to be well received; she was immediately admitted into the Superintendent's family, as governess to his two daughters; and though yet but seventeen, shewed herself capable of instructing her sex, not only in virtue, but politeness. Such was her good sense and beauty, that her master himself in a short time offered her his hand, which to his great surprise she thought proper to refuse. Actuated by a principle of gratitude, she was resolved to marry her deliverer only, even though he had lost an arm, and was otherwise disfigured by wounds in the service.

In order therefore to prevent further solicitations from others, as soon as the officer came to town upon duty, she offered him her person, which he accepted with transport, and their nuptials were solemnized as usual. But all the lines of her fortune were to be striking: the very day on which they were married the Russians laid siege to Marienburgh; the unhappy soldier had now no time to enjoy the well earned pleasures of matrimony; he was called off before consummation to an attack, from which he was never after seen to return.

In the mean time the siege went on with fury, aggravated on one side by obstinacy, on the other by revenge. This war between the two northern powers at that time was truly barbarous; the innocent peasant and the harmless virgin often shared the fate of the soldier in arms. Marienburgh was taken by assault; and such was the fury of the assailants, that not only the garrison, but almost all the inhabitants, men, women, and children, were put to the sword; at length when the carnage was pretty well over, Catherina was found hid in an oven.

She had been hitherto poor, but still was free; she was now to conform to her hard fate, and learn what it was to be a slave: in this situation, however, she behaved with piety and humility; and though misfortunes had abated her vivacity, yet she was cheerful. The fame of her merit and resignation reached even Prince Menzikoff, the Russian General; he desired to see her, was struck with her beauty, bought her from the soldier, her master, and placed her under the direction of his own sister. Here she was treated with all the respect which her merit deserved, while her beauty every day improved with her good fortune.

She had not been long in this situation, when Peter the Great paying the prince a visit, Catherina happened to come in with some dry fruits, which she served round with peculiar modesty. The mighty monarch saw, and was struck with her beauty. He returned the next day, called for the beautiful slave, asked her several questions, and found her understanding even more perfect than her person.

He had been forced when young to marry from motives of interest, he was now resolved to marry pursuant to his own inclinations. He immediately enquired the history of the fair Livonian, who was not yet eighteen. He traced her through the vale of obscurity, through all the vicissitudes of her fortune, and found her truly great in them all. The meanness of her birth was no obstruction to his design; their nuptials were solemnised in private: the prince assuring his courtiers, that virtue alone was the properest ladder to a throne.

We now see Catherina, from the low mud-walled cottage, empress of the greatest kingdom upon earth. The poor solitary wanderer is now surrounded by thousands, who find happiness in her smile. She, who formerly wanted a meal, is now capable of diffusing plenty upon whole nations. To her fortune she owed part of this pre-eminence, but to her virtues more.

She ever after retained those great qualities which first placed her on a throne; and while the extraordinary prince, her husband, laboured for the reformation of his male subjects, she studied in her turn the improvement of her own sex. She altered their dresses, introduced mixed assemblies, instituted an order of female knighthood; and, at length, when she had greatly filled all the stations of empress, friend, wife, and mother, bravely died without regret; regretted by all. Adieu.

LETTER LXIII.—*From Lien Chi Altangi, to Fum Hoam, first President of the Ceremonial Academy, at Pekin, in China.*

IN every letter I expect accounts of some new revolutions in China, some strange occurrence in the state, or disaster among my private acquaintance. I open every packet with tremulous expectation, and am agreeably disappointed when I find my friends and my country continuing in felicity. I wander, but they are at rest; they suffer few changes but what pass in my own restless imagination; it is only the rapidity of my own motion gives an imaginary swiftness to objects which are in some measure immovable.

Yet believe me, my friend, that even China itself is imperceptibly degenerating from her ancient greatness; her laws are now more venal, and her merchants are more deceitful than formerly; the very arts and sciences have run to decay. Observe the carvings on our ancient bridges; figures that add grace even to nature. There is not an artist now in all the empire that can imitate their beauty. Our manufactures in porcelain too are inferior to what we once were famous for; and even Europe now begins to excel us. There was a time when China was the receptacle of strangers, when all were welcome who either came to improve the state, or admire its greatness; now the empire is shut up from every foreign improvement; and the very inhabitants discourage each other from prosecuting their own internal advantages.

Whence this degeneracy in a state so little subject to external revolutions; how happens it that China, which is now more powerful than ever, which is less subject to foreign invasions, and even assisted in some discoveries by her connexions with Europe; whence comes it, I say, that the empire is thus declining so fast into barbarity?

This decay is surely from Nature, and not the result of voluntary degeneracy. In a period of two or three thousand years she seems at proper intervals to produce great minds, with an effort resembling that which introduces the vicissitudes of seasons. They rise up at once, continue for an age, enlighten the world, fall like ripened corn, and mankind again gradually relapse into pristine barbarity. We little ones look around, are amazed at the decline, seek after the causes of this invisible decay, attribute to want of encouragement what really proceeds from want of power, are astonished to find every art and every science in the decline, not considering that autumn is over, and fatigued Nature begins to repose for some succeeding effort.

Some periods have been remarkable for the production of men of extraordinary stature; others for producing some particular animals in great abundance; some for excessive plenty; and others again for seemingly causeless famine. Nature which shews herself so very different in her visible productions, must surely differ also from herself in the production of minds; and while she astonishes one age with the strength and stature of a Milo or a Maximin, may bless another with the wisdom of a Plato, or the goodness of an Antonine.

Let us not then attribute to accident the falling off of every nation; but to the natural revolution of things. Often in the darkest ages there has appeared some one man of surprising abilities, who, with all his understanding, failed to bring his barbarous age into refinement: all mankind seemed to sleep, till Nature gave the general call, and then the whole world seemed at once roused at the voice; science triumphed in every country, and the brightness of a single genius seemed lost in a galaxy of contiguous glory.

Thus the enlightened periods in every age have been universal. At the time when China first began to emerge from barbarity, the western world was equally rising into refinement; when we had our *Yau*, they had their *Sesostris*. In succeeding ages, Confucius and Pythagoras seem born nearly together, and a train of philosophers then sprung up as well in Greece as in China. The period of renewed barbarity began to have an universal spread much about the same time, and continued for several centuries, till in the year of the Christian æra 1400, the Emperor Yonglo arose, to revive the learning of the east; while about the same time the Medicean family laboured in Italy to raise infant genius from the cradle: thus we see politeness spreading over every part of the world in one age, and barbarity succeeding in another; at one period a blaze of light diffusing itself over the whole world, and at another all mankind wrapped up in the profoundest ignorance.

Such has been the situation of things in times past; and such probably it will ever be. China, I have observed, has evidently begun to degenerate from its former politeness; and were the learning of the Europeans at present candidly considered, the decline would perhaps appear to have already taken place. We should find among the natives of the west the study of morality displaced for mathematical disquisition, or metaphysical subtleties; we should find learning to begin to separate from the useful duties and concerns of life, while none ventured to aspire after that character, but they who know much more than is truly amusing or useful. We should find every great attempt suppressed by prudence, and the rapturous sublimity in writing cooled by a cautious fear of offence. We should find few of those daring spirits, who bravely venture to be wrong, and who are willing to hazard much for the sake of great acquisitions. Providence has indulged the world with a period of almost four hundred years' refinement; does it not now by degrees sink us into our former ignorance, leaving us only the love of wisdom, while it deprives us of its advantage? Adieu.

LETTER LXIV.—*From the same.*

THE princes of Europe have found out a manner of rewarding their subjects who have behaved well, by presenting them with about two yards of blue ribbon, which is worn about the shoulder. They who are honoured with this mark of distinction are called knights, and the king himself is always the head of the order. This is a very frugal method of recompensing the most important services; and it is very fortunate for kings that their subjects are satisfied with such trifling rewards. Should a nobleman happen to lose his leg in battle, the king presents him with two yards of ribbon, and he is paid for the loss of his limb. Should an ambassador spend all his paternal fortune in supporting the honour of his country abroad, the king presents him with two yards of ribbon, which is to be considered as an equivalent to his estate. In short, while an European king has a yard of blue or green ribbon left, he need be under no apprehensions of wanting statesmen, generals, and soldiers.

I cannot sufficiently admire those kingdoms in which men with large patrimonial estates are willing thus to undergo real hardships for empty favours. A person, already possessed of a competent fortune, who undertakes to enter the career of ambition, feels many real inconveniences from his station, while it procures him no real happiness that he was not possessed of before. He could eat, drink, and sleep, before he became a courtier, as well, perhaps better than when invested with his authority. He could command flatterers in a private station, as well as in his public capacity, and indulge at home every favourite inclination, uncensured and unseen by the people.

What real good then does an addition to a fortune already sufficient procure? Not any. Could the great man by having his fortune increased, increase also his appetites, then precedence might be attended with real amusement.

Was he by having his one thousand made two, thus enabled to enjoy two wives, or eat two dinners; then indeed he might be excused for undergoing some pain, in order to extend the sphere of his enjoyments. But on the contrary, he finds his desire for pleasure often lessen, as he takes pains to be able to improve it; and his capacity of enjoyment diminishes as his fortune happens to encrease.

Instead therefore of regarding the great with envy, I generally consider them with some share of compassion. I look upon them as a set of good-natured misguided people, who are indebted to us and not to themselves for all the happiness they enjoy. For our pleasure, and not their own, they sweat under a cumbrous heap of finery; for our pleasure the lacquied train, the slow parading pageant, with all the gravity of grandeur, moves in review; a single coat, or a single footman, answers all the purposes of the most indolent refinement as well; and those who have twenty, may be said to keep one for their own pleasure, and the other nineteen merely for ours. So true is the observation of Confucius, *that we take greater pains to persuade others that we are happy, than in endeavouring to think so ourselves.*

But though this desire of being seen, of being made the subject of discourse, and of supporting the dignities of an exalted station, be troublesome enough to the ambitious; yet it is well for society that there are men thus willing to exchange ease and safety, for danger and a ribbon. We lose nothing by their vanity, and it would be unkind to endeavour to deprive a child of its rattle. If a duke or a duchess are willing to carry a long train for our entertainment, so much the worse for themselves; if they choose to exhibit in public with a hundred lacquies and mameluks in their equipage for our entertainment, still so much the worse for themselves; it is the spectators alone who give and receive the pleasure; they only the sweating figures that swell the pageant.

A mandarine who took pride in appearing with a number of jewels on every part of his robe, was once accosted by an old sly bonze, who followed him through several streets, and bowing often to the ground, thanked him for his jewels. What does the man mean? cried the mandarine. Friend, I never gave thee any of my jewels. No, replied the other; but you have let me look at them, and that is all the use you can make of them yourself; so there is no difference between us, except that you have the trouble of watching them, and that is an employment I don't much desire. Adieu.

LETTER LXV.—*From the same.*

THOUGH not very fond of seeing a pageant myself, yet I am generally pleased with being in the crowd which sees it; it is amusing to observe the effect which such a spectacle has upon the variety of faces, the pleasure it excites in some, the envy in others, and the wishes it raises in all. With this design I lately went to see the entry of a foreign ambassador, resolved to make one in the mob, to shout as they shouted, to fix with earnestness upon the same frivolous objects, and participate for a while the pleasures and the wishes of the vulgar.

Struggling here for some time, in order to be first to see the cavalcade as it passed, some one of the crowd unluckily happened to tread upon my shoe, and tore it in such a manner, that I was utterly unqualified to march forward with the main body, and obliged to fall back in the rear. Thus rendered incapable of being a spectator of the show myself, I was at least willing to observe the spectators, and limped behind like one of the invalids which follow the march of an army.

In this plight, as I was considering the eagerness that appeared on every face, how some bustled to get foremost, and others contented themselves with taking a transient peep when they could; how some praised the four black servants, that were stuck behind one of the equipages, and some the ribbons that decorated the horses' necks in another; my attention was called off to an object more extraordinary than any I had yet seen: a poor cobbler sat in his stall by the way side, and continued to work while the crowd passed by, without testifying the smallest share of curiosity. I own his want of attention excited mine; and as I stood in need of his assistance, I thought it best to employ a philosophic cobbler on this occasion: perceiving my business, therefore, he desired me to enter and sit down, took my shoe in his lap, and began to mend it with his usual indifference and taciturnity.

'How, my friend, said I to him, can you continue to work while all those fine things are passing by your door?' 'Very fine they are, master, returned the cobbler, for those that like them, to be sure; but what are all those fine things to me? You don't know what it is to be a cobbler, and so much the better for yourself. Your bread is baked, you may go and see the sights the whole day, and eat a warm supper when you come home at night; but for me, if I should run hunting after all these fine folk, what should I get by my journey but an appetite, and, God help me, I have too much of that at home already, without stirring out for it. Your people who may eat four meals a day and a supper at night, are but a bad example to such a one as I. No, master, as God has called me into this world in order to mend old shoes, I have no business with fine folk, and they no business with me.' I here interrupted him with a smile. 'See this last, master, continues he, and this hammer; this last and hammer are the two best friends I have in this world; nobody else will be my friend, because I want a friend. The great folks you saw pass by just now have five hundred friends, because they have no occasion for them; now, while I stick to my good friends here, I am very contented; but when I ever so little run after sights and fine things, I begin to hate my work, I grow sad, and have no heart to mend shoes any longer.'

This discourse only served to raise my curiosity to know more of a man whom Nature had thus formed into a philosopher. I therefore insensibly led him into an history of his adventures: 'I have lived, said he, a wandering life, now five and fifty years, here to-day and gone to-morrow; for it was my misfortune, when I was young, to be fond of changing.' *You have been a traveller then, I presume*, interrupted I. 'I can't boast much of travelling, continued he, for I have never left the parish in which I was born but three times in my life, that I can remember; but then there is not a street in the whole neighbourhood that I have not lived in, at some time or another. When I began to settle and to take to my business in one street, some unforeseen misfortune, or a desire of trying my luck elsewhere, has removed me, perhaps a whole mile away from my former customers, while some more lucky cobbler would come into my place, and make a handsome fortune among friends of my making: there was one who actually died in a stall that I had left, worth seven pounds seven shillings, all in hard gold, which he had quilted into the waistband of his breeches.'

I could not but smile at these migrations of a man by the fire-side, and continued to ask if he had ever been married. 'Ay, that I have, master, replied he, for sixteen long years; and a weary life I had of it, heaven knows. My wife took it into her head, that the only way to thrive in this world, was to save money, so though our comings-in was but about three shillings a week, all ever she could lay her hands upon she used to hide away from me, though we were obliged to starve the whole week after for it.

'The first three years we used to quarrel about this every day, and I always got the better; but she had a hard spirit, and still continued to hide as usual; so that I was at last tired of quarrelling and getting the better, and she scraped and scraped at pleasure, till I was almost starved to death. Her conduct drove me at last in despair to the ale-house; here I used to sit with people who hated home like myself, drank while I had money left, and run in score when any body would trust me; till at last the landlady, coming one day with a long bill when I was from home, and putting it into my wife's hands, the length of it effectually broke her heart. I searched the whole stall after she was dead for money, but she had hidden it so effectually, that with all my pains I could never find a farthing.'

By this time my shoe was mended, and satisfying the poor artist for his trouble, and rewarding him besides for his information, I took my leave, and returned home to lengthen out the amusement his conversation afforded, by communicating it to my friend. Adieu.

LETTER LXVI.—*From Lien Chi Altangi to Hingpo, by the way of Moscow.*

GENEROSITY properly applied will supply every other external advantage in life, but the love of those we converse with; it will procure esteem and a conduct resembling real affection, but actual love is the spontaneous production of the mind, no generosity can purchase, no rewards encrease, nor no liberality continue it, the very person who is obliged has it not in his power to force his lingering affections upon the object he should love, and voluntarily mix passion with gratitude.

Imparted fortune, and well-placed liberality, may procure the benefactor good will, may load the person obliged, with the sense of the duty he lies under to retaliate; this is gratitude: and simple gratitude, untinctured with love, is all the return an ingenuous mind can bestow for former benefits.

But gratitude and love are almost opposite affections; love is often an involuntary passion, placed upon our compassions without our consent, and frequently conferred without our previous esteem.

We love some men, we know not why; our tenderness is naturally excited in all their concerns; we excuse their faults with the same indulgence, and approve their virtues with the same applause with which we consider our own. While we entertain the passion it pleases us; we cherish it with delight, and give it up with reluctance, and love for love is all the reward we expect or desire.

Gratitude, on the contrary, is never conferred, but where there have been previous endeavours to excite it; we consider it as a debt, and our spirits wear a load till we have discharged the obligation. Every acknowledgment of gratitude is a circumstance of humiliation; and some are found to submit to frequent mortifications of this kind; proclaiming what obligations they owe, merely because they think it in some measure cancels the debt.

Thus love is the most easy and agreeable, and gratitude the most humiliating affection of the mind; we never reflect on the man we *love*, without exulting in our choice, while he who has bound us to him by *benefits* alone, rises to our idea as a person to whom we have, in some measure, forfeited our freedom. Love and gratitude are seldom therefore found in the same breast without impairing each other; we may tender the one or the other singly to those we converse with, but cannot command both together. By attempting to increase, we diminish them; the mind becomes bankrupt under too large obligations; all additional benefits lessen every hope of future return, and bar up every avenue that leads to tenderness.

In all our connexions with society therefore, it is not only generous, but prudent, to appear insensible of the value of those favours we bestow, and endeavour to make the obligation seem as slight as possible. Love must be taken by stratagem, and not by open force. We should seem ignorant that we oblige, and leave the mind at full liberty to give or refuse its affections; for constraint may indeed leave the receiver still grateful, but it will certainly produce disgust.

If to procure gratitude be our only aim, there is no great art in making the acquisition; a benefit conferred demands a just acknowledgment, and we have a right to insist upon our due. But it were much more prudent to forego our right on such an occasion, and exchange it, if we can, for love. We receive but little advantage from repeated protestations of gratitude, but they cost him very much from whom we exact them in return; exacting a grateful acknowledgment, is demanding a debt by which the creditor is not advantaged, and the debtor pays with reluctance.

As *Mencius* the Philosopher was travelling in the pursuit of wisdom, night overtook him at the foot of a gloomy mountain, remote from the habitations of men. Here as he was straying, while rain and thunder conspired to make solitude still more hideous, he perceived a hermit's cell, and approaching, asked for shelter: Enter, cries the hermit, in a severe tone, men deserve not to be obliged, but it would be imitating their ingratitude, to treat them as they deserve. Come in: examples of vice may sometimes strengthen us in the ways of virtue.

After a frugal meal, which consisted of roots and tea, Mencius could not repress his curiosity to know why the hermit had retired from mankind, the actions of whom taught the truest lessons of wisdom. Mention not the name of man, cries the hermit, with indignation; here let me live retired from a base ungrateful world; here among the beasts of the forest, I shall find no flatterers; the lion is a generous enemy, and the dog a faithful friend, but man, base man, can poison the bowl, and smile while he presents it. *You have been used ill by mankind?* interrupted the philosopher shrewdly. Yes, returned the hermit, on mankind I have exhausted my whole fortune, and this staff, and that cup, and those roots, are all that I have in

return. *Did you bestow your fortune, or did you only lend it?*
returned Mencius. I bestowed it, undoubtedly, replied the
other, for where were the merit of being a money lender? *Did
they ever own that they received it?* still adds the philosopher.
A thousand times, cries the hermit, they every day loaded me
with professions of gratitude for obligations received, and
solicitations for future favours. *If then,* says Mencius, smiling,
*you did not lend your fortune, in order to have it returned, it is
unjust to accuse them of ingratitude; they owned themselves obliged,
you expected no more, and they certainly earned each favour, by
frequently acknowledging the obligation.* The hermit was struck
with the reply, and surveying his guest with emotion, I have
heard of the great Mencius, and you certainly are the man;
I am now fourscore years old, but still a child in wisdom, take
me back to the school of man, and educate me as one of the
most ignorant and the youngest of your disciples!

Indeed, my son, it is better to have friends in our passage
through life than grateful dependents; and as love is a more
willing, so it is a more lasting tribute than extorted obligation.
As we are uneasy when greatly obliged, gratitude once refused,
can never after be recovered: the mind that is base enough to
disallow the just return, instead of feeling any uneasiness upon
recollection, triumphs in its new acquired freedom, and in some
measure is pleased with conscious baseness.

Very different is the situation of disagreeing friends, their
separation produces mutual uneasiness. Like that divided being
in fabulous creation, their sympathetic souls once more desire
their former union, the joys of both are imperfect, their gayest
moments tinctured with uneasiness; each seeks for the smallest
concessions to clear the way to a wished for explanation; the
most trifling acknowledgment, the slightest accident serves to
effect a mutual reconciliation.

But instead of pursuing the thought, permit me to soften the
severity of advice, by an European story, which will fully
illustrate my meaning.

A fiddler and his wife, who had rubbed through life, as most
couples usually do, sometimes good friends, at others not quite
so well, one day happened to have a dispute, which was conducted with becoming spirit on both sides. The wife was sure
she was right, and the husband was resolved to have his own
way. What was to be done in such a case? The quarrel grew
worse by explanations, and at last the fury of both rose to such
a pitch, that they made a vow never to sleep together in the

same bed for the future. This was the most rash vow that could be imagined, for they still were friends at bottom, and besides they had but one bed in the house; however, resolved they were to go through with it, and at night the fiddle-case was laid in bed between them, in order to make a separation. In this manner they continued for three weeks; every night the fiddle-case being placed as a barrier to divide them.

By this time, however, each heartily repented of their vow, their resentment was at an end, and their love began to return; they wished the fiddle-case away, but both had too much spirit to begin. One night, however, as they were both lying awake with the detested fiddle-case between them, the husband happened to sneeze, to which the wife, as is usual in such cases, bid God bless him; *Ay, but,* returns the husband, *woman, do you say that from your heart?* Indeed, I do, my poor Nicholas, cries his wife, I say it with all my heart. *If so then,* says the husband, *we had as good remove the fiddle-case.*

LETTER LXVII.—*From the same.*

BOOKS, my son, while they teach us to respect the interests of others, often make us unmindful of our own; while they instruct the youthful reader to grasp at social happiness, he grows miserable in detail, and attentive to universal harmony, often forgets that he himself has a part to sustain in the concert. I dislike therefore the philosopher who describes the inconveniences of life in such pleasing colours that the pupil grows enamoured of distress, longs to try the charms of poverty, meets it without dread, nor fears its inconveniences, till he severely feels them.

A youth, who has thus spent his life among books, new to the world, and unacquainted with man, but by philosophic information, may be considered as a being, whose mind is filled with the vulgar errors of the wise; utterly unqualified for a journey through life, yet confident of his own skill in the direction, he sets out with confidence, blunders on with vanity, and finds himself at last undone.

He first has learned from books, and then lays it down as a maxim, that all mankind are virtuous or vicious in excess; and he has been long taught to detest vice and love virtue: warm therefore in attachments, and stedfast in enmity, he treats every creature as a friend or foe; expects from those he loves unerring integrity, and consigns his enemies to the reproach of wanting every virtue. On this principle he proceeds; and here begin his disappointments: upon a closer inspection of human nature, he perceives, that he should have moderated his friendship, and softened his severity; for he often finds the excellencies of one part of mankind clouded with vice, and the faults of the other brightened with virtue; he finds no character so sanctified that has not its failings, none so infamous, but has somewhat to attract our esteem; he beholds impiety in lawn, and fidelity in fetters.

He now therefore, but too late, perceives that his regard should have been more cool, and his hatred less violent; that the truly wise seldom court romantic friendships with the good, and avoid, if possible, the resentment even of the wicked: every moment gives him fresh instances that the bonds of friendship are broken if drawn too closely, and that those whom he has treated with disrespect more than retaliate the injury: at length therefore he is obliged to confess, that he has declared war upon the vicious half of mankind, without being able to form an alliance among the virtuous to espouse his quarrel.

Our book-taught philosopher, however, is now too far advanced to recede; and though poverty be the just consequence of the many enemies his conduct has created, yet he is resolved to meet it without shrinking: philosophers have described poverty in most charming colours; and even his vanity is touched, in thinking, that he should shew the world, in himself one more example of patience, fortitude, and resignation. *Come, then, O Poverty! for what is there in thee dreadful to the* WISE; *temperance, health, and frugality, walk in thy train; cheerfulness and liberty are ever thy companions. Shall any be ashamed of thee of whom Cincinnatus was not ashamed? the running brook, the herbs of the field can amply satisfy nature; man wants but little, nor that little long; come, then, O Poverty, while kings stand by and gaze with admiration, at the true philosopher's resignation.*

The goddess appears; for Poverty ever comes at the call: but, alas! he finds her by no means the charming figure books and his warm imagination had painted. As when an eastern bride whom her friends and relations had long described as a model of perfection, pays her first visit, the longing bridegroom lifts the veil to see a face he had never seen before; but instead of a countenance, blazing with beauty like the sun, he beholds deformity shooting icicles to his heart; such appears Poverty to her new entertainer; all the fabric of enthusiasm is at once demolished, and a thousand miseries rise upon its ruins, while Contempt, with pointing finger, is foremost in the hideous procession.

The poor man now finds that he can get no kings to look at him while he is eating; he finds that in proportion as he grows poor, the world turns its back upon him, and gives him leave to act the philosopher in all the majesty of solitude; it might be agreeable enough to play the philosopher, while we are conscious that mankind are spectators; but what signifies wearing the mask of sturdy contentment, and mounting the stage of restraint, when not one creature will assist at the exhibition! Thus is he forsaken of men, while his fortitude wants the satisfaction even of self-applause; for either he does not feel his present calamities, and that is natural *insensibility*, or he disguises his feelings, and that is *dissimulation*.

Spleen now begins to take up the man; not distinguishing in his resentments, he regards all mankind with detestation, and commencing man-hater, seeks solitude to be at liberty to rail.

It has been said, that he who retires to solitude is either a beast or an angel. The censure is too severe, and the praise unmerited; the discontented being, who retires from society, is generally some good-natured man, who has begun life without experience, and knew not how to gain it in his intercourse with mankind. Adieu.

LETTER LXVIII.—*From Lien Chi Altangi, to Fum Hoam, first President of the Ceremonial Academy, at Pekin in China.*

I FORMERLY acquainted thee, most grave *Fum*, with the excellence of the *English* in the art of healing. The *Chinese* boast their skill in pulses, the *Siamese* their botanical knowledge, but the *English* advertising physicians alone, of being the great restorers of health, the dispensers of youth, and the insurers of longevity. I can never enough admire the sagacity of this country for the encouragement given to professors of this art; with what indulgence does she foster up those of her own growth, and kindly cherish those that come from abroad. Like a skilful gardener she invites them from every foreign climate to herself. Here every great exotic strikes root as soon as imported, and feels the genial beam of favour; while the mighty metropolis, like one vast munificent dunghill, receives them indiscriminately to her breast, and supplies each with more than native nourishment.

In other countries the physician pretends to cure disorders in the lump; the same doctor who combats the gout in the toe, shall pretend to prescribe for a pain in the head, and he who at one time cures a consumption, shall at another give drugs for a dropsy. How absurd and ridiculous! this is being a mere jack of all trades. Is the animal machine less complicated than a brass pin? Not less than ten different hands are required to make a pin; and shall the body be set right by one single operator?

The *English* are sensible of the force of this reasoning; they have therefore one doctor for the eyes, another for the toes; they have their sciatica doctors, and inoculating doctors; they have one doctor who is modestly content with securing them from bugbites, and five hundred who prescribe for the bite of mad dogs.

The learned are not here retired with vicious modesty from public view; for every dead wall is covered with their names, their abilities, their amazing cures, and places of abode. Few patients can escape falling into their hands, unless blasted by lightning, or struck dead with some sudden disorder: it may sometimes happen, that a stranger who does not understand *English,* or a countryman who cannot read, dies without ever hearing of the vivifying drops, or restorative electuary; but for my part, before I was a week in town, I had learned to bid the whole catalogue of disorders defiance, and was perfectly acquainted with the names and the medicines of every great man, or great woman of them all.

But as nothing pleases curiosity more than anecdotes of the great, however minute or trifling, I must present you, inadequate as my abilities are to the subject, with some account of those personages who lead in this honourable profession.

The first upon the list of glory, is doctor *Richard Rock,* F.U.N. This great man is short of stature, is fat, and waddles as he walks. He always wears a white three-tail'd wig, nicely combed, and frizzled upon each cheek. Sometimes he carries a cane, but a hat never; it is indeed very remarkable, that this extraordinary personage should never wear an hat, but so it is, he never wears an hat. He is usually drawn at the top of his own bills, sitting in his arm chair, holding a little bottle between his finger and thumb, and surrounded with rotten teeth, nippers, pills, packets, and gally-pots. No man can promise fairer nor better than he; for as he observes, *Be your disorder never so far gone, be under no uneasiness, make yourself quite easy, I can cure you.*

The next in fame, though by some reckoned of equal pretensions, is doctor *Timothy Franks*, F.O.G.H., living in a place called the *Old Bailey*. As *Rock* is remarkably squab, his great rival *Franks* is as remarkably tall. He was born in the year of the Christian æra 1692, and is, while I now write, exactly sixty-eight years, three months, and four days old. Age, however, has no ways impaired his usual health and vivacity, I am told he generally walks with his breast open. This gentleman, who is of a mixed reputation, is particularly remarkable for a becoming assurance, which carries him greatly through life; for, except doctor *Rock*, none are more blessed with the advantages of face than doctor *Franks*.

And yet the great have their foibles as well as the little. I am almost ashamed to mention it. Let the foibles of the great rest in peace. Yet I must impart the whole to my friend. These two great men are actually now at variance; yes, my dear *Fum Hoam*, by the head of our grandfather, they are now at variance like mere men, mere common mortals. The champion *Rock* advises the world to beware of bogtrotting quacks, while *Franks* retorts the wit and the sarcasm (for they have both a world of wit) by fixing on his rival the odious appellation of *Dumplin Dick*. He calls the serious doctor *Rock, Dumplin Dick!* Head of *Confucius*, what profanation! *Dumplin Dick!* What a pity, ye powers, that the learned, who were born mutually to assist in enlightening the world, should thus differ among themselves, and make even the profession ridiculous! Sure the world is wide enough, at least, for two great personages to figure in; men of science should leave controversy to the little world below them; and then we might see *Rock* and *Franks* walking together hand in hand, smiling onward to immortality.

Next to these is doctor *Walker*, preparator of his own medicines. This gentleman is remarkable for an aversion to quacks; frequently cautioning the public to be careful into what hands they commit their safety: by which he would insinuate, that if they did not employ him alone, they must be undone. His public spirit is equal to his success. Not for himself, but his country, is the gally-pot prepared and the drops sealed up with proper directions for any part of the town or country. All this is for his country's good: so that he is now grown old in the practice of physic and virtue; and to use his own elegance of expression, *There is not such another medicine as his in the world again*.

This, my friend, is a formidable triumvirate; and yet, formidable as they are, I am resolved to defend the honour of *Chinese* physic against them all. I have made a vow to summon doctor *Rock* to a solemn disputation in all the mysteries of the profession, before the face of every *Philomath*, student in astrology, and member of the learned societies. I adhere to, and venerate the doctrines of old *Wang-shu-ho*. In the very teeth of opposition I will maintain, *That the heart is the son of the liver, which has the kidneys for its mother, and the stomach for its wife.*[1] I have therefore drawn up a disputation challenge, which is to be sent speedily, to this effect:

I, *Lien Chi Altangi*, D.N.R.P., native of *Honan* in *China*, to *Richard Rock*, F.U.N., native of *Garbage-alley* in *Wapping*, defiance. Though, Sir, I am perfectly sensible of your importance, though no stranger to your studies in the paths of nature, yet there may be many things in the art of physic with which you are yet unacquainted. I know full well a doctor thou art, great *Rock*, and so am I. Wherefore I challenge, and do hereby invite you to a trial of learning upon hard problems, and knotty physical points. In this debate we will calmly investigate the whole theory and practice of medicine, botany and chemistry; and I invite all the *Philomaths*, with many of the lecturers in medicine, to be present at the dispute: which, I hope, will be carried on with due decorum, with proper gravity, and as befits men of erudition and science, among each other. But before we meet face to face, I would thus publicly, and in the face of the whole world, desire you to answer me one question; I ask it with the same earnestness with which you have often solicited the public; answer me, I say, at once, without having recourse to your physical dictionary, which of those three disorders incident to the human body, is the most fatal, the *syncope, parenthesis,* or *apoplexy*? I beg your reply may be as public as this my demand.[2] I am, as hereafter may be, your admirer or your rival. Adieu.

LETTER LXIX.—*To the same.*

INDULGENT Nature seems to have exempted this island from many of those epidemic evils which are so fatal in other parts of the world. A want of rain but for a few days beyond the expected season in China, spreads famine, desolation, and terror,

[1] See Du Halde, vol. ii, fol. p. 185.
[2] The day after this was published, the editor received an answer, in which the doctor seems to be of opinion, that the apoplexy is most fatal.

over the whole country; the winds that blow from the brown bosom of the western desert are impregnated with death in every gale; but in this fortunate land of Britain, the inhabitant courts health in every breeze, and the husbandman ever sows in joyful expectation.

But though the nation be exempt from real evils, think not, my friend, that it is more happy on this account than others. They are afflicted, it is true, with neither famine nor pestilence, but then there is a disorder peculiar to the country, which every season makes strange ravages among them; it spreads with pestilential rapidity, and infects almost every rank of people; what is still more strange, the natives have no name for this peculiar malady, though well known to foreign physicians by the appellation of *Epidemic terror*.

A season is never known to pass in which the people are not visited by this cruel calamity in one shape or another, seemingly different, though ever the same; one year it issues from a baker's shop in the shape of a six-penny loaf, the next it takes the appearance of a comet with a fiery tail, a third it threatens like a flat-bottomed boat, and a fourth it carries consternation at the bite of a mad dog. The people, when once infected, lose their relish for happiness, saunter about with looks of despondence, ask after the calamities of the day, and receive no comfort but in heightening each other's distress. It is insignificant how remote or near, how weak or powerful the object of terror may be, when once they resolve to fright and be frighted, the merest trifles sow consternation and dismay, each proportions his fears, not to the object, but to the dread he discovers in the countenance of others; for when once the fermentation is begun, it goes on of itself, though the original cause be discontinued which first set it in motion.

A dread of mad dogs is the *epidemic terror* which now prevails, and the whole nation is at present actually groaning under the malignity of its influence. The people sally from their houses with that circumspection which is prudent in such as expect a mad dog at every turning. The physician publishes his prescription, the beadle prepares his halter, and a few of unusual bravery arm themselves with boots and buff gloves, in order to face the enemy if he should offer to attack them. In short, the whole people stand bravely upon their defence, and seem by their present spirit to show a resolution of not being tamely bit by mad dogs any longer.

Their manner of knowing whether a dog be mad or no, somewhat resembles the ancient European custom of trying witches. The old woman suspected was tied hand and foot and thrown into the water. If she swam, then she was instantly carried off to be burnt for a witch, if she sunk, then indeed she was acquitted of the charge, but drowned in the experiment. In the same manner a crowd gather round a dog suspected of madness, and they begin by teasing the devoted animal on every side; if he attempts to stand upon the defensive and bite, then is he unanimously found guilty, for *a mad dog always snaps at every thing*; if, on the contrary, he strives to escape by running away, then he can expect no compassion, *for mad dogs always run straight forward before them*.

It is pleasant enough for a neutral being like me, who have no share in those ideal calamities, to mark the stages of this national disease. The terror at first feebly enters with a disregarded story of a little dog, that had gone through a neighbouring village, that was thought to be mad by several that had seen him. The next account comes, that a mastiff ran through a certain town, and had bit five geese, which immediately run mad, foamed at the bill, and died in great agonies soon after. Then comes an affecting history of a little boy bit in the leg, and gone down to be dipt in the salt water; when the people have sufficiently shuddered at that, they are the next congealed with a frightful account of a man who was said lately to have died from a bite he had received some years before. This relation only prepares the way for another, still more hideous, as how the master of a family, with seven small children, were all bit by a mad lap dog, and how the poor father first perceived the infection by calling for a draught of water, where he saw the lap dog swimming in the cup.

When epidemic terror is thus once excited, every morning comes loaded with some new disaster; as in stories of ghosts each loves to hear the account, though it only serves to make him uneasy, so here each listens with eagerness, and adds to the tidings with new circumstances of peculiar horror. A lady for instance, in the country, of very weak nerves has been frighted by the barking of a dog; and this, alas! too frequently happens. The story soon is improved and spreads, that a mad dog had frighted a lady of distinction. These circumstances begin to grow terrible before they have reached the neighbouring village, and there the report is that a lady of quality was *bit* by a mad mastiff. This account every moment gathers new strength and grows more dismal as it approaches the capital, and by the time it has arrived in town the lady is described, with wild eyes, foaming mouth, running mad upon all four, barking like a dog, biting her servants, and at last smothered between two beds by the advice of her doctors: while the mad mastiff is in the mean time ranging the whole country over, slavering at the mouth, and seeking whom he may devour.

My landlady, a good-natured woman, but a little credulous, waked me some mornings ago before the usual hour with horror and astonishment in her looks; she desired me if I had any regard for my safety, to keep within; for a few days ago so dismal an accident had happened, as to put all the world upon their guard. A mad dog down in the country, she assured me, had bit a farmer, who soon becoming mad ran into his own yard, and bit a fine brindled cow; the cow quickly became as mad as the man, began to foam at the mouth, and raising herself up, walked about on her hind legs, sometimes barking like a dog, and sometimes attempting to talk like the farmer. Upon examining the grounds of this story, I found my landlady had it from one neighbour, who had it from another neighbour, who heard it from very good authority.

Were most stories of this nature thoroughly examined, it would be found that numbers of such as have been said to suffer were no way injured, and that of those who have been actually bitten, not one in a hundred was bit by a mad dog. Such accounts in general therefore only serve to make the people miserable by false terrors, and sometimes fright the patient into actual frenzy, by creating those very symptoms they pretended to deplore.

But even allowing three or four to die in a season of this terrible death (and four is probably too large a concession), yet still it is not considered, how many are preserved in their health and in their property by this devoted animal's services. The midnight robber is kept at a distance, the insidious thief is often detected, the healthful chase repairs many a worn constitution, and the poor man finds in his dog a willing assistant, eager to lessen his toil, and content with the smallest retribution.

A dog, says one of the English poets, 'is an honest creature, and I am a friend to dogs.' Of all the beasts that graze the lawn or hunt the forest, a dog is the only animal, that leaving his fellows, attempts to cultivate the friendship of man; to man he looks in all his necessities with a speaking eye for assistance; exerts for him all the little service in his power with cheerful-

ness and pleasure; for him bears famine and fatigue with patience
and resignation; no injuries can abate his fidelity, no distress
induce him to forsake his benefactor; studious to please, and
fearing to offend, he is still an humble stedfast dependant, and
in him alone fawning is not flattery. How unkind then to
torture this faithful creature who has left the forest, to claim
the protection of man; how ungrateful a return to the trusty
animal for all its services. Adieu.

LETTER LXX.—*From Lien Chi Altangi to Hingpo, by the way
of Moscow.*

THE Europeans are themselves blind, who describe Fortune
without sight. No first rate beauty ever had finer eyes, or saw
more clearly; they who have no other trade but seeking their
fortune, need never hope to find her; coquette-like she flies
from her close pursuers, and at last fixes on the plodding
mechanic, who stays at home, and minds his business.

I am amazed how men can call her blind, when by the company
she keeps she seems so very discerning. Wherever you see a
gaming-table, be very sure Fortune is not there; wherever you
see an house with the doors open, be very sure Fortune is not
there; when you see a man whose pocket-holes are laced with
gold, be satisfied Fortune is not there; wherever you see a
beautiful woman good-natured and obliging, be convinced
Fortune is never there. In short, she is ever seen accompanying
industry, and as often trundling a wheelbarrow, as lolling in a
coach and six.

If you would make Fortune your friend, or to personize her
no longer, if you desire, my son, to be rich and have money, be
more eager to save than to acquire: when people say, *Money is
to be got here, and money is to be got there,* take no notice; mind
your own business; stay where you are; and secure all you can
get, without stirring. When you hear that your neighbour has
picked up a purse of gold in the street, never run out into the
same street, looking about you in order to pick up such another:
or when you are informed that he has made a fortune in one
branch of business, never change your own, in order to be his
rival. Do not desire to be rich all at once; but patiently add
farthing to farthing. Perhaps you despise the petty sum; and
yet they who want a farthing, and have no friend that will
lend them it, think farthings very good things. *Whang* the

foolish miller, when he wanted a farthing in his distress, found that no friend would lend, because they knew he wanted. Did you ever read the story of *Whang* in our books of Chinese learning; he, who despising small sums, and grasping at all, lost even what he had?

Whang, the miller, was naturally avaricious; nobody loved money better than he, or more respected those that had it. When people would talk of a rich man in company, *Whang* would say, I know him very well; he and I have been long acquainted; he and I are intimate; he stood for a child of mine: but if ever a poor man was mentioned, he had not the least knowledge of the man; he might be very well for ought he knew; but he was not fond of many acquaintances, and loved to choose his company.

Whang, however, with all his eagerness for riches, was in reality poor; he had nothing but the profits of his mill to support him, but though these were small they were certain; while his mill stood and went, he was sure of eating, and his frugality was such, that he every day laid some money by, which he would at intervals count and contemplate with much satisfaction. Yet still his acquisitions were not equal to his desires, he only found himself above want, whereas he desired to be possessed of affluence.

One day as he was indulging these wishes, he was informed, that a neighbour of his had found a pan of money under ground, having dreamed of it three nights running before. These tidings were daggers to the heart of poor *Whang*. Here am I, says he, toiling and moiling from morning till night for a few paltry farthings, while neighbour *Hunks* only goes quietly to bed, and dreams himself into thousands before morning. O that I could dream like him, with what pleasure would I dig round the pan; how slyly would I carry it home; not even my wife should see me; and then, O the pleasure of thrusting one's hand into a heap of gold up to the elbow!

Such reflections only served to make the miller unhappy; he discontinued his former assiduity, he was quite disgusted with small gains, and his customers began to forsake him. Every day he repeated the wish, and every night laid himself down in order to dream. Fortune that was for a long time unkind, at last however seemed to smile upon his distresses, and indulged him with the wished-for vision. He dreamed, that under a certain part of the foundation of his mill, there was concealed a monstrous pan of gold and diamonds, buried deep in the ground, and covered with a large flat stone. He rose up, thanked the stars, that were at last pleased to take pity on his sufferings, and concealed his good luck from every person, as is usual in money dreams, in order to have the vision repeated the two succeeding nights, by which he should be certain of its veracity. His wishes in this also were answered, he still dreamed of the same pan of money, in the very same place.

Now, therefore, it was past a doubt; so getting up early the third morning, he repairs alone, with a mattock in his hand, to the mill, and began to undermine that part of the wall which the vision directed. The first omen of success that he met was a broken mug; digging still deeper, he turns up a house tile, quite new and entire. At last, after much digging, he came to the broad flat stone, but then so large, that it was beyond one man's strength to remove it. Here, cried he, in raptures to himself, here it is; under this stone there is room for a very large pan of diamonds indeed. I must e'en go home to my wife, and tell her the whole affair, and get her to assist me in turning it up. Away therefore he goes, and acquaints his wife with every circumstance of their good fortune. Her raptures on this occasion easily may be imagined; she flew round his neck, and embraced him in an agony of joy; but those transports however did not delay their eagerness to know the exact sum: returning therefore speedily together to the place where *Whang* had been digging, there they found—not indeed the expected treasure, but the mill, their only support, undermined and fallen. Adieu.

LETTER LXXI.—*From Lien Chi Altangi, to Fum Hoam, first President of the Ceremonial Academy at Pekin, in China.*

THE people of *London* are as fond of walking as our friends of *Pekin* of riding; one of the principal entertainments of the citizens here in summer is to repair about nightfall to a garden not far from town, where they walk about, shew their best clothes and best faces, and listen to a concert provided for the occasion.

I accepted an invitation a few evenings ago from my old friend, the man in black, to be one of a party that was to sup there, and at the appointed hour waited upon him at his lodgings. There I found the company assembled and expecting my arrival. Our party consisted of my friend in superlative finery, his stockings rolled, a black velvet waistcoat which was formerly new, and his grey wig combed down in imitation of hair. A pawnbroker's widow, of whom, by the bye, my friend was a professed admirer, dressed out in green damask, with three gold rings on every finger. Mr. *Tibbs*, the second-rate beau I have formerly described, together with his lady, in flimsy silk, dirty gauze instead of linen, and an hat as big as an umbrella.

Our first difficulty was in settling how we should set out. Mrs. *Tibbs* had a natural aversion to the water, and the widow being a little in flesh, as warmly protested against walking; a coach was therefore agreed upon; which being too small to carry five, Mr. *Tibbs* consented to sit in his wife's lap.

In this manner therefore we set forward, being entertained by the way with the bodings of Mr. *Tibbs*, who assured us, he did not expect to see a single creature for the evening above the degree of a cheesemonger; that this was the last night of the gardens, and that consequently we should be pestered with the nobility and gentry from *Thames-street* and *Crooked-lane*, with several other prophetic ejaculations probably inspired by the uneasiness of his situation.

The illuminations began before we arrived, and I must confess, that upon entering the gardens, I found every sense overpaid with more than expected pleasure; the lights every where glimmering through the scarcely moving trees; the full-bodied concert bursting on the stillness of the night, the natural concert of the birds in the more retired part of the Grove, vying with that which was formed by art; the company gaily dressed, looking satisfaction, and the table spread with various delicacies, all conspired to fill my imagination with the visionary happiness of the *Arabian* lawgiver, and lifted me into an extasy of admiration. Head of *Confucius*, cried I to my friend, this is fine! this unites rural beauty with courtly magnificence; if we except the virgins of immortality that hang on every tree, and may be plucked at every desire, I don't see how this falls short of *Mahomet's Paradise!* As for virgins, cried my friend, it is true, they are a fruit that don't much abound in our gardens here; but if ladies as plenty as apples in autumn, and as complying as any *houri* of them all, can content you, I fancy we have no need to go to heaven for Paradise.

I was going to second his remarks, when we were called to a consultation by Mr. *Tibbs* and the rest of the company, to know in what manner we were to lay out the evening to the greatest advantage. Mrs. *Tibbs* was for keeping the genteel walk of the garden, where she observed there was always the very best company; the widow, on the contrary, who came but once a season, was for securing a good standing-place to see the water-works, which she assured us would begin in less than an hour at farthest; a dispute therefore began, and as it was managed between two of very opposite characters, it threatened to grow more bitter at every reply. Mrs. *Tibbs* wondered how people could pretend to know the polite world who had received all their rudiments of breeding behind a counter; to which the other replied, that tho' some people sat behind counters, yet they could sit at the head of their own tables too, and carve three good dishes of hot meat whenever they thought proper, which was more than some people could say for themselves, that hardly knew a rabbit and onions from a green goose and gooseberries.

It is hard to say where this might have ended, had not the husband, who probably knew the impetuosity of his wife's disposition, proposed to end the dispute by adjoining to a box, and try if there was any thing to be had for supper that was supportable. To this we all consented, but here a new distress arose; Mr. and Mrs. *Tibbs* would sit in none but a genteel box, a box where they might see and be seen, one, as they expressed it, in the very focus of public view; but such a box was not easy to be obtained, for though we were perfectly convinced of our own gentility, and the gentility of our appearance, yet we found it a difficult matter to persuade the keepers of the boxes to be of our opinion; they chose to reserve genteel boxes for what they judged more genteel company.

At last however we were fixed, though somewhat obscurely, and supplied with the usual entertainment of the place. The widow found the supper excellent, but Mrs. *Tibbs* thought every thing detestable: Come, come, my dear, cried the husband, by way of consolation, to be sure we can't find such dressing here as we have at lord Crump's or lady Crimp's; but for Vauxhall dressing it is pretty good; it is not their victuals indeed I find fault with, but their wine; their wine, cried he, drinking off a glass, indeed, is most abominable.

By this last contradiction the widow was fairly conquered in point of politeness. She perceived now that she had no pretensions in the world to taste, her very senses were vulgar, since she had praised detestable custard, and smacked at wretched wine; she was therefore content to yield the victory, and for the rest of the night to listen and improve. It is true, she would now and then forget herself, and confess she was pleased, but they soon brought her back again to miserable refinement. She once praised the painting of the box in which we were sitting, but was soon convinced that such paltry pieces ought rather to excite horror than satisfaction; she ventured again to commend one of the singers, but Mrs. *Tibbs* soon let her know, in the style of a connoisseur, that the singer in question had neither ear, voice, nor judgment.

Mr. *Tibbs* now willing to prove that his wife's pretensions to music were just, entreated her to favour the company with a song; but to this she gave a positive denial, For you know very well, my dear, says she, that I am not in voice to day, and when one's voice is not equal to one's judgment, what signifies singing; besides as there is no accompaniment, it would be but spoiling music. All these excuses however were overruled by the rest of the company, who, though one would think they already had music enough, joined in the entreaty. But particularly the widow, now willing to convince the company of her breeding, pressed so warmly that she seemed determined to take no refusal. At last then the lady complied, and after humming for some minutes, began with such a voice and such affectation, as I could perceive gave but little satisfaction to any except her husband. He sat with rapture in his eye, and beat time with his hand on the table.

You must observe, my friend, that it is the custom of this country, when a lady or gentleman happens to sing, for the company to sit as mute and motionless as statues. Every feature, every limb must seem to correspond in fixed attention, and while the song continues, they are to remain in a state of universal petrifaction. In this mortifying situation we had continued for some time, listening to the song, and looking with tranquillity, when the master of the box came to inform us, that the water-works were going to begin. At this information I could instantly perceive the widow bounce from her seat; but correcting herself, she sat down again, repressed by motives of good breeding. Mrs. *Tibbs*, who had seen the water-works an hundred times, resolved not to be interrupted, continued her song without any share of mercy, nor had the smallest pity on our impatience. The widow's face, I own, gave me high entertainment; in it I could plainly read the struggle she felt between good breeding and curiosity; she talked of the water-works the whole evening before, and seemed to have come merely in order to see them; but then she could not bounce out in the very middle of a song, for that would be forfeiting all pretensions to high life, or high-lived company ever after: Mrs. *Tibbs* therefore kept on singing, and we continued to listen, till at last, when the song was just concluded, the waiter came to inform us that the water-works were over!

The water-works over, cried the widow! the water-works over already, that's impossible, they can't be over so soon! It is not my business, replied the fellow, to contradict your ladyship, I'll run again and see; he went, and soon returned with a confirmation of the dismal tidings. No ceremony could now bind my friend's disappointed mistress, she testified her displeasure in the openest manner; in short, she now began to find fault in turn, and at last, insisted upon going home, just at the time that Mr. and Mrs. *Tibbs* assured the company, that the polite hours were going to begin, and that the ladies would instantaneously be entertained with the horns. Adieu.

LETTER LXXII.—*From the same.*

NOT far from this city lives a poor tinker, who has educated seven sons, all at this very time in arms and fighting for their country, and what reward do you think has the tinker from the state for such important services? None in the world; his sons, when the war is over, may probably be whipped from parish to parish as vagabonds, and the old man, when past labour, may die a prisoner in some house of correction.

Such a worthy subject in China would be held in universal reverence; his services would be rewarded, if not with dignities, at least with an exemption from labour; he would take the left hand at feasts, and mandarines themselves would be proud to show their submission. The *English* laws punish vice, the *Chinese* laws do more, they reward virtue!

Considering the little encouragements given to matrimony here, I am not surprised at the discouragements given to propagation. Would you believe it, my dear *Fum Hoam*, there are laws made, which even forbid the people marrying each other. By the head of *Confucius* I jest not; there are such laws in being here; and yet their law-givers have neither been instructed among the *Hottentots* nor imbibed their principles of equity from the natives of *Anamaboo*.

There are laws which ordain, that no man shall marry a woman against her own consent. This though contrary to what we are taught in *Asia* and though in some measure a clog upon matrimony, I have no great objection to. There are laws which ordain, that no woman shall marry against her father and mother's consent, unless arrived at an age of maturity; by which is understood those years, when women with us are generally past child-bearing. This must be a clog upon matrimony, as it is more difficult for the lover to please three than one, and much more difficult to please old people than young ones. The law ordains, that the consenting couple shall take a long time to consider before they marry; this is a very great clog, because people love to have all rash actions done in a hurry. It is ordained, that all marriages shall be proclaimed before celebration; this is a severe clog, as many are ashamed to have their marriage made public, from motives of vicious modesty, and many afraid from views of temporal interest. It is ordained, that there is nothing sacred in the ceremony, but that it may be dissolved to all intents and purposes by the authority of any civil magistrate. And yet opposite to this it is ordained, that the priest shall be paid a large sum of money for granting his sacred permission.

Thus you see, my friend, that matrimony here is hedged round with so many obstructions, that those who are willing to break through or surmount them must be contented, if at last they find it a bed of thorns. The laws are not to blame, for they have deterred the people from engaging as much as they could. It is indeed become a very serious affair in *England*, and none but serious people are generally found willing to engage. The young, the gay, and the beautiful, who have motives of passion only to induce them, are seldom found to embark, as those inducements are taken away, and none but the old, the ugly, and the mercenary are seen to unite, who, if they have any posterity at all, will probably be an ill-favoured race like themselves.

What gave rise to those laws might have been some such accidents as these. It sometimes happened, that a miser who had spent all his youth, in scraping up money to give his daughter such a fortune as might get her a mandarine husband, found his expectations disappointed at last, by her running away with his footman: this must have been a sad shock to the poor disconsolate parent, to see his poor daughter in a one horse chaise, when he had designed her for a coach and six: what a stroke from Providence! to see his dear money go to enrich a beggar; all Nature cried out at the profanation!

It sometimes happened also, that a lady who had inherited all the titles, and all the nervous complaints of nobility, thought fit to impair her dignity and mend her constitution, by marrying a farmer; this must have been a sad shock to her inconsolable relations, to see so fine a flower snatched from a flourishing family, and planted in a dunghill; this was an absolute inversion of the first principles of things.

In order, therefore, to prevent the great from being thus contaminated by vulgar alliances, the obstacles to matrimony have been so contrived, that the rich only can marry amongst the rich, and the poor, who would leave celibacy, must be content to increase their poverty with a wife. Thus have their laws fairly inverted the inducements to matrimony; Nature tells us, that beauty is the proper allurement of those who are rich, and money of those who are poor; but things here are so contrived, that the rich are invited to marry by that fortune which they do not want, and the poor have no inducement, but that beauty which they do not feel.

An equal diffusion of riches through any country ever constitutes its happiness. Great wealth in the possession of one stagnates, and extreme poverty with another keeps him in unambitious indigence; but the moderately rich are generally active; not too far removed from poverty to fear its calamities; nor too near extreme wealth to slacken the nerve of labour, they still remain between both in a state of continual fluctuation. How impolitic therefore are those laws which promote the accumulation of wealth among the rich, more impolitic still in attempting to increase the depression on poverty.

Bacon, the English philosopher, compares money to manure; if gathered in heaps, says he, it does no good; on the contrary, it becomes offensive. But being spread, though never so thinly, over the surface of the earth, it enriches the whole country. Thus the wealth a nation possesses must expatiate, or it is of no benefit to the public; it becomes rather a grievance, where matrimonial laws thus confine it to a few.

But this restraint upon matrimonial community, even considered in a physical light, is injurious. As those who rear up animals take all possible pains to cross the strain in order to improve the breed; so in those countries, where marriage is most free, the inhabitants are found every age to improve in stature and in beauty; on the contrary, where it is confined to a *caste*, a *tribe* or an *horde*, as among the Gaurs, the Jews, or the Tartars, each division soon assumes a family likeness, and every tribe degenerates into peculiar deformity. From hence it may be easily inferred, that if the mandarines here are resolved only to marry among each other, they will soon produce a posterity with mandarine faces; and we shall see the heir of some honourable family, scarce equal to the abortion of a country farmer.

These are a few of the obstacles to marriage here, and it is certain, they have in some measure answered the end, for celibacy is both frequent and fashionable. Old bachelors appear abroad without a mask, and old maids, my dear *Fum Hoam*, have been absolutely known to ogle. To confess in friendship, if I were an Englishman, I fancy I should be an old bachelor myself; I should never find courage to run through all the adventures prescribed by the law. I could submit to court my mistress herself upon reasonable terms, but to court her father, her mother, and a long tribe of cousins, aunts, and relations, and then stand the butt of a whole country church; I would as soon turn tail and make love to her grandmother.

I can conceive no other reason for thus loading matrimony with so many prohibitions, unless it be that the country was thought already too populous, and this was found to be the most effectual means of thinning it. If this was the motive, I cannot but congratulate the wise projectors on the success of their scheme. Hail, O ye dim-sighted politicians, ye weeders of men! 'Tis yours to clip the wing of industry, and convert Hymen to a broker. 'Tis yours to behold small objects with a microscopic eye, but to be blind to those which require an extent of vision. 'Tis yours, O ye discerners of mankind, to lay the line between society, and weaken that force by dividing, which should bind with united vigour. 'Tis yours, to introduce national real distress, in order to avoid the imaginary distresses of a few. Your actions can be justified by an hundred reasons like truth, they can be opposed by but a few reasons, and those reasons are true. Farewell.

LETTER LXXIII.—*From Lien Chi Altangi to Fum Hoam, first President of the Ceremonial Academy, at Pekin in China.*

AGE that lessens the enjoyment of life increases our desire of living. Those dangers, which, in the vigour of youth we had learned to despise, assume new terrors as we grow old. Our caution increasing as our years increase, fear becomes at last the prevailing passion of the mind; and the small remainder of life is taken up in useless efforts to keep off our end, or provide for a continued existence.

Strange contradiction in our nature, and to which even the wise are liable! If I should judge of that part of life which lies before me by that which I have already seen, the prospect is hideous. Experience tells me, that my past enjoyments have brought no real felicity; and sensation assures me, that those I have felt are stronger than those which are yet to come. Yet experience and sensation in vain persuade; hope, more powerful than either, dresses out the distant prospect in fancied beauty, some happiness in long perspective still beckons me to pursue, and, like a losing gamester, every new disappointment increases my ardour to continue the game.

Whence, my friend, this increased love of life, which grows upon us with our years; whence comes it, that we thus make greater efforts to preserve our existence, at a period when it becomes scarce worth the keeping? Is it that Nature, attentive to the preservation of mankind, increases our wishes to live, while she lessens our enjoyments; and, as she robs the senses of every pleasure, equips imagination in the spoil? Life would be insupportable to an old man, who, loaded with infirmities, feared death no more than when in the vigour of manhood; the numberless calamities of decaying nature, and the consciousness of surviving every pleasure, would at once induce him with his own hand to terminate the scene of misery; but happily the contempt of death forsakes him at a time when it could only be prejudicial; and life acquires an imaginary value, in proportion as its real value is no more.

Our attachment to every object around us increases, in general, from the length of our acquaintance with it. I would not choose, says a *French* philosopher, to see an old post pulled up, with which I have been long acquainted. A mind long habituated to a certain set of objects, insensibly becomes fond of seeing them; visits them from habit, and parts from them with reluctance: from hence proceeds the avarice of the old in every kind of possession. They love the world and all it produces; they love life and all its advantages; not because it gives them pleasure, but because they have known it long.

Chinvang, the Chaste, ascending the throne of China, commanded that all who were unjustly detained in prison, during the preceding reigns, should be set free. Among the number who came to thank their deliverer on this occasion, there appeared a majestic old man, who, falling at the emperor's feet, addressed him as follows: 'Great father of China, behold a wretch, now eighty-five years old, who was shut up in a dungeon at the age of twenty-two. I was imprisoned, though a stranger to crime, or without even being confronted by my accusers. I have now lived in solitude and darkness for more than fifty years, and am grown familiar with distress. As yet dazzled with the splendour of that sun to which you have restored me, I have been wandering the streets to find some friend that would assist, or relieve, or remember me; but my friends, my family, and relations, are all dead, and I am forgotten. Permit me then, O Chinvang, to wear out the wretched remains of life in my former prison; the walls of my dungeon are, to me, more pleasing than the most splendid palace; I have not long to live, and shall be unhappy except I spend the rest of my days where my youth was passed; in that prison from whence you were pleased to release me.'

The old man's passion for confinement is similar to that we all have for life. We are habituated to the prison, we look round with discontent, are displeased with the abode, and yet the length of our captivity only increases our fondness for the cell. The trees we have planted, the houses we have built, or the posterity we have begotten, all serve to bind us closer to earth, and embitter our parting. Life sues the young like a new acquaintance; the companion, as yet unexhausted, is at once instructive and amusing, 'tis company pleases, yet for all this it is but little regarded. To us, who are declined in years, life appears like an old friend; its jests have been anticipated in former conversation; it has no new story to make us smile, no new improvement with which to surprise, yet still we love it; destitute of every agreement, still we love it; husband the wasting treasure with increased frugality, and feel all the poignancy of anguish in the fatal separation.

Sir Philip Mordaunt was young, beautiful, sincere, brave, an Englishman. He had a complete fortune of his own, and the love of the king his master, which was equivalent to riches. Life opened all her treasure before him, and promised a long succession of future happiness. He came, tasted of the entertainment, but was disgusted even in the beginning. He professed an aversion to living, was tired of walking round the same circle; had tried every enjoyment, and found them all grow weaker at every repetition. 'If life be in youth so displeasing, cried he to himself, what will it appear when age comes on; if it be at present indifferent, sure it will then be execrable.' This thought embittered every reflection; till, at last, with all the serenity of perverted reason, he ended the debate with a pistol! Had this self-deluded man been apprized, that existence grows more desirable to us the longer we exist, he would then have faced old age without shrinking, he would have boldly dared to live, and served that society, by his future assiduity, which he basely injured by his desertion. Adieu.

LETTER LXXIV.—*From Lien Chi Altangi, to Fum Hoam, first President of the Ceremonial Academy, at Pekin, in China.*

IN reading the newspapers here, I have reckoned up not less than twenty-five great men, seventeen very great men, and nine very extraordinary men in less than the compass of half a year. These, say the gazettes, are the men that posterity are to gaze at with admiration; these the names that fame will be employed in holding up for the astonishment of succeeding ages. Let me see—forty-six great men in half a year, amounts to just ninety-two in a year.—I wonder how posterity will be able to remember them all, or whether the people, in future times, will have any other business to mind, but that of getting the catalogue by heart.

Does the mayor of a corporation make a speech? he is instantly set down for a great man. Does a pedant digest his common place book into a folio? he quickly becomes great. Does a poet string up trite sentiments in rhyme? he also becomes the great man of the hour. How diminutive soever the object of admiration, each is followed by a crowd of still more diminutive admirers. The shout begins in his train, onward he marches towards immortality, looks back at the pursuing crowd with self-satisfaction; catching all the oddities, the whimsies, the absurdities, and the littlenesses of conscious greatness, by the way.

I was yesterday invited by a gentleman to dinner, who promised that our entertainment should consist of an haunch of venison, a turtle, and a great man. I came, according to appointment. The venison was fine, the turtle good, but the great man insupportable. The moment I ventured to speak, I was at once contradicted with a snap. I attempted, by a second and a third assault, to retrieve my lost reputation, but was still beat back with confusion. I was resolved to attack him once more from entrenchment, and turned the conversation upon the government of China: but even here he asserted, snapped, and contradicted as before. Heavens, thought I, this man pretends to know China even better than myself! I looked round to see who was on my side, but every eye was fixed in admiration on the great man; I therefore, at last thought proper to sit silent, and act the pretty gentleman during the ensuing conversation.

When a man has once secured a circle of admirers, he may be as ridiculous here as he thinks proper; and it all passes for elevation of sentiment, or learned absence. If he transgresses the common forms of breeding, mistakes even a teapot for a tobacco-box, it is said, that his thoughts are fixed on more important objects: to speak and act like the rest of mankind is to be no greater than they. There is something of oddity in the very idea of greatness; for we are seldom astonished at a thing very much resembling ourselves.

When the Tartars make a Lama, their first care is to place him in a dark corner of the temple; here he is to sit half concealed from view, to regulate the motion of his hands, lips, and eyes; but, above all, he is enjoined gravity and silence. This, however, is but the prelude to his apotheosis: a set of emissaries are despatched among the people to cry up his piety, gravity, and love of raw flesh; the people take them at their word, approach the Lama, now become an idol, with the most humble prostration; he receives their addresses without motion, commences a god, and is ever after fed by his priests with the spoon of immortality. The same receipt in this country serves to make a great man. The idol only keeps close, sends out his little emissaries to be hearty in his praise; and straight, whether statesman or author, he is set down in the list of fame, continuing to be praised while it is fashionable to praise, or while he prudently keeps his minuteness concealed from the public.

I have visited many countries, and have been in cities without number, yet never did I enter a town which could not produce ten or twelve of those little great men; all fancying themselves known to the rest of the world, and complimenting each other upon their extensive reputation. It is amusing enough when two of those domestic prodigies of learning mount the stage of ceremony, and give and take praise from each other. I have been present when a German doctor, for having pronounced a panegyric upon a certain monk, was thought the most ingenious man in the world; till the monk soon after divided this reputation by returning the compliment; by which means they both marched off with universal applause.

The same degree of undeserved adulation that attends our great man while living, often also follows him to the tomb. It frequently happens that one of his little admirers sits down big with the important subject, and is delivered of the history of his life and writings. This may properly be called the revolutions of a life between the fireside and the easy-chair. In this we learn, the year in which he was born, at what an early age he gave symptoms of uncommon genius and application, together with some of his smart sayings, collected by his aunt and mother, while yet but a boy. The next book introduces him to the University, where we are informed of his amazing progress in learning, his excellent skill in darning stockings, and his new invention for papering books to save the covers. He next makes his appearance in the republic of letters, and publishes his folio. Now the colossus is reared, his works are eagerly bought up by all the purchasers of scarce books. The learned societies invite him to become a member; he disputes against some foreigner with a long Latin name, conquers in the controversy, is complimented by several authors of gravity and importance, is excessively fond of egg-sauce with his pig, becomes president of a literary club, and dies in the meridian of his glory. Happy they, who thus have some little faithful attendant, who never forsakes them, but prepares to wrangle and to praise against every opposer; at once ready to increase their pride while living, and their character when dead. For you and I, my friend, who have no humble admirer thus to attend us, we, who neither are, nor ever will be great men, and who do not much care whether we are great men or no, at least let us strive to be honest men, and to have common sense.

LETTER LXXV.—*To the same.*

THERE are numbers in this city who live by writing new books; and yet there are thousands of volumes in every large library unread and forgotten. This, upon my arrival, was one of those contradictions which I was unable to account for. Is it possible, said I, that there should be any demand for new books, before those already published are read? Can there be so many employed in producing a commodity, with which the market is already overstocked; and with goods also better than any of modern manufacture!

What at first view appeared an inconsistence, is a proof at once of this people's wisdom and refinement. Even allowing the works of their ancestors better written than theirs, yet those of the moderns acquire a real value, by being marked with the impression of the times. Antiquity has been in the possession of others, the present is our own; let us first therefore learn to know what belongs to ourselves, and then, if we have leisure, cast our reflections back to the reign of *Shonou*, who governed twenty thousand years before the creation of the moon.

The volumes of antiquity, like medals, may very well serve to amuse the curious, but the works of the moderns, like the current coin of a kingdom, are much better for immediate use; the former are often prized above their intrinsic value, and kept with care, the latter seldom pass for more than they are worth, and are often subject to the merciless hands of sweating critics, and clipping compilers; the works of antiquity were ever praised, those of the moderns read; the treasures of our ancestors have our esteem, and we boast the passion; those of contemporary genius engage our heart, although we blush to own it. The visits we pay the former resemble those we pay the great; the ceremony is troublesome, and yet such as we would not choose to forego; our acquaintance with modern books, is like sitting with a friend; our pride is not flattered in the interview, but it gives more internal satisfaction.

In proportion as society refines, new books must ever become more necessary. Savage rusticity is reclaimed by oral admonition alone; but the elegant excesses of refinement are best corrected by the still voice of studious enquiry. In a polite age, almost every person becomes a reader, and receives more instruction from the press than the pulpit. The preaching bonze may instruct the illiterate peasant; but nothing less than the insinuating address of a fine writer, can win its way to a heart already relaxed in all the effeminacy of refinement. Books are necessary to correct the vices of the polite, but those vices are ever changing, and the antidote should be changed accordingly; should still be new.

Instead, therefore, of thinking the number of new publications here too great, I could wish it still greater, as they are the most useful instruments of reformation. Every country must be instructed either by *writers* or *preachers*; but as the number of readers increases, the number of hearers is proportionably diminished, the writer becomes more useful, and the preaching bonze less necessary.

Instead, therefore, of complaining that writers are overpaid, when their works procure them a bare subsistence, I should imagine it the duty of a state not only to encourage their numbers, but their industry. A bonze is rewarded with immense riches for instructing only a few, even of the most ignorant, of the people; and sure the poor scholar should not beg his bread, who is capable of instructing a million.

Of all rewards, I grant, the most pleasing to a man of real merit, is fame; but a polite age, of all times, is that in which scarce any share of merit can acquire it. What numbers of fine writers in the latter empire of Rome, when refinement was carried to the highest pitch, have missed that fame and immortality which they had fondly arrogated to themselves! How many Greek authors, who wrote at that period when Constantinople was the refined mistress of the empire, now rest either not printed, or not read, in the libraries of Europe! Those who came first, while either state as yet was barbarous, carried all the reputation away. Authors, as the age refined, became more numerous, and their numbers destroyed their fame. It is but natural, therefore, for the writer, when conscious that his works will not procure him fame hereafter, to endeavour to make them turn out to his temporal interest here.

Whatever be the motives which induce men to write, whether avarice or fame, the country becomes most wise and happy, in which they most serve for instructors. The countries where sacerdotal instruction alone is permitted, remain in ignorance, superstition, and hopeless slavery. In England, where there are as many new books published as in all the rest of Europe together, a spirit of freedom and reason reigns among the people; they have been often known to act like fools, they are generally found to think like men.

The only danger that attends a multiplicity of publications, is that some of them may be calculated to injure, rather than benefit society. But where writers are numerous, they also serve as a check upon each other; and perhaps a literary inquisition is the most terrible punishment that can be conceived, to a literary transgressor.

But, to do the English justice, there are but few offenders of this kind, their publications in general aim at mending either the heart, or improving the common weal. The dullest writer talks of virtue, and liberty, and benevolence, with esteem; tells his true story, filled with good and wholesome advice; warns against slavery, bribery, or the bite of a mad dog, and dresses up his little useful magazine of knowledge and entertainment, at least with a good intention. The dunces of France, on the other hand, who have less encouragement, are more vicious. Tender hearts, languishing eyes, Leonora in love at thirteen, extatic transports, stolen blisses, are the frivolous subjects of their frivolous memoirs. In England, if a bawdy blockhead thus breaks in on the community, he sets his whole fraternity in a roar; nor can he escape, even though he should fly to nobility for shelter.

Thus even dunces, my friend, may make themselves useful. But there are others whom Nature has blest with talents above the rest of mankind; men capable of thinking with precision, and impressing their thought with rapidity; beings who diffuse those regards upon mankind, which others contract and settle upon themselves. These deserve every honour from that community of which they are more peculiarly the children; to such I would give my heart, since to them I am indebted for its humanity. Adieu.

LETTER LXXVI.—*From Hingpo to Lien Chi Altangi, by the way of Moscow.*

I STILL remain at *Terki* where I have received that money, which was remitted here in order to release me from captivity. My fair companion still improves in my esteem; the more I know her mind, her beauty becomes more poignant; she appears charming, even among the daughters of *Circassia*.

Yet were I to examine her beauty with the art of a statuary, I should find numbers here that far surpass her; Nature has not granted her all the boasted *Circassian* regularity of feature, and yet she greatly exceeds the fairest of the country, in the art of seizing the affections. Whence, have I often said to myself, this resistless magic that attends even moderate charms? Though I regard the beauties of the country with admiration, every interview weakens the impression, but the form of Zelis grows upon my imagination, I never behold her without an increase of tenderness and respect. Whence this injustice of the mind in preferring imperfect beauty to that which Nature seems to have finished with care? whence the infatuation, that he whom a comet could not amaze, should be astonished at a meteor! When reason was thus fatigued to find an answer, my imagination pursued the subject, and this was the result.

I fancied myself placed between two landscapes, this called *the region of Beauty*, and that *the valley of the Graces*; the one adorned with all that luxuriant nature could bestow; the fruits of various climates adorned the trees, the grove resounded with music, the gale breathed perfume, every charm that could arise from symmetry and exact distribution were here conspicuous, the whole offering a prospect of pleasure without end. *The Valley of the Graces* on the other hand, seemed by no means so inviting; the streams and the groves appeared just as they usually do in frequented countries; no magnificent parterres, no concert in the grove, the rivulet was edged with weeds, and the rook joined its voice to that of the nightingale. All was simplicity and nature.

The most striking objects ever first allure the traveller; I entered *The Region of Beauty* with increased curiosity, and promised myself endless satisfaction in being introduced to the presiding goddess. I perceived several strangers, who entered with the same design, and what surprised me not a little, was to see several others hastening to leave this abode of seeming felicity.

After some fatigue, I had at last the honour of being introduced to the goddess, who represented Beauty in person. She was seated on a throne, at the foot of which stood several strangers lately introduced like me; all gazing on her form in extasy. *Ah, what eyes! what lips! how clear her complexion! how perfect her shape!* at these exclamations Beauty with downcast eyes, would endeavour to counterfeit modesty, but soon again looking round as if to confirm every spectator in his favourable sentiments, sometimes she would attempt to allure us by smiles; and at intervals would bridle back, in order to inspire us with respect as well as tenderness.

This ceremony lasted for some time, and had so much employed our eyes, that we had forgot all this while that the goddess was silent. We soon, however, began to perceive the defect: *What,* said we, among each other, *are we to have nothing but languishing airs, soft looks, and inclinations of the head; will the goddess only deign to satisfy our eyes?* Upon this one of the company stepped up to present her with some fruits he had gathered by the way. She received the present most sweetly smiling, and with one of the whitest hands in the world, but still not a word escaped her lips.

I now found that my companions grew weary of their homage; they went off one by one, and resolving not to be left behind, I offered to go in my turn; when just at the door of the temple I was called back by a female, whose name was *Pride* and who seemed displeased at the behaviour of the company. *Where are you hastening?* said she to me with an angry air, *the goddess of Beauty is here.* I have been to visit her, Madam, replied I, and find her more beautiful even than report had made her. *And why then will you leave her?* added the female. I have seen her long enough, returned I; I have got all her features by heart. Her eyes are still the same. Her nose is a very fine one, but it is still just now such a nose, as it was half an hour ago: could she throw a little more mind into her face, perhaps I should be for wishing to have more of her company. *What signifies,* replied my female, *whether she has a mind or not; has she any occasion for a mind, so formed as she is by nature? If she had a common face, indeed, there might be some reason for thinking to improve it; but when features are already perfect, every alteration would but impair them. A fine face is already at the point of perfection, and a fine lady should endeavour to keep it so; the impression it would receive from thought, would but disturb its whole economy.*

To this speech I gave no reply, but made the best of my way to the valley of the Graces. Here I found all those who before had been my companions in *The Region of Beauty*, now upon the same errand.

As we entered the valley, the prospect insensibly seemed to improve; we found every thing so natural, so domestic, and pleasing, that our minds, which before were congealed in admiration, now relaxed into gaiety and good-humour. We had designed to pay our respects to the presiding goddess, but she was nowhere to be found. One of our companions asserted that her temple lay to the right; another, to the left; a third insisted that it was straight before us; and a fourth, that we had left it behind. In short, we found everything familiar and charming, but could not determine where to seek for the Grace in person.

In this agreeable incertitude we passed several hours, and though very desirous of finding the goddess, by no means impatient of the delay. Every part of the valley presented some minute beauty, which without offering itself at once, stole upon the soul, and captivated us with the charms of our retreat. Still, however, we continued to search, and might still have continued, had we not been interrupted by a voice which, though we could not see from whence it came, addressed us in this manner:

'If you would find the goddess of Grace, seek her not under one form, for she assumes a thousand. Ever changing under the eye of inspection, her variety, rather than her figure, is pleasing.

In contemplating her beauty, the eye glides over every perfection with giddy delight, and, capable of fixing no where, is charmed with the whole.[1] She is now Contemplation with solemn look, again Compassion with humid eye; she now sparkles with joy, soon every feature speaks distress: her looks at times invite our approach, at others repress our presumption; the goddess cannot be properly called beautiful under any one of these forms, but by combining them all, she becomes irresistibly pleasing.' Adieu.

LETTER LXXVII.—*From Lien Chi Altangi, to Fum Hoam, first President of the Ceremonial Academy, at Pekin, in China.*

THE shops of London are as well furnished as those of Pekin. Those of London have a picture hung at their door, informing the passengers what they have to sell, as those at Pekin have a board to assure the buyer, that they have no intentions to cheat him.

I was this morning to buy silk for a night-cap; immediately upon entering the mercer's shop, the master and his two men, with wigs plastered with powder, appeared to ask my commands. They were certainly the civilest people alive; if I but looked, they flew to the place where I cast my eye; every motion of mine sent them running round the whole shop for my satisfaction. I informed them that I wanted what was good, and they shewed me not less than forty pieces, and each was better than the former; the prettiest pattern in nature, and the fittest in the world for night-caps. My very good friend, said I to the mercer, you must not pretend to instruct me in silks, I know these in particular to be no better than your mere flimsy *Bungees. That may be,* cried the mercer, who I afterwards found had never contradicted a man in his life, *I can't pretend to say but they may; but I can assure you, my Lady Trail has had a sacque from this piece this very morning.* But friend, said I, though my lady has chosen a sacque from it, I see no necessity that I should wear it for a night-cap. *That may be,* returned he again, *yet what becomes a pretty lady, will at any time look well on a handsome gentlemen.* This short compliment was thrown in so very seasonably upon my ugly face, that even though I disliked the silk, I desired him to cut me off the pattern of a night-cap.

While this business was consigned to his journeyman, the master himself took down some pieces of silk still finer than

'Vultus nimium lubricus aspici.'—HOR.

any I had yet seen, and spreading them before me, *There*, cries he, *there's beauty, my Lord Snakeskin has bespoke the fellow to this for the birth-night this very morning; it would look charmingly in waistcoats.* But I don't want a waistcoat, replied I: *Not want a waistcoat?* returned the mercer, *then I would advise you to buy one; when waistcoats are wanted, you may depend upon it they will come dear. Always buy before you want, and you are sure to be well used, as they say in Cheapside.* There was so much justice in his advice, that I could not refuse taking it; besides, the silk, which was really a good one, increased the temptation, so I gave orders for that too.

As I was waiting to have my bargains measured and cut, which I know not how, they executed but slowly; during the interval, the mercer entertained me with the modern manner of some of the nobility receiving company in their morning gowns; *Perhaps, Sir,* adds he, *you have a mind to see what kind of silk is universally worn.* Without waiting for my reply, he spreads a piece before me, which might be reckoned beautiful even in China. *If the nobility,* continues he, *were to know I sold this to any under a Right Honourable, I should certainly lose their custom; you see, my Lord, it is at once rich, tasty, and quite the thing.* I am no Lord, interrupted I.—*I beg pardon,* cried he, *but be pleased to remember, when you intend buying a morning gown, that you had an offer from me of something worth money. Conscience, Sir, conscience is my way of dealing; you may buy a morning gown now, or you may stay till they become dearer and less fashionable, but it is not my business to advise.* In short, most reverend Fum, he persuaded me to buy a morning gown also, and would probably have persuaded me to have bought half the goods in his shop, if I had staid long enough, or was furnished with sufficient money.

Upon returning home, I could not help reflecting with some astonishment, how this very man with such a confined education and capacity, was yet capable of turning me as he thought proper, and moulding me to his inclinations! I knew he was only answering his own purposes, even while he attempted to appear solicitous about mine; yet by a voluntary infatuation, a sort of passion compounded of vanity and good nature, I walked into the snare with my eyes open, and put myself to future pain in order to give him immediate pleasure. The wisdom of the ignorant, somewhat resembles the instinct of animals; it is diffused in but a very narrow sphere, but within that circle it acts with vigour, uniformity, and success. Adieu.

LETTER LXXVIII.—*From the same.*

FROM my former accounts you may be apt to fancy the English the most ridiculous people under the sun. They are indeed ridiculous: yet every other nation in Europe is equally so; each laughs at each, and the Asiatic at all.

I may, upon another occasion, point out what is most strikingly absurd in other countries; I shall at present confine myself only to France. The first national peculiarity a traveller meets upon entering that kingdom, is an odd sort of a staring vivacity in every eye, not excepting even the children; the people, it seems, have got it into their heads that they have more wit than others, and so stare in order to look smart.

I know not how it happens, but there appears a sickly delicacy in the faces of their finest women. This may have introduced the use of paint, and paint produces wrinkles: so that a fine lady shall look like an hag at twenty-three. But as in some measure they never appear young, so it may be equally asserted, that they actually think themselves never old; a gentle Miss shall prepare for new conquests at sixty, shall hobble a rigadoon when she can scarce walk without a crutch, she shall affect the girl, play her fan and her eyes, and talk of sentiments, bleeding hearts, and expiring for love, when actually dying with age. Like a departing philosopher, she attempts to make her last moments the most brilliant of her life.

Their civility to strangers is what they are chiefly proud of; and to confess sincerely, their beggars are the very politest beggars I ever knew; in other places, a traveller is addressed with a piteous whine, or a sturdy solemnity, but a French beggar shall ask your charity with a very genteel bow, and thank you for it with a smile and shrug.

Another instance of this people's breeding I must not forget. An Englishman would not speak his native language in a company of foreigners, where he was sure that none understood him; a travelling Hottentot himself would be silent if acquainted only with the language of his country; but a Frenchman shall talk to you whether you understand his language or not; never troubling his head whether you have learned French, still he keeps up the conversation, fixes his eyes full in your face, and asks a thousand questions, which he answers himself for want of a more satisfactory reply.

But their civility to foreigners is not half so great as their admiration of themselves. Every thing that belongs to them and their nation is great; magnificent beyond expression; quite romantic! every garden is a paradise, every hovel a palace, and every woman an angel. They shut their eyes close, throw their mouths wide open, and cry out in a rapture: *Sacre!* What beauty! *O Ciel* what taste, *mort de ma vie*, what grandeur, was ever any people like ourselves? we are the nation of men, and all the rest no better than two-legged barbarians.

I fancy the French would make the best cooks in the world, if they had but meat; as it is, they can dress you out five different dishes from a nettle-top, seven from a dock leaf, and twice as many from a frog's haunches; these eat prettily enough when one is a little used to them, are easy of digestion, and seldom over-load the stomach with crudities. They seldom dine under seven hot dishes; it is true, indeed, with all this magnificence, they seldom spread a cloth before the guests; but in that I cannot be angry with them; since those who have got no linen upon their backs, may very well be excused for wanting it upon their tables.

Even religion itself loses its solemnity among them. Upon their roads, at about every five miles distance, you see an image of the Virgin Mary dressed up in grim head-clothes, painted cheeks, and an old red petticoat; before her a lamp is often seen burning, at which, with the saint's permission, I have frequently lighted my pipe. Instead of the Virgin, you are sometimes presented with a crucifix, at other times with a wooden Saviour, fitted out in complete garniture, with sponge, spear, nails, pincers, hammer, beeswax, and vinegar-bottle. Some of these images, I have been told, came down from heaven; if so, in heaven they have but bungling workmen.

In passing through their towns, you frequently see the men sitting at the doors knitting stockings, while the care of culti-vating the ground and pruning the vines falls to the women. This is perhaps the reason why the fair sex are granted some peculiar privileges in this country; particularly, when they can get horses, of riding without a side-saddle.

But I begin to think you may find this description pert and dull enough; perhaps it is so, yet in general it is the manner in which the French usually describe foreigners; and it is but just to *force* a part of that ridicule back upon them, which they attempt to lavish on others. Adieu.

LETTER LXXIX.—*From the same.*

THE two theatres, which serve to amuse the citizens here, are again opened for the winter. The mimetic troops, different from those of the state, begin their campaign when all the others quit the field; and at a time when the Europeans cease to destroy each other in reality, they are entertained with mock battles upon the stage.

The dancing master once more shakes his quivering feet; the carpenter prepares his paradise of paste-board; the hero resolves to cover his forehead with brass, and the heroine begins to scour up her copper tail, preparative to future operations; in short, all are in motion, from the theatrical letter-carrier in yellow clothes, to Alexander the Great that stands on a stool.

Both houses have already commenced hostilities. War, open war! and no quarter received or given! Two singing women, like heralds, have begun the contest; the whole town is divided on this solemn occasion; one has the finest pipe, the other the finest manner; one curtesies to the ground, the other salutes the audience with a smile; one comes on with modesty which asks, the other with boldness which extorts applause; one wears powder, the other has none; one has the longest waist, but the other appears most easy; all, all is important and serious; the town as yet perseveres in its neutrality, a cause of such moment demands the most mature deliberation, they continue to exhibit, and it is very possible this contest may continue to please to the end of the season.

But the generals of either army, have, as I am told, several reinforcements to lend occasional assistance. If they produce a pair of diamond buckles at one house, we have a pair of eyebrows that can match them at the other. If we outdo them in our attitude, they can overcome us by a shrug; if we can bring more children on the stage, they can bring more guards in red clothes, who strut and shoulder their swords to the astonishment of every spectator.

They tell me here, that people frequent the theatre in order to be instructed as well as amused. I smile to hear the assertion. If I ever go to one of their playhouses, what with trumpets, hallooing behind the stage, and bawling upon it, I am quite dizzy before the performance is over. If I enter the house with any sentiments in my head, I am sure to have none going away, the whole mind being filled with a dead march, a funeral procession, a cat-call, a jig, or a tempest.

There is perhaps nothing more easy than to write properly for the English theatre; I am amazed that none are apprenticed to the trade. The author, when well acquainted with the value of thunder and lightning, when versed in all the mystery of scene-shifting and trap-doors; when skilled in the proper periods to introduce a wire-walker, or a water-fall; when instructed in every actor's peculiar talent, and capable of adapting his speeches to the supposed excellence; when thus instructed, knows all that can give a modern audience pleasure. One player shines in an exclamation, another in a groan, a third in a horror, a fourth in a start, a fifth in a smile, a sixth faints, and a seventh fidgets round the stage with peculiar vivacity; that piece therefore will succeed best where each has a proper opportunity of shining; the actor's business is not so much to adapt himself to the poet, as the poet's to adapt himself to the actor.

The great secret, therefore, of tragedy-writing at present, is a perfect acquaintance with theatrical *ah's* and *oh's*, a certain number of these interspersed with *gods! tortures, racks,* and *damnation,* shall distort every actor almost into convulsions, and draw tears from every spectator; a proper use of these will infallibly fill the whole house with applause. But above all, a whining scene must strike most forcibly. I would advise, from my present knowledge of the audience, the two favourite players of the town to introduce a scene of this sort in every play. Towards the middle of the last act, I would have them enter with wild looks and out-spread arms; there is no necessity for speaking, they are only to groan at each other, they must vary the tones of exclamation and despair through the whole theatrical gamut, wring their figures into every shape of distress, and when their calamities have drawn a proper quantity of tears from the sympathetic spectators, they may go off in dumb solemnity at different doors, clasping their hands, or slapping their pocket-holes; this, which may be called a tragic panto-mime, will answer every purpose of moving the passions, as well as words could have done, and it must save those expenses which go to reward an author.

All modern plays that would keep the audience alive, must be conceived in this manner, and indeed, many a modern play is made up on no other plan. This is the merit that lifts up the heart, like opium, into a rapture of insensibility, and can dismiss the mind from all the fatigue of thinking: this is the eloquence that shines in many a long forgotten scene, which has been reckoned excessive fine upon acting; this the lightning that flashes no less in the hyperbolical tyrant, *who breakfasts on the wind*, than in the little Norval, *as harmless as the babe unborn*. Adieu.

LETTER LXXX.—*From the same.*

I HAVE always regarded the spirit of mercy, which appears in the Chinese laws, with admiration. An order for the execution of a criminal is carried from court by slow journies of six miles a day, but a pardon is sent down with the most rapid despatch. If five sons of the same father be guilty of the same offence, one of them is forgiven, in order to continue the family and comfort his aged parents in their decline.

Similar to this, there is a spirit of mercy breathes through the laws of England, which some erroneously endeavour to suppress; the laws however seem unwilling to punish the offender, or to furnish the officers of justice with every means of acting with severity. Those who arrest debtors are denied the use of arms, the nightly watch is permitted to repress the disorders of the drunken citizens only with clubs; justice in such a case seems to hide her terrors, and permits some offenders to escape rather than load any with a punishment disproportioned to the crime.

Thus it is the glory of an Englishman, that he is not only governed by laws, but that these are also tempered by mercy; a country restrained by severe laws, and those too executed with severity (as in Japan) is under the most terrible species of tyranny; a royal tyrant is generally dreadful to the great, but numerous penal laws grind every rank of people, and chiefly those least able to resist oppression, the poor.

It is very possible thus for a people to become slaves to laws of their own enacting, as the Athenians were to those of Draco. 'It might first happen (says the historian) that men with peculiar talents for villainy attempted to evade the ordinances already established; their practices therefore soon brought on a new law levelled against them; but the same degree of cunning which had taught the knave to evade the former statutes, taught him to evade the latter also; he flew to new shifts, while justice pursued with new ordinances; still however he kept his proper distance, and whenever one crime was judged penal by the state, he left committing it in order to practise some unforbidden species of villainy. Thus the criminal against whom the threatenings were denounced always escaped free; while the simple rogue alone felt the rigour of justice. In the mean time penal laws become numerous, almost every person in the state unknowingly at different times offended, and was every moment subject to a malicious prosecution.' In fact, penal laws, instead of preventing crimes, are generally enacted after the commission; instead of repressing the growth of ingenious villainy, only multiply deceit, by putting it upon new shifts and expedients of practising with impunity.

Such laws, therefore, resemble the guards which are sometimes imposed upon tributary princes, apparently indeed to secure them from danger, but in reality, to confirm their captivity.

Penal laws, it must be allowed, secure property in a state, but they also diminish personal security in the same proportion: There is no positive law how equitable soever, that may not be sometimes capable of injustice. When a law enacted to make theft punishable with death, happens to be equitably executed, it can at best only guard our possessions; but when by favour or ignorance justice pronounces a wrong verdict, it then attacks our lives, since in such a case the whole community suffers with the innocent victim; if therefore in order to secure the effects of one man, I should make a law which may take away the life of another, in such a case to attain a smaller good, I am guilty of a greater evil; to secure society in the possession of a bauble, I render a real and valuable possession precarious. And indeed the experience of every age may serve to vindicate the assertion: No law could be more just then that called *lesæ Majestatis*, when Rome was governed by Emperors. It was but reasonable, that every conspiracy against the administration should be detected and punished; yet what terrible slaughters succeeded in consequence of its enacting; proscription, stranglings, poisonings, in almost every family of distinction, yet all done in a legal way; every criminal had his trial, and lost his life by a majority of witnesses.

And such will ever be the case, where punishments are numerous, and where a weak, vicious, but above all, where a mercenary magistrate is concerned in their execution; such a man desires to see penal laws increased, since he too frequently has it in his power to turn them into instruments of extortion; in such hands the more laws, the wider means, not of satisfying justice, but of satiating avarice.

A mercenary magistrate who is rewarded in proportion, not to his integrity, but to the number he convicts, must be a person of the most unblemished character, or he will lean on the side of cruelty; and when once the work of injustice is begun, it is impossible to tell how far it will proceed; it is said of the Hyena, that naturally it is no way ravenous, but when once it has tasted human flesh, it becomes the most voracious animal of the forest, and continues to persecute mankind ever after: A corrupt magistrate may be considered as a human Hyena, he begins perhaps by a private snap, he goes on to a morsel among friends, he proceeds to a meal in public, from a meal he advances to a surfeit, and at last sucks blood like a vampire.

Not in such hands should the administration of justice be entrusted, but to those who know how to reward as well as to punish; it was a fine saying of Nangfu the emperor, who being told that his enemies had raised an insurrection in one of the distant provinces; Come then, my friends, said he, follow me, and I promise you that we shall quickly destroy them; he marched forward, and the rebels submitted upon his approach. All now thought that he would take the most signal revenge, but were surprised to see the captives treated with mildness and humanity. How! cries his first minister, is this the manner in which you fulfil your promise? your royal word was given that your enemies should be destroyed, and behold you have pardoned all, and even caressed some! I promised, replied the emperor, with a generous air, to *destroy* my enemies, I have fulfilled my word, for see they are enemies no longer; I have made *friends* of them.

This, could it always succeed, were the true method of destroying the enemies of a state; well it were if rewards and mercy alone could regulate the commonwealth; but since punishments are sometimes necessary, let them at least be rendered terrible, by being executed but seldom, and let justice lift her sword rather to terrify than revenge. Adieu.

LETTER LXXXI.—*From the same.*

I HAVE as yet given you but a short and imperfect description of the Ladies of England. Woman, my friend, is a subject not easily understood, even in China; what therefore can be expected from my knowledge of the sex in a country where they are universally allowed to be riddles, and I but a stranger?

To confess a truth, I was afraid to begin the description, lest the sex should undergo some new revolution before it was finished; and my picture should thus become old before it could

well be said to have ever been new.   To-day they are lifted upon
stilts, to-morrow they lower their heels and raise their heads;
their clothes at one time are bloated out with whalebone; at
present they have laid their hoops aside and are become as
slim as mermaids.   All, all is in a state of continual fluctuation,
from the Mandarine's wife, who rattles through the streets in
her chariot, to the humble sempstress, who clatters over the
pavement in iron-shod pattens.

What chiefly distinguishes the sex at present is the train.
As a lady's quality or fashion was once determined here by the
circumference of her hoop, both are now measured by the length
of her tail.   Women of moderate fortunes are contented with
tails moderately long; but ladies of true taste and distinction
set no bounds to their ambition in this particular.   I am told
the lady Mayoress, on days of ceremony, carries one longer
than a bell-wether of Bantam, whose tail you know is trundled
along in a wheel-barrow.

Sun of China, what contradictions do we find in this strange
world! not only the people of different countries think in opposition to each other, but the inhabitants of a single island are
often found inconsistent with themselves; would you believe
it? this very people, my Fum, who are so fond of seeing their
women with long tails, at the same time dock their horses to
the very rump!!!

But you may easily guess that I am no way displeased with
a fashion which tends to increase a demand for the commodities
of the East, and is so very beneficial to the country in which I
was born.   Nothing can be better calculated to increase the
price of silk than the present manner of dressing.   A lady's
train is not bought but at some expense, and after it has swept
the public walks for a very few evenings, is fit to be worn no
longer: more silk must be bought in order to repair the breach,
and some ladies of peculiar economy are thus found to patch
up their tails eight or ten times in a season.   This unnecessary
consumption may introduce poverty here, but then we shall be
the richer for it in China.

The man in black, who is a professed enemy to this manner
of ornamenting the tail, assures me, there are numberless
inconveniences attending it, and that a lady dressed up to the
fashion is as much a cripple as any in Nankin.   But his chief
indignation is levelled at those who dress in this manner, without
a proper fortune to support it.   He assures me, that he has
known some, who would have a tail, though they wanted a

petticoat, and others, who, without any other pretensions, fancied they became ladies merely from the addition of three superfluous yards of ragged silk; I know a thrifty good woman, continues he, who thinking herself obliged to carry a train like her betters, never walks from home without the uneasy apprehensions of wearing it out too soon; every excursion she makes gives her new anxiety, and her train is every bit as importunate, and wounds her peace as much, as the bladder we sometimes see tied to the tail of a cat.

Nay, he ventures to affirm, that a train may often bring a lady into the most critical circumstances; for should a rude fellow, says he, offer to come up to ravish a kiss, and the lady attempt to avoid it, in retiring she must necessarily tread upon her train, and thus fall fairly upon her back, by which means every one knows,—her clothes may be spoiled.

The ladies here make no scruple to laugh at the smallness of a Chinese slipper, but I fancy our wives at China would have a more real cause of laughter, could they but see the immoderate length of an European train. Head of Confucius! to view a human being crippling herself with a great unwieldy tail for our diversion; backward she cannot go, forward she must move but slowly, and if ever she attempts to turn round, it must be in a circle not smaller than that described by the wheeling crocodile, when it would face an assailant. And yet to think that all this confers importance and majesty! to think that a lady acquires additional respect from fifteen yards of trailing taffety! I can't contain; ha, ha, ha! this is certainly a remnant of European barbarity; the female Tartar dressed in sheepskins is in far more convenient drapery. Their own writers have sometimes inveighed against the absurdity of this fashion, but perhaps it has never been ridiculed so well as upon the Italian theatre, where Pasquariello being engaged to attend on the countess of Fernambroco, having one of his hands employed in carrying her muff, and the other her lap dog, he bears her train majestically along by sticking it in the waistband of his breeches. Adieu.

LETTER LXXXII.—*From the same.*

A DISPUTE has for some time divided the philosophers of Europe; it is debated, whether arts and sciences are more serviceable or prejudicial to mankind. They, who maintain the cause of literature, endeavour to prove their usefulness from the impossibility of a large number of men subsisting in a small tract of country without them; from the pleasure which attends the acquisition; and from the influence of knowledge in promoting practical morality.

They who maintain the opposite opinion, display the happiness and innocence of those uncultivated nations who live without learning; urge the numerous vices which are to be found only in polished society, enlarge upon the oppression, the cruelty and the blood which must necessarily be shed, in order to cement civil society, and insist upon the happy equality of conditions in a barbarous state, preferable to the unnatural subordination of a more refined constitution.

This dispute, which has already given so much employment to speculative indolence, has been managed with much ardour, and (not to suppress our sentiments) with but little sagacity. They who insist that the sciences are useful in *refined* society are certainly right, and they who maintain that *barbarous* nations are more happy without them, are right also; but when one side for this reason attempts to prove them as universally useful to the solitary barbarian, as to the native of a crowded common-wealth; or when the other endeavours to banish them as prejudicial to all society, even from populous states as well as from the inhabitants of the wilderness, they are both wrong; since that knowledge which makes the happiness of a refined European, would be a torment to the precarious tenant of an Asiatic wild.

Let me, to prove this, transport the imagination for a moment to the midst of a forest in Siberia. There we behold the inhabitant, poor indeed, but equally fond of happiness with the most refined philosopher of China. The earth lies uncultivated and uninhabited for miles around him; his little family and he the sole and undisputed possessors. In such circumstances Nature and Reason will induce him to prefer a hunter's life to that of cultivating the earth. He will certainly adhere to that manner of living which is carried on at the smallest expense of labour, and that food which is most agreeable to the appetite; he will prefer indolent though precarious luxury to a laborious though permanent competence, and a knowledge of his own happiness will determine him to persevere in native barbarity.

In like manner his happiness will incline him to bind himself by no law: Laws are made in order to secure present property, but he is possessed of no property which he is afraid to lose, and desires no more than will be sufficient to sustain him; to enter into compacts with others, would be undergoing a voluntary obligation without the expectance of any reward. He and his countrymen are tenants, not rivals, in the same inexhaustible forest; the encreased possessions of one by no means diminishes the expectations arising from equal assiduity in another; there are no need of laws therefore to repress ambition, where there can be no mischief attending its most boundless gratifications.

Our solitary Siberian will, in like manner, find the sciences not only entirely useless in directing his practice, but disgusting even in speculation. In every contemplation our curiosity must be first excited by the *appearances* of things, before our reason undergoes the fatigue of investigating the *causes*. Some of those appearances are produced by experiment, others by minute enquiry; some arise from a knowledge of foreign climates, and others from an intimate study of our own. But there are few objects in comparison which present themselves to the inhabitant of a barbarous country; the game he hunts, or the transient cottage he builds, make up the chief objects of his concern; his curiosity therefore must be proportionably less; and if that is diminished, the reasoning faculty will be diminished in proportion.

Besides, sensual enjoyment adds wings to curiosity. We consider few objects with ardent attention, but those which have some connection with our wishes, our pleasures, or our necessities. A desire of enjoyment first interests our passions in the pursuit, points out the object of investigation, and Reason then comments where sense has led the way. An encrease in the number of our enjoyments therefore necessarily produces an encrease of scientific research; but in countries where almost every enjoyment is wanting, Reason there seems destitute of its great inspirer, and speculation is the business of fools, when it becomes its own reward.

The barbarous Siberian is too wise, therefore, to exhaust his time in quest of knowledge, which neither curiosity prompts, nor pleasure impels him to pursue. When told of the exact admeasurement of a degree upon the equator at Quito, he feels no pleasure in the account; when informed that such a discovery tends to promote navigation and commerce, he finds himself no way interested in either. A discovery which some have pursued at the hazard of their lives, affects him with neither astonishment nor pleasure. He is satisfied with thoroughly understanding the few objects which contribute to his own felicity, he knows the properest places where to lay the snare for the sable, and discerns the value of furs with more than European sagacity. More extended knowledge would only serve to render him unhappy; it might lend a ray to shew him the misery of his situation, but could not guide him in his efforts to avoid it. Ignorance is the happiness of the poor.

The misery of a being endowed with sentiments above its capacity of fruition, is most admirably described in one of the fables of Locman, the Indian moralist. 'An elephant that had been peculiarly serviceable in fighting the battles of Wistnow, was ordered by the god to wish for whatever he thought proper, and the desire should be attended with immediate gratification. The elephant thanked his benefactor on bended knees, and desired to be endowed with the reason and the faculties of a man. Wistnow was sorry to hear the foolish request, and endeavoured to dissuade him from his misplaced ambition; but finding it to no purpose, gave him at last such a portion of wisdom as could correct even the Zendavesta of Zoroaster. The reasoning elephant went away rejoicing in his new acquisition, and though his body still retained its ancient form, he found his appetites and passions entirely altered. He first considered that it would not only be more comfortable, but also more becoming to wear clothes; but unhappily he had no method of making them himself, nor had he the use of speech to demand them from others, and this was the first time he felt real anxiety. He soon perceived how much more elegantly men were fed than he, therefore he began to loath his usual food and longed for those delicacies which adorn the tables of Princes; but here again he found it impossible to be satisfied; for though he could easily obtain flesh, yet he found it impossible to dress it in any degree of perfection. In short, every pleasure that contributed to the felicity of mankind, served only to render him more miserable, as he found himself utterly deprived of the power of enjoyment. In this manner he led a repining, discontented life, detesting himself and displeased with his ill-judged ambition, till at last his benefactor Wistnow, taking compassion on his forlorn situation, restored him to the ignorance and the happiness which he was originally formed to enjoy.'

No, my friend, to attempt to introduce the sciences into a nation of wandering barbarians, is only to render them more miserable than even Nature designed they should be. A life of simplicity is best fitted to a state of solitude.

The great law-giver of Russia attempted to improve the desolate inhabitants of Siberia, by sending among them some of the politest men of Europe. The consequence has shewn, that the country was as yet unfit to receive them; they languished for a time with a sort of exotic malady, every day degenerated from themselves, and, at last, instead of rendering the country more polite, they conformed to the soil, and put on barbarity.

No, my friend, in order to make the sciences useful in any country, it must first become populous; the inhabitants must go through the different stages of hunter, shepherd, and husbandman: then when property becomes valuable, and consequently gives cause for injustice; then when laws are appointed to repress injury, and secure possession, when men, by the sanction of those laws, become possessed of superfluity, when luxury is thus introduced and demands its continual supply, then it is that the sciences become necessary and useful; the state then cannot subsist without them; they must then be introduced at once to teach men to draw the greatest possible quantity of pleasure from circumscribed possession; and to restrain them within the bounds of moderate enjoyment.

The sciences are not the cause of luxury, but its consequence, and this destroyer thus brings with it an antidote which resists the virulence of its own poison. By asserting that luxury introduces the sciences, we assert a truth; but if with those, who reject the utility of learning, we assert that the sciences also introduce luxury, we shall be at once false, absurd, and ridiculous. Adieu.

LETTER LXXXIII.—*From Lien Chi Altangi to Hingpo, by the way of Moscow.*

You are now arrived at an age, my son, when pleasure dissuades from application, but rob not by present gratification all the succeeding period of life of its happiness. Sacrifice a little pleasure at first to the expectance of greater. The study of a very few years will make the rest of life completely easy.

But instead of continuing the subject myself, take the following instructions borrowed from a modern philosopher of China.[1] 'He who has begun his fortune by study will certainly confirm it by perseverance. The love of books damps the passion for pleasure, and when this passion is once extinguished, life

---

[1] A translation of this passage may also be seen in Du Halde, vol. ii, fol. p. 47 and 58. This extract will at least serve to shew that fondness for humour which appears in the writings of the Chinese.

is then cheaply supported; thus a man being possessed of more than he wants, can never be subject to great disappointments, and avoids all those meannesses which indigence sometimes unavoidably produces.

'There is unspeakable pleasure attending the life of a voluntary student. The first time I read an excellent book, it is to me just as if I had gained a new friend. When I read over a book I have perused before, it resembles the meeting with an old one. We ought to lay hold of every incident in life for improvement, the trifling as well as the important. It is not one diamond alone which gives lustre to another, a common coarse stone is also employed for that purpose. Thus I ought to draw advantage from the insults and contempt I meet with from a worthless fellow. His brutality ought to induce me to self-examination, and correct every blemish that may have given rise to his calumny.

'Yet with all the pleasures and profits which are generally produced by learning, parents often find it difficult to induce their children to study. They often seem dragged to what wears the appearance of application. Thus being dilatory in the beginning, all future hopes of eminence are entirely cut off. If they find themselves obliged to write two lines more polite than ordinary, their pencil then seems as heavy as a millstone, and they spend ten years in turning two or three periods with propriety.

'These persons are most at a loss when a banquet is almost over; the plate and the dice go round, that the number of little verses which each is obliged to repeat may be determined by chance. The booby, when it comes to his turn, appears quite stupid and insensible. The company divert themselves with his confusion; and sneers, winks, and whispers are circulated at his expense. As for him, he opens a pair of large heavy eyes, stares at all about him, and even offers to join in the laugh, without ever considering himself as the burthen of all their good humour.

'But it is of no importance to read much, except you be regular in your reading. If it be interrupted for any considerable time, it can never be attended with proper improvement. There are some who study for one day with intense application, and repose themselves for ten days after. But wisdom is a coquette, and must be courted with unabating assiduity.

'It was a saying of the ancients, that a man never opens a book, without reaping some advantage by it. I say with them, that every book can serve to make us more expert, except romances, and these are no better than instruments of debauchery. They are dangerous fictions, where love is the ruling passion.

'The most indecent strokes there pass for turns of wit; intrigue and criminal liberties for gallantry and politeness. Assignations, and even villainy, are put in such strong lights, as may inspire even grown men with the strongest passion; how much more therefore ought the youth of either sex to dread them, whose reason is so weak, and whose hearts are so susceptible of passion!

'To slip in by a back-door, or leap a wall, are accomplishments that when handsomely set off enchant a young heart. It is true the plot is commonly wound up by a marriage, concluded with the consent of parents, and adjusted by every ceremony prescribed by law. But as in the body of the work there are many passages that offend good morals, overthrow laudable customs, violate the laws, and destroy the duties most essential to society, virtue is thereby exposed to the most dangerous attacks.

'But, say some, the authors of these romances have nothing in view, but to represent vice punished, and virtue rewarded. Granted. But will the greater number of readers take notice of these punishments and rewards? Are not their minds carried to something else? Can it be imagined that the art with which the author inspires the love of virtue, can overcome that crowd of thoughts which sway them to licentiousness? To be able to inculcate virtue by so leaky a vehicle, the author must be a philosopher of the first rank. But in our age we can find but few first-rate philosophers.

'Avoid such performances where vice assumes the face of virtue; seek wisdom and knowledge without ever thinking you have found them. A man is wise while he continues in the pursuit of wisdom; but when he once fancies that he has found the object of his enquiry, he then becomes a fool. Learn to pursue virtue from the man that is blind, who never makes a step without first examining the ground with his staff.

'The world is like a vast sea, mankind like a vessel sailing on its tempestuous bosom. Our prudence is its sails, the sciences serve us for oars, good or bad fortune are the favourable or contrary winds, and judgment is the rudder; without this last the vessel is tossed by every billow, and will find shipwreck in every breeze. In a word, obscurity and indigence are the parents of vigilance and economy; vigilance and economy, of riches and honour; riches and honour, of pride and luxury; pride and luxury, of impurity and idleness; and impurity and idleness again produce indigence and obscurity. Such are the revolutions of life.' Adieu.

LETTER LXXXIV.—*From Lien Chi Altangi, to Fum Hoam, first President of the Ceremonial Academy, at Pekin, in China.*

I FANCY the character of a poet is in every country the same, fond of enjoying the present, careless of the future, his conversation that of a man of sense, his actions those of a fool! of fortitude able to stand unmoved at the bursting of an earthquake, yet of sensibility to be affected by the breaking of a tea-cup; such is his character, which considered in every light, is the very opposite of that which leads to riches.

The poets of the west are as remarkable for their indigence as their genius, and yet among the numerous hospitals designed to relieve the poor, I have heard of but one erected for the benefit of decayed authors. This was founded by Pope Urban VIII, and called the retreat of the incurables, intimating, that it was equally impossible to reclaim the patients, who sued for reception, from poverty, or from poetry. To be sincere, were I to send you an account of the lives of the western poets, either ancient or modern, I fancy you would think me employed in collecting materials for an history of human wretchedness.

Homer is the first poet and beggar of note among the ancients; he was blind, and sung his ballads about the streets; but it is observed, that his mouth was more frequently filled with verses than with bread. Plautus the comic poet was better off; he had two trades, he was a poet for his diversion, and helped to turn a mill in order to gain a livelihood. Terence was a slave, and Boethius died in a jail.

Among the Italians, Paulo Burghese, almost as good a poet as Tasso, knew fourteen different trades, and yet died because he could get employment in none. Tasso himself, who had the most amiable character of all poets, has often been obliged to borrow a crown from some friend, in order to pay for a month's subsistence; he has left us a pretty sonnet, addressed to his cat, in which he begs the light of her eyes to write by, being too poor to afford himself a candle. But Bentivoglio, poor Bentivoglio! chiefly demands our pity. His comedies will last with the Italian language; he dissipated a noble fortune in acts of charity and benevolence; but falling into misery in his old age, was refused to be admitted into an hospital which he himself had erected.

In Spain, it is said, the great Cervantes died of hunger; and it is certain that the famous Camoens ended his days in an hospital.

If we turn to France, we shall there find even stronger instances of the ingratitude of the public. Vaugelas, one of the politest writers, and one of the honestest men of his time, was surnamed the Owl, from his being obliged to keep within all day, and venture out only by night, through fear of his creditors. His last will is very remarkable; after having bequeathed all his worldly substance to the discharging his debts, he goes on thus: But as there still may remain some creditors unpaid, even after all that I have shall be disposed of, in such a case, it is my last will, that my body should be sold to the surgeons to the best advantage, and that the purchase should go to the discharging those debts which I owe to society; so that if I could not, while living, at least when dead, I may be useful.

Cassander was one of the greatest geniuses of his time, yet all his merit could not procure him a bare subsistence. Being be degrees driven into an hatred of all mankind from the little pity he found amongst them, he even ventured at last ungratefully to impute his calamities to Providence. In his last agonies, when the priest entreated him to rely on the justice of Heaven, and ask mercy from him that made him. *If God*, replies he, *has shewn me no justice here, what reason have I to expect any from him hereafter?* But being answered, that a suspension of justice was no argument that should induce us to doubt of its reality; let me entreat you, continued his confessor, by all that is dear, to be reconciled to God, your father, your maker, and friend. *No*, replied the exasperated wretch, *you know the manner in which He left me to live;* (and pointing to the straw on which he was stretched) *and you see the manner in which He leaves me to die!*

But the sufferings of the poet in other countries are nothing when compared to his distresses here; the names of Spenser and Otway, Butler and Dryden, are every day mentioned as a national reproach; some of them lived in a state of precarious indigence, and others literally died of hunger.

At present the few poets of England no longer depend on the Great for subsistence, they have now no other patrons but the public, and the public, collectively considered, is a good and generous master. It is, indeed, too frequently mistaken as to the merits of every candidate for favour; but to make amends, it is never mistaken long. A performance indeed may be forced for a time into reputation, but destitute of real merit it soon sinks; time, the touchstone of what is truly valuable, will soon discover the fraud, and an author should never arrogate to himself any share of success till his works have been read at least ten years with satisfaction.

A man of letters at present, whose works are valuable, is perfectly sensible of their value. Every polite member of the community, by buying what he writes, contributes to reward him. The ridicule therefore of living in a garret, might have been wit in the last age, but continues such no longer, because no longer true. A writer of real merit now may easily be rich if his heart be set only on fortune: and for those who have no merit, it is but fit that such should remain in merited obscurity. He may now refuse an invitation to dinner, without fearing to incur his patron's displeasure, or to starve by remaining at home. He may now venture to appear in company with just such clothes as other men generally wear, and talk even to princes, with all the conscious superiority of wisdom. Though he cannot boast of fortune here, yet he can bravely assert the dignity of independence. Adieu.

LETTER LXXXV.—*From the same.*

I HAVE interested myself so long in all the concerns of this people, that I am almost become an Englishman; I now begin to read with pleasure of their taking towns or gaining battles, and secretly wish disappointment to all the enemies of Britain. Yet still my regard to mankind fills me with concern for their contentions. I could wish to see the disturbances of Europe once more amicably adjusted: I am an enemy to nothing in this good world but war; I hate fighting between rival states: I hate it between man and man; I hate fighting even between women!

I already informed you, that while Europe was at variance, we were also threatened from the stage with an irreconcilable opposition, and that our singing women were resolved to sing at each other to the end of the season. O my friend, those fears were just. They are not only determined to sing at each other to the end of the season, but what is worse, to sing the same song, and what is still more insupportable, to make us pay for hearing.

If they be for war, for my part I should advise them to have

a public congress, and there fairly squall at each other. What
signifies sounding the trumpet of defiance at a distance, and
calling in the town to fight their battles? I would have them
come boldly into one of the most open and frequented streets,
face to face, and there try their skill in quavering.

However this may be, resolved I am that they shall not touch
one single piece of silver more of mine. Though I have ears for
music, thanks to heaven, they are not altogether asses' ears.
What! Polly and the Pick-pocket to-night, Polly and the
Pick-pocket to-morrow night, and Polly and the Pick-pocket
again; I want patience. I will hear no more. My soul is out
of tune, all jarring discord, and confusion. Rest, rest, ye dear
three clinking shillings in my pocket's bottom; the music you
make is more harmonious to my spirit, than cat-gut, rosin, or
all the nightingales that ever chirruped in petticoats.

But what raises my indignation to the greatest degree, is that
this piping does not only pester me on the stage, but is my
punishment in private conversation. What is it to me, whether
the *fine pipe* of one, or the *great manner* of the other be preferable? what care I, if one has a better top, or the other a nobler
bottom? how am I concerned, if one sings from the stomach, or
the other sings with a snap? yet paltry as these matters are,
they make a subject of debate wherever I go, and this musical
dispute, especially among the fair sex, almost always ends in a
very unmusical altercation.

Sure the spirit of contention is mixed into the very constitution of the people; divisions among the inhabitants of other
countries arise only from their higher concerns, but subjects
the most contemptible are made an affair of party here, the
spirit is carried even into their amusements. The very ladies,
whose duty should seem to allay the impetuosity of the opposite
sex, become themselves party champions, engage in the thickest
of the fight, scold at each other, and shew their courage, even at
the expense of their lovers and their beauty.

There are even a numerous set of poets who help to keep up
the contention, and write for the stage. Mistake me not, I do
not mean pieces to be acted upon it, but panegyrical verses on
the performers, for that is the most universal method of writing
for the stage at present. It is the business of the stage poet
therefore to watch the appearance of every new player at his
own house, and so come out next day with a flaunting copy of
newspaper verses. In these Nature and the actor may be set
to run races, the player always coming off victorious; or Nature

may mistake him for herself; or old Shakespeare may put on his winding-sheet and pay him a visit; or the tuneful Nine may strike up their harps in his praise; or should it happen to be an actress, Venus, the beauteous queen of Love, and the naked Graces, are ever in waiting: the lady must be herself a goddess bred and born; she must—but you shall have a specimen of one of these poems, which may convey a more precise idea.

ON SEEING MRS. *** PERFORM IN THE CHARACTER OF ****

> To you, bright fair, the Nine address their lays,
> And tune my feeble voice to sing thy praise.
> The heart-felt power of every charm divine,
> Who can withstand their all-commanding shine?
> See how she moves along with every grace,
> While soul-brought tears steal down each shining face,
> She speaks, 'tis rapture all and nameless bliss,
> Ye gods, what transport e'er compar'd to this.
> As when in Paphian groves the queen of Love,
> With fond complaint address'd the listening Jove,
> 'Twas joy, and endless blisses all around,
> And rocks forgot their hardness at the sound.
> Then first, at last even Jove was taken in,
> And felt her charms, without disguise, within.

And yet, think not, my friend, that I have any particular animosity against the champions who are at the head of the present commotion; on the contrary, I could find pleasure in their music, if served up at proper intervals; if I heard it only on proper occasions, and not about it wherever I go. In fact, I could patronize them both; and as an instance of my condescension in this particular, they may come and give me a song at my lodging, on any evening when I 'm at leisure, provided they keep a becoming distance, and stand, while they continue to entertain me, with decent humility at the door.

You perceive I have not read the seventeen books of Chinese ceremonies to no purpose. I know the proper share of respect due to every rank in society. Stage-players, fire-eaters, singing women, dancing-dogs, wild beasts, and wire-walkers, as their efforts are exerted for our amusement, ought not *entirely* to be despised. The laws of every country should allow them to play their tricks at least with impunity. They should not be branded with the ignominious appellation of vagabonds; at least they deserve a rank in society equal to the mystery of barbers, or undertakers, and could my influence extend so far, they should be allowed to earn even forty or fifty pounds a year, if eminent in their profession.

I am sensible, however, that you will censure me of profusion in this respect, bred up as you are in the narrow prejudices of eastern frugality. You will undoubtedly assert, that such a stipend is too great for so useless an employment. Yet how will your surprise increase, when told, that though the law holds them as vagabonds, many of them earn more than a thousand a year. You are amazed. There is cause for amazement. A vagabond with a thousand a year is indeed a curiosity in Nature; a wonder far surpassing the flying fish, petrified crab, or travelling lobster. However, from my great love to the profession, I would willingly have them divested of part of their contempt, and part of their finery; the law should kindly take them under the wing of protection, fix them into a corporation, like that of the barbers, and abridge their ignominy and their pensions. As to their abilities in other respects, I would leave that entirely to the public, who are certainly in this case the properest judges—whether they despise them or no.

Yes, my *Fum,* I would abridge their pensions. A theatrical warrior who conducts the battles of the stage, should be cooped up with the same caution as a Bantam cock that is kept for fighting. When one of those animals is taken from its native dunghill, we retrench it both in the quantity of its food, and the number of its seraglio: players should in the same manner be fed, not fattened; they should be permitted to get their bread, but not eat the people's bread into the bargain; and instead of being permitted to keep four mistresses, in conscience they should be contented only with two.

Were stage-players thus brought into bounds, perhaps we should find their admirers less sanguine, and consequently less ridiculous in patronizing them. We should no longer be struck with the absurdity of seeing the same people, whose valour makes such a figure abroad, apostrophizing in the praise of a bouncing blockhead, and wrangling in the defence of a copper-tail'd actress at home.

I shall conclude my letter with the sensible admonition of *Mé* the philosopher. 'You love harmony, says he, and are charmed with music. I do not blame you for hearing a fine voice, when you are in your closet with a lovely parterre under your eye, or in the night time, while perhaps the moon diffuses her silver rays. But is a man to carry this passion so far as to let a company of comedians, musicians, and singers, grow rich upon his exhausted fortune? If so, he resembles one of those dead bodies, whose brains the embalmers have picked out through its ears.' Adieu.

LETTER LXXXVI.—*From the same.*

OF all the places of amusement where gentlemen and ladies are entertained, I have not been yet to visit Newmarket. This, I am told, is a large field, where, upon certain occasions, three or four horses are brought together, then set a running, and that horse which runs swiftest wins the wager.

This is reckoned a very polite and fashionable amusement here, much more followed by the nobility, than partridge fighting at Java, or paper kites at Madagascar; several of the great here, I am told, understand as much of farriery as their grooms; and a horse, with any share of merit, can never want a patron among the nobility.

We have a description of this entertainment almost every day in some of the gazettes, as for instance: 'On such a day the Give and Take Plate was run for between his Grace's Crab, his Lordship's Periwinkle, and 'Squire Smackem's Slamerkin. All rode their own horses. There was the greatest concourse of nobility that has been known here for several seasons. The odds were in favour of Crab in the beginning, but Slamerkin, after the first heat, seemed to have the match hollow; however, it was soon seen, that Periwinkle improved in wind, which at last, turned out accordingly; Crab was run to a standstill, Slamerkin was knocked up, and Periwinkle was brought in with universal applause.' Thus you see Periwinkle received universal applause, and no doubt his Lordship came in for some share of that praise which was so liberally bestowed upon Periwinkle. Sun of China! how glorious must the Senator appear in his cap and leather breeches, his whip crossed in his mouth, and thus coming to the goal amongst the shouts of grooms, jockeys, pimps, stable-bred Dukes, and degraded Generals!

From the description of this princely amusement, now transcribed, and from the great veneration I have for the characters of its principal promoters, I make no doubt but I shall look upon an horse-race with becoming reverence, predisposed as I am by a similar amusement, of which I have lately been a spectator; for just now I happened to have an opportunity of being present at a Cart-race.

Whether this contention between three carts of different parishes was promoted by a subscription among the nobility, or whether the grand-jury in council assembled, had gloriously combined to encourage plaustral merit, I cannot take upon me to determine; but certain it is, the whole was conducted with the utmost regularity and decorum, and the company, which made a brilliant appearance, were universally of opinion, that the sport was high, the running fine, and the riders influenced by no bribe.

It was run on the road from London to a village called Brentford, between a turnip cart, a dust cart, and a dung cart; each of the owners condescending to mount and be his own driver. The odds at starting were Dust against Dung, five to four; but after half a mile going, the knowing ones found themselves all on the wrong side, and it was Turnip against the field, brass to silver.

Soon however the contest became more doubtful; Turnip indeed kept the way, but it was perceived that Dung had better bottom. The road re-echoed with the shouts of the spectators; Dung against Turnip! Turnip against Dung! was now the universal cry; neck and neck; one rode lighter, but the other had more judgment. I could not but particularly observe the ardour with which the fair sex espoused the cause of the different riders on this occasion; one was charmed with the unwashed beauties of Dung; another was captivated with the patibulary aspect of Turnip: while in the mean time unfortunate gloomy Dust, who came whipping behind, was cheered by the encouragements of some, and pity of all.

The contention now continued for some time, without a possibility of determining to whom victory designed the prize. The winning-post appeared in view, and he who drove the turnip cart, assured himself of success; and successful he might have been, had his horse been as ambitious as he; but upon approaching a turn from the road, which led homewards, the horse fairly stood still, and refused to move a foot farther. The dung cart had scarce time to enjoy this temporary triumph, when it was pitched headlong into a ditch by the wayside, and the rider left to wallow in congenial mud. Dust in the mean time soon came up, and not being far from the post, came in amidst the shouts and acclamations of all the spectators, and greatly caressed by all the quality of Brentford. Fortune was kind only to one, who ought to have been favourable to all; each had peculiar merit, each laboured hard to earn the prize, and each richly deserved the cart he drove.

I do not know whether this description may not have anticipated that which I intended giving of Newmarket. I am told there is little else to be seen even there. There may be some minute differences in the dress of the spectators, but none at all in their understandings; the quality of Brentford are as remarkable for politeness and delicacy, as the breeders of Newmarket. The quality of Brentford drive their own carts, and the honourable fraternity of Newmarket ride their own horses. In short, the matches in one place are as rational as those in the other; and it is more than probable, that turnips, dust, and dung, are all that can be found to furnish out description in either.

Forgive me, my friend, but a person like me, bred up in a philosophic seclusion, is apt to regard perhaps with too much asperity, those occurrences which sink man below his station in Nature, and diminish the intrinsic value of humanity.

LETTER LXXXVII.—*From Fum Hoam to Lien Chi Altangi.*

You tell me the people of Europe are wise; but where lies their wisdom? You say they are valiant too; but I have some reasons to doubt of their valour. They are engaged in war among each other, yet apply to the Russians, their neighbours and ours, for assistance. Cultivating such an alliance argues at once imprudence and timidity. All subsidies paid for such an aid is strengthening the Russians, already too powerful, and weakening the employers, already exhausted by intestine commotions.

I cannot avoid beholding the Russian empire as the natural enemy of the more western parts of Europe; as an enemy already possessed of great strength, and from the nature of the government, every day threatening to become more powerful. This extensive empire, which, both in Europe and Asia, occupies almost a third of the old world, was, about two centuries ago, divided into separate kingdoms and dukedoms, and from such a division consequently feeble. Since the times, however, of John Basilides, it has increased in strength and extent; and those untrodden forests, those innumerable savage animals which formerly covered the face of the country, are now removed, and colonies of mankind planted in their room. A kingdom thus enjoying peace internally, possessed of an unbounded extent of dominion, and learning the military art at the expense of others abroad, must every day grow more powerful; and it is probable, we shall hear Russia, in future times, as formerly, called the Officina Gentium.

It was long the wish of Peter, their great monarch, to have a fort in some of the western parts of Europe; many of his schemes and treaties were directed to this end, but happily for Europe he failed in them all. A fort in the power of this people would be like the possession of a floodgate; and whenever ambition, interest, or necessity prompted, they might then be able to deluge the whole world with a barbarous inundation.

Believe me, my friend, I cannot sufficiently contemn the politicians of Europe, who thus make this powerful people arbitrators in their quarrel. The Russians are now at that period between refinement and barbarity, which seems most adapted to military achievement; and if once they happen to get footing in the western parts of Europe, it is not the feeble efforts of the sons of effeminacy and dissention, that can serve to remove them. The fertile valley and soft climate, will ever be sufficient inducements to draw whole myriads from their native deserts, the trackless wild, or snowy mountain.

History, experience, reason, nature, expand the book of wisdom before the eyes of mankind, but they will not read. We have seen with terror a winged phalanx of famished locusts each singly contemptible, but from multitude become hideous, cover, like clouds, the face of day, and threaten the whole world with ruin. We have seen them settling on the fertile plains of India and Egypt, destroying in an instant the labours and the hopes of nations; sparing neither the fruit of the earth nor the verdure of the fields, and changing into a frightful desert, landscapes of once luxuriant beauty. We have seen myriads of ants issuing together from the southern desert, like a torrent whose source was inexhaustible, succeeding each other without end, and renewing their destroyed forces with unwearied perseverance, bringing desolation wherever they came, banishing men and animals, and, when destitute of all subsistence, in heaps infecting the wilderness which they had made! Like these have been the migrations of men. When as yet savage, and almost resembling their brute partners in the forest, subject like them only to the instincts of Nature, and directed by hunger alone in the choice of an abode, how have we seen whole armies starting wild at once from their forests and their dens: Goths, Huns, Vandals, Saracens, Turks, Tartars, myriads of men, animals in human form, without country, without name, without laws, out-powering by numbers all opposition, ravaging cities, overturning empires and, after having destroyed whole nations, and spread extensive desolation, how have we seen them sink oppressed by some new enemy, more barbarous and even more unknown than they! Adieu.

LETTER LXXXVIII.—*From Lien Chi Altangi, to Fum Hoam, first President of the Ceremonial Academy at Pekin, in China.*

As the instruction of the fair sex in this country is entirely committed to the care of foreigners, as their language-masters, music-masters, hair-frizzers, and governesses, are all from abroad, I had some intentions of opening a female academy myself, and made no doubt, as I was quite a foreigner, of meeting a favourable reception.

In this I intended to instruct the ladies in all the conjugal mysteries; wives whould be taught the art of managing husbands, and maids the skill of properly choosing them; I would teach a wife how far she might venture to be sick without giving disgust; she should be acquainted with the great benefits of the cholic in the stomach, and all the thorough-bred insolence of fashion; maids should learn the secret of nicely distinguishing every competitor; they should be able to know the difference between a pedant and a scholar, a citizen and a prig, a squire and his horse, a beau and his monkey; but chiefly they should be taught the art of managing their smiles, from the contemptuous simper to the long laborious laugh.

But I have discontinued the project; for what would signify teaching ladies the manner of governing or choosing husbands, when marriage is at present so much out of fashion, that a lady is very well off, who can get any husband at all. Celibacy now prevails in every rank of life, the streets are crowded with old bachelors, and the houses with ladies who have refused good offers, and are never likely to receive any for the future.

The only advice, therefore, I could give the fair sex as things stand at present, is to get husbands as fast as they can. There is certainly nothing in the whole creation, not even Babylon in ruins, more truly deplorable than a lady in the virgin bloom of sixty-three, or a battered unmarried beau, who squibs about from place to place, shewing his pig-tail wig and his ears. The one appears to my imagination in the form of a double night-cap, or a roll of pomatum, the other in the shape of an electuary, or a box of pills.

I would once more therefore advise the ladies to get husbands. I would desire them not to discard an old lover without very sufficient reasons, nor treat the new with ill-nature till they know him false; let not prudes allege the falseness of the sex, coquettes the pleasures of long courtship, or parents the necessary preliminaries of penny for penny. I have reasons that would silence even a casuist in this particular. In the first place, therefore, I divide the subject into fifteen heads, and then *sic argumentor*—but not to give you and myself the spleen, be contented at present with an Indian tale.

In a winding of the river Amidar, just before it falls into the Caspian sea, there lies an island unfrequented by the inhabitants of the Continent. In this seclusion, blest with all that wild uncultivated Nature could bestow, lived a princess and her two daughters. She had been wrecked upon the coast while her children as yet were infants, who of consequence, though grown up, were entirely unacquainted with man. Yet, unexperienced as the young ladies were in the opposite sex, both early discovered symptoms, the one of prudery, the other of being a coquette. The eldest was ever learning maxims of wisdom and discretion from her mamma, while the youngest employed all her hours in gazing at her own face in a neighbouring fountain.

Their usual amusement in this solitude was fishing. Their mother had taught them all the secrets of the art: she shewed them which were the most likely places to throw out the line, what baits were most proper for the various seasons, and the best manner to draw up the finny prey, when they had hooked it. In this manner they spent their time, easy and innocent, till one day, the Princess being indisposed, desired them to go and catch her a sturgeon or a shark for supper, which she fancied might sit easy on her stomach. The daughters obeyed, and clapping on a gold fish, the usual bait on those occasions, went and sat upon one of the rocks, letting the gilded hook glide down with the stream.

On the opposite shore, farther down, at the mouth of the river, lived a diver for pearls; a youth, who, by long habit in his trade, was almost grown amphibious; so that he could remain whole hours at the bottom of the water, without ever fetching breath. He happened to be at that very instant diving, when the ladies were fishing with the gilded hook. Seeing therefore the bait, which to him had the appearance of real gold, he was resolved to seize the prize, but both hands being already filled with pearl oysters, he found himself obliged to snap at it with his mouth: The consequence is easily imagined; the hook, before unperceived, was instantly fastened in his jaw, nor could he, with all his efforts or his floundering, get free.

'Sister, cries the youngest Princess, I have certainly caught a monstrous fish; I never perceived any thing struggle so at the end of my line before; come, and help me to draw it in.' They

both now therefore assisted in fishing up the Diver on shore; but
nothing could equal their surprise upon seeing him. 'Bless my
eyes, cries the prude, what have we got here; this is a very
odd fish to be sure; I never saw any thing in my life look so
queer; what eyes, what terrible claws, what a monstrous snout;
I have read of this monster somewhere before, it certainly must
be a *Tanlang* that eats women; let us throw it back into the sea
where we found it.'

The Diver in the mean time stood upon the beach, at the end
of the line, with the hook in his mouth, using every art that he
thought could best excite pity, and particularly looking extremely tender, which is usual in such circumstances. The
coquette, therefore, in some measure influenced by the innocence
of his looks, ventured to contradict her companion. 'Upon my
word, sister, says she, I see nothing in the animal so very terrible
as you are pleased to apprehend; I think it may serve well
enough for a change. Always sharks, and sturgeons, and
lobsters, and crawfish, make me quite sick. I fancy a slice of
this nicely grilladed, and dressed up with shrimp-sauce, would
be very pretty eating. I fancy mamma would like a bit with
pickles above all things in the world; and if it should not sit
easy on her stomach, it will be time enough to discontinue it
when found disagreeable, you know.' 'Horrid, cries the prude,
would the girl be poisoned? I tell you it is a *Tanlang*; I have read
of it in twenty places. It is every where described as the most
pernicious animal that ever infested the ocean. I am certain
it is the most insidious, ravenous creature in the world; and is
certain destruction if taken internally.' The youngest sister
was now therefore obliged to submit; both assisted in drawing
the hook with some violence from the Diver's jaw; and he
finding himself at liberty, bent his breast against the broad
wave and disappeared in an instant.

Just at this juncture the mother came down to the beach, to
know the cause of her daughters' delay; they told her every
circumstance, describing the monster they had caught. The
old lady was one of the most discreet women in the world; she
was called the black-eyed Princess, from two black eyes she had
received in her youth, being a little addicted to boxing in her
liquor. 'Alas, my children,' cries she, what have you done; the
fish you caught was a man-fish; one of the most tame domestic
animals in the world. We could have let him run and play
about the garden, and he would have been twenty times more
entertaining than our squirrel or monkey.' 'If that be all, says

the young coquette, we will fish for him again. If that be all, I 'll hold three tooth-picks to one pound of snuff, I catch him whenever I please.' Accordingly they threw in their line once more, but with all their gilding, and paddling, and assiduity, they could never after catch the Diver. In this state of solitude and disappointment they continued for many years, still fishing, but without success; till, at last, the genius of the place, in pity to their distresses, changed the prude into a shrimp, and the coquette into an oyster. Adieu.

LETTER LXXXIX.—*From the same.*

I AM amused, my dear Fum, with the labours of some of the learned here. One shall write you a whole folio on the dissection of a caterpillar. Another shall swell his works with a description of the plumage on the wing of a butterfly; a third shall see a little world on a peach leaf, and publish a book to describe what his readers might see more clearly in two minutes, only by being furnished with eyes and a microscope.

I have frequently compared the understandings of such men to their own glasses. Their field of vision is too contracted to take in the whole of any but minute objects; they view all Nature bit by bit; now the proboscis, now the antennæ, now the pinnæ of—a flea. Now the polypus comes to breakfast upon a worm; now it is kept up to see how long it will live without eating; now it is turned inside outward; and now it sickens and dies. Thus they proceed, laborious in trifles, constant in experiment, without one single abstraction, by which alone knowledge may be properly said to increase; till, at last, their ideas, ever employed upon minute things, contract to the size of the diminutive object, and a single mite shall fill their whole mind's capacity.

Yet believe me, my friend, ridiculous as these men are to the world, they are set up as objects of esteem for each other. They have particular places appointed for their meetings; in which one shows his cockle-shell, and is praised by all the society; another produces his powder, makes some experiments that result in nothing, and comes off with admiration and applause; a third comes out with the important discovery of some new process in the skeleton of a mole, and is set down as the accurate and sensible; while one still more fortunate than the rest, by pickling, potting, and preserving monsters, rises into unbounded reputation.

The labours of such men, instead of being calculated to amuse the public, are laid out only in diverting each other. The world becomes very little the better or the wiser, for knowing what is the peculiar food of an insect, that is itself the food of another, which in its turn is eaten by a third; but there are men who have studied themselves into an habit of investigating and admiring such minutiæ. To these such subjects are pleasing, as there are some who contentedly spend whole days in endeavouring to solve enigmas, or disentangle the puzzling sticks of children.

But of all the learned, those who pretend to investigate remote antiquity, have least to plead in their own defence, when they carry this passion to a faulty excess. They are generally found to supply by conjecture the want of record, and then by perseverance are wrought up into a confidence of the truth of opinions, which even to themselves at first appeared founded only in imagination.

The Europeans have heard much of the kingdom of China: its politeness, arts, commerce, laws, and morals, are, however, but very imperfectly known among them. They have, even now, in their Indian warehouse numberless utensils, plants, minerals, and machines, of the use of which they are entirely ignorant; nor can any among them even make a probable guess, for what they might have been designed. Yet though this people be so ignorant of the present real state of China, the philosophers I am describing have entered into long, learned, laborious disputes, about what China was two thousand years ago. China and European happiness are but little connected even at this day; but European happiness and China two thousand years ago have certainly no connection at all. However, the learned have written on and pursued the subject through all the labyrinths of antiquity; though the early dews and the tainted gale be passed away, though no footsteps remain to direct the doubtful chase, yet still they run forward, open upon the uncertain scent, and though in fact they follow nothing, are earnest in the pursuit. In this chase however they all take different ways. One, for example, confidently assures us, that China was peopled by a colony from Egypt. Sesostris, he observes, led his army as far as the Ganges; therefore, if he went so far, he might still have gone as far as China, which is but about a thousand miles from thence; therefore he did go to China; therefore China was not peopled before he went there; therefore it was peopled by him. Besides, the Egyptians have pyramids; the Chinese have in like manner their porcelain tower; the Egyptians used to light up candles upon every rejoicing, the Chinese have lanthorns upon the same occasions; the Egyptians had their great river, so have the Chinese; but what serves to put the matter past a doubt is, that the ancient Kings of China and those of Egypt were called by the same names. The emperor Ki is certainly the same with king Atoes; for, if we only change *K* into *A*, and *i* into *toes*, we shall have the name Atoes; and with equal ease *Menes* may be proved to be the same with the emperor *Yu*; therefore the Chinese are a colony from Egypt.

But another of the learned is entirely different from the last; and he will have the Chinese to be a colony planted by Noah just after the deluge. First, from the vast similitude there is between the name of Fohi, the founder of the Chinese monarchy, and that of Noah, the preserver of the human race: Noah, Fohi, very like each other truly; they have each but four letters, and only two of the four happen to differ. But to strengthen the argument, Fohi, as the Chinese chronicle asserts, had no father. Noah, it is true, had a father, as the European Bible tells us; but then, as this father was probably drowned in the flood, it is just the same as if he had no father at all; therefore Noah and Fohi are the same. Just after the flood, the earth was covered with mud; if it was covered with mud, it must have been incrustated mud; if it was incrustated, it was clothed with verdure; this was a fine, unembarrassed road for Noah to fly from his wicked children; he therefore did fly from them, and took a journey of two thousand miles for his own amusement; therefore Noah and Fohi are the same.

Another sect of literati, for they all pass among the vulgar for very great scholars, assert, that the Chinese came neither from the colony of Sesostris, nor from Noah, but are descended from Magog, Meshec, and Tubal, and therefore neither Sesostris, nor Noah, nor Fohi are the same.

It is thus, my friend, that indolence assumes the airs of wisdom, and while it tosses the cup and ball with infantine folly, desires the world to look on, and calls the stupid pastime, philosophy and learning. Adieu.

LETTER XC.—*From the same.*

WHEN the men of this country are once turned of thirty, they regularly retire every year at proper intervals to lie in of the *spleen.* The vulgar, unfurnished with the luxurious comforts of the soft cushion, down bed, and easy chair, are obliged when the fit is on them, to nurse it up by drinking, idleness, and ill-humour. In such dispositions, unhappy is the foreigner who happens to cross them; his long chin, tarnished coat, or pinched hat, are sure to receive no quarter. If they meet no foreigner however to fight with, they are in such cases generally content with beating each other.

The rich, as they have more sensibility, are operated upon with greater violence by this disorder. Different from the poor, instead of becoming more insolent, they grow totally unfit for opposition. A general here, who would have faced a culverin when well, if the fit be on him, shall hardly find courage to snuff a candle. An admiral, who could have opposed a broadside without shrinking, shall sit whole days in his chamber, mobbed up in double night-caps, shuddering at the intrusive breeze, and distinguishable from his wife only by his black beard and heavy eyebrows.

In the country this disorder mostly attacks the fair sex, in town it is most unfavourable to the men. A lady, who has pined whole years amidst cooing doves and complaining nightingales in rural retirement, shall resume all her vivacity in one night at a city gaming-table; her husband, who roared, hunted, and got drunk at home, shall grow splenetic in town in proportion to his wife's good humour. Upon their arrival in London, they exchange their disorders. In consequence of her parties and excursions, he puts on the furred cap and scarlet stomacher, and perfectly resembles an Indian husband, who when his wife is safely delivered permits her to transact business abroad while he undergoes all the formality of keeping his bed, and receiving all the condolence in her place.

But those who reside constantly in town, owe this disorder mostly to the influence of the weather. It is impossible to describe what a variety of transmutations an east wind shall produce; it has been known to change a Lady of fashion into a parlour couch; an Alderman into a plate of custards, and a dispenser of justice into a rat trap. Even Philosophers themselves are not exempt from its influence; it has often converted a Poet into a coral and bells, and a patriot Senator into a dumb waiter.

Some days ago I went to visit the man in black, and entered his house with that cheerfulness, which the certainty of a favourable reception always inspires. Upon opening the door of his apartment, I found him with the most rueful face imaginable in a morning gown and flannel night-cap, earnestly employed in learning to blow the German flute. Struck with the absurdity of a man in the decline of life, thus blowing away all his constitution and spirits, even without the consolation of being musical, I ventured to ask what could induce him to attempt learning so difficult an instrument so late in life. To this he made no reply, but groaning, and still holding the flute to his lip, continued to gaze at me for some moments very angrily, and then proceeded to practise his gamut as before. After having produced a variety of the most hideous tones in nature; at last turning to me, he demanded, whether I did not think he made a surprising progress in two days? You see, continues he, I have got the Ambusheer already, and as for fingering, my master tells me, I shall have that in a few lessons more. I was so much astonished with this instance of inverted ambition, that I knew not what to reply, but soon discerned the cause of all his absurdities; my friend was under a metamorphosis by the power of spleen, and flute-blowing was unluckily become his adventitious passion.

In order therefore to banish his anxiety imperceptibly, by seeming to indulge it, I began to descant on those gloomy topics by which Philosophers often get rid of their own spleen, by communicating it; the wretchedness of a man in this life, the happiness of some wrought out of the miseries of others, the necessity that wretches should expire under punishment, that rogues might enjoy affluence in tranquillity; I led him on from the inhumanity of the rich to the ingratitude of the beggar; from the insincerity of refinement to the fierceness of rusticity; and at last had the good fortune to restore him to his usual serenity of temper, by permitting him to expatiate upon all the modes of human misery.

'Some nights ago, says my friend, sitting alone by my fire, I happened to look into an account of the detection of a set of men called the thief-takers. I read over the many hideous cruelties of those haters of mankind, of their pretended friendship to wretches they meant to betray, of their sending men out to rob, and then hanging them. I could not avoid sometimes interrupting the narrative, by crying out, *Yet these are men!* As I went on, I was informed that they had lived by this practice several years, and had been enriched by the price of blood, *and yet,* cried I, *I have been sent into this world, and am desired to call these men my brothers!* I read that the very man who led the condemned wretch to the gallows, was he who falsely swore his life away; *And yet*, continued I, *that perjurer had just such a nose, such lips, such hands, and such eyes as Newton*. I at last came to the account of the wretch, that was searched after robbing one of the thief-takers of half a crown. Those of the confederacy knew that he had got but that single half-crown in the world; after a long search therefore, which they knew would be fruitless, and taking from him the half-crown, which they knew was all he had, one of the gang compassionately cried out, *Alas, poor creature, let him keep all the rest he has got, it will do him service in Newgate, where we are sending him*. This was an instance of such complicated guilt and hypocrisy, that I threw down the book in an agony of rage, and began to think with malice of all the human kind. I sat silent for some minutes, and soon perceiving the ticking of my watch beginning to grow noisy and troublesome, I quickly placed it out of hearing, and strove to resume my serenity. But the watch-man soon gave me a second alarm. I had scarcely recovered from this, when my peace was assaulted by the wind at my window; and when that ceased to blow, I listened for death-watches in the wainscot. I now found my whole system discomposed, I strove to find a resource in philosophy and reason; but what could I oppose, or where direct my blow, when I could see no enemy to combat? I saw no misery approaching, nor knew any I had to fear, yet still I was miserable. Morning came, I sought for tranquillity in dissipation, sauntered from one place of public resort to another, but found myself disagreeable to my acquaintance, and ridiculous to others. I tried at different times dancing, fencing, and riding, I solved geometrical problems, shaped tobacco-stoppers, wrote verses and cut paper. At last I placed my affections on music, and find, that earnest employment, if it cannot cure, at least will palliate every anxiety.' Adieu.

LETTER XCI.—*From the same.*

It is no unpleasing contemplation to consider the influence which soil and climate have upon the disposition of the inhabitants, the animals and vegetables of different countries. That among the brute creation is much more visible than in man, and that in vegetables more than either. In some places those plants which are entirely poisonous at home lose their deleterious quality by being carried abroad; there are serpents in Macedonia so harmless as to be used as play-things for children, and we are told, that in some parts of Fez there are lions so very timorous as to be scared away, though coming in herds, by the cries of women.

I know of no country where the influence of climate and soil is more visible than in England; the same hidden cause which gives courage to their dogs and cocks, gives also fierceness to their men. But chiefly this ferocity appears among the vulgar. The polite of every country pretty nearly resemble each other. But as in simpling, it is among the uncultivated productions of Nature, we are to examine the characteristic differences of climate and soil, so in an estimate of the genius of the people, we must look among the sons of unpolished rusticity. The vulgar English therefore may be easily distinguished from all the rest of the world, by superior pride, impatience, and a peculiar hardiness of soul.

Perhaps no qualities in the world are more susceptible of a fine polish than these; artificial complaisance and easy deference being super-induced over these, generally forms a great character; something at once elegant and majestic; affable yet sincere. Such in general are the better sort; but they who are left in primitive rudeness are the least disposed for society with others, or comfort internally, of any people under the sun.

The poor indeed of every country, are but little prone to treat each other with tenderness; their own miseries are too apt to engross all their pity; and perhaps too they give but little commiseration, as they find but little from others. But, in England, the poor treat each other upon every occasion with more than savage animosity, and as if they were in a state of open war by nature. In China, if two porters should meet in a narrow street, they would lay down their burthens, make a thousand excuses to each other for the accidental interruption, and beg pardon on their knees; if two men of the same occupation should meet here, they would first begin to scold, and at last to beat each other. One would think they had miseries enough resulting from penury and labour not to increase them by ill nature among themselves, and subjection to new penalties, but such considerations never weigh with them.

But to recompense this strange absurdity, they are in the main generous, brave and enterprising. They feel the slightest injuries with a degree of ungoverned impatience, but resist the greatest calamities with surprising fortitude. Those miseries under which any other people in the world would sink, they have often shewed they were capable of enduring; if accidentally cast upon some desolate coast, their perseverance is beyond what any other nation is capable of sustaining; if imprisoned for crimes, their efforts to escape are greater than among others. The peculiar strength of their prisons, when compared to those elsewhere, argues their hardiness; even the strongest prisons I have ever seen in other countries, would be very insufficient to confine the untameable spirit of an Englishman. In short, what man dares do in circumstances of danger, an Englishman will. His virtues seem to sleep in the calm, and are called out only to combat the kindred storm.

But the greatest eulogy of this people, is the generosity of their miscreants; the tenderness in general of their robbers and highwaymen. Perhaps no people can produce instances of the same kind, where the desperate mix pity with injustice; still shewing that they understand a distinction in crimes, and even, in acts of violence, have still some tincture of remaining virtue. In every other country robbery and murder go almost always together; here it seldom happens, except upon ill-judged resistance or pursuit. The banditti of other countries are unmerciful to a supreme degree; the highwayman and robber here are generous at least to the public, and pretend even to virtues in their intercourse among each other. Taking therefore my opinion of the English from the virtues and vices practised among the vulgar, they at once present to a stranger all their faults, and keep their virtues up only for the enquiring eye of a philosopher.

Foreigners are generally shocked at their insolence upon first coming among them; they find themselves ridiculed and insulted in every street; they meet with none of those trifling civilities, so frequent elsewhere, which are instances of mutual good will without previous acquaintance: they travel through the country either too ignorant or too obstinate to cultivate a closer acquaintance, meet every moment something to excite their disgust, and return home to characterize this as the region of spleen, insolence, and ill-nature. In short, England would be the last place in the world I would travel to by way of amusement; but the first for instruction. I would choose to have others for my acquaintance but Englishmen for my friends.

LETTER XCII.—*To the same.*

THE mind is ever ingenious in making its own distress. The wandering beggar, who has none to protect, to feed, or to shelter him, fancies complete happiness in labour and a full meal; take him from rags and want, feed, clothe, and employ him, his wishes now rise one step above his station; he could be happy were he possessed of raiment, food, and ease. Suppose his wishes gratified even in these, his prospects widen as he ascends; he finds himself in affluence and tranquillity indeed, but indolence soon breeds anxiety, and he desires not only to be freed from pain, but to be possessed of pleasure: pleasure is granted him, and this but opens his soul to ambition, and ambition will be sure to taint his future happiness, either with jealousy, disappointment, or fatigue.

But of all the arts of distress found out by man for his own torment, perhaps, that of philosophic misery is most truly ridiculous, a passion nowhere carried to so extravagant an excess, as in the country where I now reside. It is not enough to engage all the compassion of a philosopher here, that his own globe is harassed with wars, pestilence, or barbarity; he shall grieve for the inhabitants of the moon, if the situation of her imaginary mountains happen to alter; and dread the extinction of the sun, if the spots on the surface happen to encrease: one should imagine, that philosophy was introduced to make men happy, but here it serves to make hundreds miserable.

My landlady some days ago brought me the diary of a philosopher of this desponding sort, who had lodged in the apartment before me. It contains the history of a life, which seems to be one continued tissue of sorrow, apprehension, and distress. A single week will serve as a specimen of the whole.

Monday. In what a transient decaying situation are we placed, and what various reasons does philosophy furnish to to make mankind unhappy! A single grain of mustard shall continue to produce its similitude through numberless successions; yet what has been granted to this little seed has been denied to our planetary system; the mustard-seed is still unaltered, but the system is growing old, and must quickly fall to decay. How terrible will it be, when the motions of all the planets have at last become so irregular as to need repairing, when the moon shall fall into frightful paroxysms of alteration, when the earth, deviating from its ancient track, and with every other planet forgetting its circular revolutions, shall become so eccentric, that unconfined by the laws of system, it shall fly off into boundless space, to knock against some distant world, or fall in upon the sun, either extinguishing his light, or burned up by his flames in a moment. Perhaps while I write, this dreadful change is begun. Shield me from universal ruin!

Yet idiot man laughs, sings, and rejoices in the very face of the sun, and seems no way touched with his situation.

Tuesday. Went to bed in great distress, awaked and was comforted, by considering that this change was to happen at some indefinite time, and therefore, like death, the thoughts of it might easily be borne. But there is a revolution, a fixed determined revolution, which must certainly come to pass; yet which, by good fortune, I shall never feel, except in my posterity. The obliquity of the equator with the ecliptic, is now twenty minutes less than when it was observed two thousand years ago by *Piteas*. If this be the case, in six thousand the obliquity will be still less by an whole degree. This being supposed, it is evident, that our earth, as Louville has clearly proved, has a motion, by which the climates must necessarily change place, and, in the space of about one million of years, England shall actually travel to the Antarctic pole. I shudder at the change! How shall our unhappy grand-children endure the hideous climate! A million of years will soon be accomplished; they are but a moment when compared to eternity; then shall our charming country, as I may say, in a moment of time, resemble the hideous wilderness of Nova Zembla.

Wednesday. To-night, by my calculation, the long predicted comet is to make its first appearance. Heavens, what terrors are impending over our little dim speck of earth! Dreadful visitation! Are we to be scorched in its fires, or only smothered in the vapour of its tail? That is the question! Thoughtless mortals, go build houses, plant orchards, purchase estates, for to-morrow you die. But what if the comet should not come? That would be equally fatal. Comets are servants which periodically return to supply the sun with fuel. If our sun therefore should be disappointed of the expected supply, and all his fuel be in the meantime burnt out, he must expire like an exhausted taper. What a miserable situation must our earth be in without his enlivening ray? Have we not seen several neighbouring suns entirely disappear? Has not a fixed star, near the tail of the Ram, lately been quite extinguished?

Thursday. The comet has not yet appeared; I am sorry for it: first, sorry because my calculation is false; secondly, sorry lest the sun should want fuel; thirdly, sorry lest the wits should laugh at our erroneous predictions; and fourthly, sorry because if it appears to-night, it must necessarily come within the sphere of the earth's attraction; and heaven help the unhappy country on which it happens to fall.

Friday. Our whole society have been out all eager in search of the comet. We have seen not less than sixteen comets in different parts of the heavens. However we are unanimously resolved to fix upon one only to be the comet expected. That near Virgo wants nothing but a tail to fit it out completely for terrestrial admiration.

Saturday. The moon is I find at her old pranks. Her appulses, librations, and other irregularities, indeed amaze me. My daughter too is this morning gone off with a grenadier. No way surprising. I was never able to give her a relish for wisdom. She ever promised to be a mere expletive in the creation. But the moon, the moon gives me real uneasiness; I fondly fancied I had fixed her. I had thought her constant, and constant only to me; but every night discovers her infidelity, and proves me a desolate and abandoned lover. Adieu.

LETTER XCIII.—*To the same*.

It is surprising what an influence titles shall have upon the mind, even though these titles be of our own making. Like children we dress up the puppets in finery, and then stand in astonishment at the plastic wonder. I have been told of a rat-catcher here, who strolled for a long time about the villages near town, without finding any employment; at last, however, he thought proper to take the title of his Majesty's Rat-catcher in ordinary, and this succeeded beyond his expectations; when it was known that he caught rats at court, all were ready to give him countenance and employment.

But of all the people, they who make books seem most perfectly sensible of the advantage of titular dignity. All seem convinced, that a book written by vulgar hands, can neither instruct nor improve; none but Kings, Chams, and Mandarines, can write with any probability of success. If the titles inform me right, not only Kings and Courtiers, but Emperors themselves in this country, periodically supply the press.

A man here who should write, and honestly confess that he wrote for bread, might as well send his manuscript to fire the baker's oven; not one creature will read him; all must be court-bred poets, or pretend at least to be court-bred, who can expect to please. Should the caitiff fairly avow a design of emptying our pockets and filling his own, every reader would instantly forsake him; even those who wrote for bread themselves, would combine to worry him, perfectly sensible, that his attempts only served to take the bread out of their mouths.

And yet this silly prepossession the more amazes me, when I consider, that almost all the excellent productions in wit that have appeared here, were purely the offspring of necessity; their Drydens, Butlers, Otways, and Farquhars, were all writers for bread. Believe me, my friend, hunger has a most amazing faculty of sharpening the genius; and he who with a full belly, can think like a hero, after a course of fasting, shall rise to the sublimity of a demi-god.

But what will most amaze, is, that this very set of men, who are now so much depreciated by fools, are however the very best writers they have among them at present. For my own part, were I to buy an hat, I would not have it from a stocking-maker, but an hatter; were I to buy shoes, I should not go to the tailor's for that purpose. It is just so with regard to wit: did I, for my life, desire to be well served, I would apply only to those who made it their trade, and lived by it. You smile at the oddity of my opinion; but he assured, my friend, that wit is in some measure mechanical: and that a man long habituated to catch at even its resemblance, will at last be happy enough to possess the substance: by a long habit of writing he acquires a justice of thinking, and a mastery of manner, which holiday-writers, even with ten times his genius, may vainly attempt to equal.

How then are they deceived, who expect from title, dignity, and exterior circumstance, an excellence, which is in some measure acquired by habit, and sharpened by necessity; you have seen, like me, many literary reputations promoted by the influence of fashion, which have scarce survived the possessor; you have seen the poor hardly earn the little reputation they acquired, and their merit only acknowledged when they were incapable of enjoying the pleasures of popularity; such, how-ever, is the reputation worth possessing, that which is hardly earned is hardly lost. Adieu.

LETTER XCIV.—*From Hingpo in Moscow, to Lien Chi Altangi in London.*

WHERE will my disappointments end? Must I still be doomed to accuse the severity of my fortune, and shew my constancy in distress rather than moderation in prosperity? I had at least hopes of conveying my charming companion safe from the reach of every enemy, and of again restoring her to her native soil. But those hopes are now no more.

Upon leaving Terki, we took the nearest road to the dominions of Russia. We passed the Ural mountains covered in eternal snow, and traversed the forests of Ufa, where the prowling bear and shrieking hyena keep an undisputed possession. We next embarked upon the rapid river Bulija; and made the best of our way to the banks of the Wolga, where it waters the fruitful valleys of Casan.

There were two vessels in company properly equipped and armed, in order to oppose the Wolga pirates, who, we were informed, infested this river. Of all mankind, these pirates are the most terrible. They are composed of the criminals and outlawed peasants of Russia, who fly to the forests that lie along the banks of the Wolga for protection. Here they join in parties, lead a savage life, and have no other subsistence but plunder. Being deprived of houses, friends, or a fixed habitation, they become more terrible even than the tiger, and as insensible to all the feelings of humanity. They neither give quarter to those they conquer, nor receive it when overpowered themselves. The severity of the laws against them serves to increase their barbarity, and seems to make them a neutral species of beings, between the wildness of the lion and the subtility of the man. When taken alive their punishment is hideous. A floating gibbet is erected, which is let run down with the stream; here upon an iron hook stuck under their ribs, and upon which the whole weight of their body depends, they are left to expire in the most terrible agonies; some being thus found to linger several days successively.

We were but three days' voyage from the confluence of this river into the Wolga, when we perceived at a distance behind us an armed barque coming up with the assistance of sails and oars, in order to attack us. The dreadful signal of death was hung upon the mast, and our captain with his glass could easily discern them to be pirates. It is impossible to express our consternation on this occasion; the whole crew instantly came together to consult the properest means of safety. It was therefore soon determined to send off our women and valuable commodities in one of our vessels, and that the men should stay in the other and boldly oppose the enemy. This resolution was soon put into execution, and I now reluctantly parted from the beautiful Zelis for the first time since our retreat from Persia. The vessel in which she was, disappeared to my longing eyes, in proportion as that of the pirates approached us. They soon came up; but, upon examining our strength, and perhaps sensible of the manner in which we had sent off our most valuable effects, they seemed more eager to pursue the vessel we had sent away, than attack us. In this manner they continued to harass us for three days; still endeavouring to pass us without fighting. But, on the fourth day, finding it entirely impossible, and despairing to seize the expected booty, they desisted from their endeavours, and left us to pursue our voyage without interruption.

Our joy on this occasion was great; but soon a disappointment more terrible, because unexpected, succeeded. The barque, in which our women and treasure were sent off, was wrecked upon the banks of the Wolga, for want of a proper number of hands to manage her, and the whole crew carried by the peasants up the country. Of this however we were not sensible till our arrival at Moscow; where expecting to meet our separated barque, we were informed of its misfortune, and our loss. Need I paint the situation of my mind on this occasion? Need I describe all I feel, when I despair of beholding the beautiful Zelis more! Fancy had dressed the future prospect of my life in the gayest colouring; but one unexpected stroke of fortune has robbed it of every charm. Her dear idea mixes with every scene of pleasure, and without her presence to enliven it, the whole becomes tedious, insipid, insupportable. I will confess, now that she is lost, I will confess, I loved her; nor is it in the power of time, or of reason, to erase her image from my heart. Adieu.

LETTER XCV.—*From Lien Chi Altangi to Hingpo, at Moscow.*[1]

YOUR misfortunes are mine. But as every period of life is marked with its own, you must learn to endure them. Disappointed love makes the misery of youth; disappointed ambition, that of manhood; and successless avarice that of age. These three attack us through life; and it is our duty to stand upon our guard. To love, we ought to oppose dissipation, and endeavour to change the object of the affections; to ambition, the happiness of indolence and obscurity; and to avarice, the fear of soon dying. These are the shields with which we should

[1] This letter is a rhapsody from the Maxims of the philosopher Mé. Vide Lett. curieuses & edifiantes. Vide etiam Du Halde, vol. ii, p. 98.

arm ourselves; and thus make every scene of life, if not pleasing, at least supportable.

Men complain of not finding a place of repose. They are in the wrong; they have it for seeking. What they should indeed complain of is, that the heart is an enemy to that very repose they seek. To themselves alone should they impute their discontent. They seek within the short span of life to satisfy a thousand desires; each of which alone is unsatiable. One month passes and another comes on; the year ends and then begins; but man is still unchanging in folly, still blindly continuing in prejudice. To the wise man, every climate and every soil is pleasing; to him, a parterre of flowers is the famous valley of gold; to him, a little brook, *the fountain of young peach-trees*; [1] to such a man, the melody of birds is more ravishing than the harmony of a full concert; and the tincture of the cloud preferable to the touch of the finest pencil.

The life of man is a journey: a journey that must be travelled, however bad the roads or the accommodation. If, in the beginning, it is found dangerous, narrow, and difficult, it must either grow better in the end, or we shall by custom learn to bear its inequality.

But though I see you incapable of penetrating into grand principles, attend at least to a simile adapted to every apprehension. I am mounted upon a wretched ass. I see another man before me upon a sprightly horse, at which I find some uneasiness. I look behind me, and see numbers on foot stooping under heavy burdens; let me learn to pity their estate, and thank heaven for my own.

Shingfu, when under misfortunes, would in the beginning weep like a child; but he soon recovered his former tranquillity. After indulging grief for a few days, he would become, as usual, the most merry old man in all the province of Shansi. About the time that his wife died, his possessions were all consumed by fire, and his only son sold into captivity; Shingfu grieved for one day, and the next went to dance at a Mandarine's door for his dinner. The company were surprised to see the old man so merry when suffering such great losses, and the Mandarine himself coming out, asked him how he, who had grieved so much, and given way to the calamity the day before, could now be so cheerful? 'You ask me one question, cries the old man, let me answer by asking another: Which is the most durable, a hard thing, or a soft thing; that which resists, or that which

---

[1] This passage the editor does not understand.

makes no resistance?' *An hard thing to be sure*, replied the Mandarine. 'There you are wrong, returned Shingfu. I am now fourscore years old; and if you look in my mouth, you will find that I have lost all my teeth, but not a bit of my tongue.' Adieu.

LETTER XCVI. — *From Lien Chi Altangi, to Fum Hoam first President of the Ceremonial Academy, at Pekin, in China.*

THE manner of grieving for our departed friends in China is very different from that of Europe. The mourning colour of Europe is black; that of China white. When a parent or relation dies here, for they seldom mourn for friends, it is only clapping on a suit of sables, grimacing it for a few days, and all, soon forgotten, goes on as before; not a single creature missing the deceased, except perhaps a favourite house-keeper or a favourite cat.

On the contrary, with us in China it is a very serious affair. The piety with which I have seen you behave on one of these occasions should never be forgotten. I remember it was upon the death of thy grandmother's maiden sister. The coffin was exposed in the principal hall in public view. Before it were placed the figures of eunuchs, horses, tortoises, and other animals, in attitudes of grief and respect. The more distant relations of the old lady, and I among the number, came to pay our compliments of condolence, and to salute the deceased after the manner of our country. We had scarce presented our wax candles and perfumes, and given the bowl of departure, when, crawling on his belly from under a curtain, out came the reverend Fum Hoam himself, in all the dismal solemnity of distress. Your looks were set for sorrow; your clothing consisted in an hempen bag tied round the neck with a string. For two long months did this mourning continue. By night you lay stretched on a single mat, and sat on the stool of discontent by day. Pious man, who could thus set an example of sorrow and decorum to our country. Pious country, where, if we do not grieve at the departure of our friends for their sakes, at least we are taught to regret them for our own.

All is very different here; amazement all. What sort of people am I got amongst? Fum, thou son of Fo, what sort of people am I got amongst? No crawling round the coffin; no dressing up in hempen bags; no lying on mats, or sitting on stools. Gentlemen here shall put on first mourning with as sprightly an air as if preparing for a birth-night; and widows shall actually dress for another husband in their weeds for the former. The best jest of all is, that our merry mourners clap bits of muslin on their sleeves, and these are called *weepers*. Weeping muslin; alas, alas, very sorrowful truly! These weepers then it seems are to bear the whole burden of the distress.

But I have had the strongest instance of this contrast; this tragi-comical behaviour in distress upon a recent occasion. Their King, whose departure, though sudden, was not unexpected, died after a reign of many years. His age, and uncertain state of health, served in some measure to diminish the sorrow of his subjects; and their expectations from his successor seemed to balance their minds between uneasiness and satisfaction. But how ought they to have behaved on such an occasion? Surely, they ought rather to have endeavoured to testify their *gratitude* to their deceased friend, than to proclaim their *hopes* of the future. Sure even the Successor must suppose their love to wear the face of adulation, which so quickly changed the object. However, the very same day on which the old King died, they made rejoicing for the new.

For my part, I have no conception of this new manner of mourning and rejoicing in a breath; of being merry and sad; of mixing a funeral procession with a jig and a bonfire. At least, it would have been just, that they who flattered the King while living for virtues which he had not, should lament him dead for those he really had.

In this universal cause for national distress, as I had no interest myself, so it is but natural to suppose, I felt no real affliction. In all the losses of our friends, says an European philosopher, we first consider how much our own welfare is affected by their departure, and moderate our real grief just in the same proportion. Now, as I had neither received nor expected to receive favours from kings or their flatterers; as I had no acquaintance in particular with their late monarch; as I knew that the place of a king is soon supplied; and as the Chinese proverb has it, that though the world may sometimes want cobblers to mend their shoes, there is no danger of its wanting Emperors to rule their kingdoms: from such considerations, I could bear the loss of a king with the most philosophic resignation. However, I thought it my duty at least to appear sorrowful; to put on a melancholy aspect, or to set my face by that of the people.

The first company I came amongst after the news became

general, was a set of jolly companions who were drinking prosperity to the ensuing reign. I entered the room with looks of despair, and even expected applause for the superlative misery of my countenance. Instead of that I was universally condemned by the company for a grimacing son of a whore, and desired to take away my penitential phiz to some other quarter. I now corrected my former mistake, and with the most sprightly air imaginable entered a company, where they were talking over the ceremonies of the approaching funeral. Here I sat for some time with an air of pert vivacity; when one of the chief mourners immediately observing my good humour, desired me, if I pleased, to go and grin somewhere else; they wanted no disaffected scoundrels there. Leaving this company therefore, I was resolved to assume a look perfectly neutral; and have ever since been studying the fashionable air: something between jest and earnest; a complete virginity of face, uncontaminated with the smallest symptom of meaning.

But though grief be a very slight affair here, the mourning, my friend, is a very important concern. When an Emperor dies in China, the whole expense of the solemnities is defrayed from the royal coffers. When the great die here, Mandarines are ready enough to order mourning; but I do not see that they are so ready to pay for it. If they send me down from court the grey undress frock, or the black coat without pocket holes, I am willing enough to comply with their commands, and wear both; but, by the head of Confucius! to be obliged to wear black, and buy it into the bargain, is more than my tranquillity of temper can bear. What, order me to wear mourning before they know whether I can buy it or no! Fum, thou son of Fo, what sort of people am I got amongst; where being out of black is a certain symptom of poverty; where those who have miserable faces cannot have mourning, and those who have mourning will not wear a miserable face!

LETTER XCVII.—*From the same.*

IT is usual for the booksellers here, when a book has given universal pleasure upon one subject, to bring on several more upon the same plan; which are sure to have purchasers and readers from that desire which all men have to view a pleasing object on every side. The first performance serves rather to awaken than satisfy attention; and when that is once moved, the slightest effort serves to continue its progression; the merit of the first diffuses a light sufficient to illuminate the succeeding efforts; and no other subject can be relished, till that is exhausted. A stupid work coming thus immediately in the train of an applauded performance, weans the mind from the object of its pleasure; and resembles the sponge thrust into the mouth of a discharged culverin, in order to adapt it for a new explosion.

This manner, however, of drawing off a subject, or a peculiar mode of writing to the dregs, effectually precludes a revival of that subject or manner for some time for the future; the sated reader turns from it with a kind of literary nausea; and though the titles of books are the part of them most read, yet he has scarce perseverance enough to wade through the title page.

Of this number I own myself one; I am now grown callous to several subjects, and different kinds of composition: whether such originally pleased I will not take upon me to determine; but at present I spurn a new book merely upon seeing its name in an advertisement; nor have the smallest curiosity to look beyond the first leaf, even though in the second the author promises his own face neatly engraved on copper.

I am become a perfect Epicure in reading; plain beef or solid mutton will never do. I am for a Chinese dish of bear's claws and bird's nests. I am for sauce strong with assafœtida, or fuming with garlic. For this reason there are an hundred very wise, learned, virtuous, well-intended productions that have no charms for me. Thus, for the soul of me, I could never find courage nor grace enough to wade above two pages deep into *Thoughts upon God and Nature*, or *Thoughts upon Providence*, or *Thoughts upon Free Grace*, or indeed into Thoughts upon any thing at all. I can no longer meditate with Meditations for every day in the year; Essays upon divers subjects cannot allure me, though never so interesting; and as for Funeral Sermons, or even Thanksgiving Sermons, I can neither weep with the one, nor rejoice with the other.

But it is chiefly in gentle poetry, where I seldom look farther than the title. The truth is, I take up books to be told something new; but here, as it is now managed, the reader is told nothing. He opens the book, and there finds very good words, truly, and much exactness of rhyme, but no information. A parcel of gaudy images pass on before his imagination like the figures in a dream; but curiosity, induction, reason, and the whole train of affections are fast asleep. The *jucunda et idonea vitæ*; those sallies which mend the heart while they amuse the fancy, are quite forgotten: so that a reader who would take up some modern applauded performances of this kind, must, in order to be pleased, first leave his good sense behind him, take for his recompense and guide bloated and compound epithet, and dwell on paintings, just indeed, because laboured with minute exactness.

If we examine, however, our internal sensations, we shall find ourselves but little pleased with such laboured vanities; we shall find that our applause rather proceeds from a kind of contagion caught up from others, and which we contribute to diffuse, than what we privately feel. There are some subjects of which almost all the world perceive the futility; yet all combine in imposing upon each other, as worthy of praise. But chiefly this imposition obtains in literature, where men publicly contemn what they relish with rapture in private, and approve abroad what has given disgust at home. The truth is, we deliver those criticisms in public which are supposed to be best calculated not to do justice to the author, but to impress others with an opinion of our superior discernment.

But let works of this kind, which have already come off with such applause, enjoy it all. It is neither my wish to diminish, as I was never considerable enough to add to their fame. But for the future I fear there are many poems, of which I shall find spirits to read but the title. In the first place, all odes upon winter, or summer, or autumn; in short all odes, epodes, and monodies whatsoever, shall hereafter be deemed too polite, classical, obscure, and refined, to be read, and entirely above human comprehension. Pastorals are pretty enough—for those that like them—but to me Thyrsis is one of the most insipid fellows I ever conversed with; and as for Corydon, I do not choose his company. Elegies and epistles are very fine to those to whom they are addressed; and as for epic poems, I am generally able to discover the whole plan in reading the two first pages.

Tragedies, however, as they are now made, are good instructive moral *sermons* enough; and it would be a fault not to be pleased with *good things*. There I learnt several great truths; as, that it is impossible to see into the ways of futurity; that punishment always attends the villain, that love is the fond soother of the human breast, that we should not resist heaven's will, for in resisting heaven's will, heaven's will is resisted; with several other sentiments equally new, delicate and striking. Every new tragedy therefore I shall go to see; for reflections of this nature make a tolerable harmony, when mixed up with a proper quantity of drum, trumpet, thunder, lightning, or the scene shifter's whistle. Adieu.

LETTER XCVIII.—*From the same.*

I HAD some intentions lately of going to visit Bedlam, the place where those who go mad are confined. I went to wait upon the man in black to be my conductor, but I found him preparing to go to Westminster-hall, where the English hold their courts of justice. It gave me some surprise to find my friend engaged in a law-suit, but more so when he informed me that it had been depending for several years. *How is it possible*, cried I, *for a man who knows the world to go to law ? I am well acquainted with the courts of justice in China, they resemble rat-traps every one of them, nothing more easy to get in, but to get out again is attended with some difficulty, and more cunning than rats are generally found to possess!*

Faith, replied my friend, I should not have gone to law, but that I was assured of success before I began; things were presented to me in so alluring a light, that I thought by barely declaring myself a candidate for the prize, I had nothing more to do but to enjoy the fruits of the victory. Thus have I been upon the eve of an imaginary triumph every term these ten years, have travelled forward with victory ever in my view, but ever out of reach; however, at present I fancy we have hampered our antagonist in such a manner, that without some unforeseen demur, we shall this very day lay him fairly on his back.

If things be so situated, said I, *I don't care if I attend you to the courts, and partake in the pleasure of your success. But prithee*, continued I, as we set forward, *what reasons have you to think an affair at last concluded, which has given you so many former disappointments?* My lawyer tells me, returned he, that I have Salkeld and Ventris strong in my favour, and that there are no less than fifteen cases in point. *I understand*, said I, *those are two of your judges who have already declared their opinions.* Pardon me, replied my friend, Salkeld and Ventris are lawyers who some hundred years ago gave their opinion on cases similar to mine; these opinions which make for me my lawyer is to cite, and those opinions which look another way, are cited by the lawyer employed by my antagonist; as I observed, I have Salkeld and Ventris for me, he has Coke and Hales for him, and he that has most opinions, is most likely to carry his cause. *But where is the necessity*, cried I, *of prolonging a suit by citing the opinions and reports of others, since the same good sense which determined lawyers in former ages may serve to guide your judges at this day? They at that time gave their opinions only from the light of reason, your judges have the same light at present to direct them, let me even add a greater, as in former ages, there were many prejudices from which the present is happily free. If arguing from authorities be exploded from every other branch of learning, why should it be particularly adhered to in this? I plainly foresee how such a method of investigation must embarrass every suit, and even perplex the student, ceremonies will be multiplied, formalities must increase, and more time will thus be spent in learning the arts of litigation than in the discovery of right.*

I see, cries my friend, that you are for a speedy administration of justice, but all the world will grant that the more time that is taken up in considering any subject the better it will be understood. Besides, it is the boast of an Englishman, that his property is secure, and all the world will grant that a deliberate administration of justice is the best way to *secure his property*. Why have we so many lawyers, *but to secure our property*; why so many formalities, but *to secure our property?* Not less than one hundred thousand families live in opulence, elegance and ease, merely by *securing our property*.

To embarrass justice, returned I, by a multiplicity of laws, or to hazard it by a confidence in our judges, are, I grant, the opposite rocks on which legislative wisdom has ever split; in one case, the client resembles that Emperor, who is said to have been suffocated with the bedclothes, which were only designed to keep him warm; in the other, to that town which let the enemy take possession of its walls, in order to shew the world how little they depended upon aught but courage for safety: But bless me, what numbers do I see here—all in black—how is it possible that half this multitude find employment? Nothing so easily conceived, returned my companion, they live by watching each other. For instance, the catchpole watches the man in debt, the attorney watches the catchpole, the counsellor watches the attorney, the solicitor the counsellor, and all find sufficient employment. I conceive you, interrupted I, they watch each other, but it is the client that pays them all for watching; it puts me in mind of a Chinese Fable, which is entitled, *Five animals at a meal.*

A grasshopper, filled with dew, was merrily singing under a

shade; a whangam that eats grasshoppers had marked it for its prey, and was just stretching forth to devour it; a serpent that had for a long time fed only on whangams, was coiled up to fasten on the whangam; a yellow bird was just upon the wing to dart upon the serpent; a hawk had just stooped from above to seize the yellow bird; all were intent on their prey, and unmindful of their danger: So the whangam eat the grasshopper, the serpent eat the whangam, the yellow bird the serpent, and the hawk the yellow bird; when sousing from on high, a vulture gobbled up the hawk, grasshopper, whangam, and all in a moment.

I had scarce finished my fable, when the lawyer came to inform my friend, that his cause was put off till another term, that money was wanted to retain, and that all the world was of opinion, that the very next hearing would bring him off victorious. If so, then cries my friend, I believe it will be my wisest way to continue the cause for another term, and in the mean time, my friend here and I will go and see Bedlam. Adieu.

LETTER XCIX.—*From the same.*

I LATELY received a visit from the little beau, who I found had assumed a new flow of spirits with a new suit of clothes. Our discourse happened to turn upon the different treatment of the fair sex here and in Asia, with the influence of beauty in refining our manners and improving our conversation.

I soon perceived he was strongly prejudiced in favour of the Asiatic method of treating the sex, and that it was impossible to persuade him, but that a man was happier who had four wives at his command, than he who had only one. 'It is true, cries he, your men of fashion in the East are slaves, and under some terrors of having their throats squeezed in a bow-string; but what then, they can find ample consolation in a seraglio; they make indeed an indifferent figure in conversation abroad, but then they have a seraglio to console them at home. I am told they have no balls, drums, nor operas, but then they have got a seraglio; they may be deprived of wine and French cookery, but they have a seraglio; a seraglio, a seraglio, my dear creature, wipes off every inconvenience in the world.

'Besides, I am told, your Asiatic beauties are the most convenient women alive, for they have no souls; positively there is nothing in Nature I should like so much as ladies without souls; soul, here, is the utter ruin of half the sex. A girl of eighteen shall have soul enough to spend an hundred pounds in the turning of a trump. Her mother shall have soul enough to ride a sweepstake match at a horse-race; her maiden aunt shall have soul enough to purchase the furniture of a whole toy-shop, and others shall have soul enough to behave as if they had no souls at all.'

With respect to the soul, interrupted I, the Asiatics are much kinder to the fair sex than you imagine; instead of one soul, Fohi, the idol of China, gives every woman three, the Bramines give them fifteen; and even Mahomet himself, no where excludes the sex from Paradise. Abulfeda reports, that an old woman one day importuning him to know what she ought to do in order to gain Paradise; *My good lady*, answered the Prophet, *old women never get there*. What, never get to Paradise? returned the matron in a fury. *Never*, says he, *for they always grow young by the way*.

No, Sir, continued I, the men of Asia behave with more deference to the sex than you seem to imagine. As you of Europe say grace, upon sitting down to dinner, so it is the custom in China to say grace, when a man goes to bed to his wife. *And may I die*, returned my companion, *but a very pretty ceremony; for seriously, Sir, I see no reason why a man should not be as grateful in one situation as in the other. Upon honour, I always find myself much more disposed to gratitude, on the couch of a fine woman, than upon sitting down to a sirloin of beef.*

Another ceremony, said I, resuming the conversation, in favour of the sex amongst us, is the bride's being allowed after marriage, *her three days of freedom*. During this interval, a thousand extravagances are practised by either sex. The lady is placed upon the nuptial bed, and numberless monkey tricks are played round to divert her. One gentleman smells her perfumed handkerchief, another attempts to untie her garters, a third pulls off her shoe to play hunt the slipper, another pretends to be an idiot, and endeavours to raise a laugh by grimacing; in the mean time, the glass goes briskly about, till ladies, gentlemen, wife, husband, and all are mixed together in one inundation of arrack punch.

'Strike me dumb, deaf, and blind, cried my companion, but very pretty; there's some sense in your Chinese ladies' con-descensions; but among us, you shall scarce find one of the whole sex that shall hold her good humour for three days together. No later than yesterday I happened to say some civil things to a citizen's wife of my acquaintance, not because I loved, but because I had charity; and what do you think was the tender creature's reply! Only that she detested my pigtail wig, high-heeled shoes, and sallow complexion. That is all. Nothing more! Yes, by the heavens, though she was more ugly than an unpainted actress, I found her more insolent than a thorough bred woman of quality.'

He was proceeding in this wild manner, when his invective was interrupted by the man in black, who entered the apartment, introducing his niece, a young lady of exquisite beauty. Her very appearance was sufficient to silence the severest satirist of the sex; easy without pride, and free without impudence, she seemed capable of supplying every sense with pleasure; her looks, her conversation were natural and unconstrained; she had neither been taught to languish nor ogle, to laugh without a jest, or sigh without sorrow. I found that she had just returned from abroad, and had been conversant in the manners of the world. Curiosity prompted me to ask several questions, but she declined them all. I own I never found myself so strongly prejudiced in favour of apparent merit before; and could willingly have prolonged our conversation, but the company after some time withdrew. Just, however, before the little beau took his leave, he called me aside, and requested I would change him a twenty pound bill, which as I was incapable of doing, he was contented with borrowing half a crown. Adieu.

LETTER C.—*From Lien Chi Altangi to Hingpo, by the way of Moscow.*

FEW virtues have been more praised by moralists, than generosity; every practical treatise of Ethics tends to increase our sensibility of the distresses of others, and to relax the grasp of frugality. Philosophers that are poor, praise it because they are gainers by its effects; and the opulent Seneca himself has written a treatise on benefits, though he was known to give nothing away.

But among the many who have enforced the duty of giving, I 'm surprised there are none to inculcate the ignominy of receiving, to shew that by every favour we accept, we in some measure forfeit our native freedom, and that a stage of continual dependence on the generosity of others, is a life of gradual debasement.

Were men taught to despise the receiving obligations with the same force of reasoning and declamation that they are instructed to confer them, we might then see every person in society filling up the requisite duties of his station with cheerful industry, neither relaxed by hope, nor sullen from disappointment.

Every favour a man receives, in some measure sinks him below his dignity, and in proportion to the value of the benefit, or the frequency of its acceptance, he gives up so much of his natural independence. He therefore, who thrives upon the unmerited bounty of another, if he has any sensibility, suffers the worst of servitude; the shackled slave may murmur without reproach, but the humble dependent is taxed with ingratitude upon every symptom of discontent; the one may rave round the walls of his cell, but the other lingers in all the silence of mental confinement. To increase his distress, every new obligation but adds to the former load which kept the vigorous mind from rising; till at last, elastic no longer, it shapes itself to constraint, and puts on habitual servility.

It is thus with the feeling mind; but there are some who, born without any share of sensibility, receive favour after favour, and still cringe for more, who accept the offer of generosity with as little reluctance as the wages of merit, and even make thanks for past benefits an indirect petition for new; such I grant can suffer no debasement from dependence, since they were originally as vile as was possible to be; dependence degrades only the ingenuous, but leaves the sordid mind in pristine meanness. In this manner therefore long continued generosity is misplaced, or it is injurious; it either finds a man worthless, or it makes him so; and true it is, that the person who is contented to be *often* obliged, ought not to have been obliged at all.

Yet while I describe the meanness of a life of continued dependence, I would not be thought to include those natural or political subordinations which subsist in every society, for in such, though dependence is exacted from the inferior, yet the obligation on either side is mutual. The son must rely upon his parent for support, but the parent lies under the same obligations to give, that the other has to expect; the subordinate officer must receive the commands of his superior, but for this obedience the former has a right to demand an intercourse of favour; such is not the dependence I would depreciate, but that where every expected favour must be the result of mere benevolence in the giver, where the benefit can be kept without remorse, or transferred without injustice. The character of a legacy-hunter, for instance, is detestable in some countries, and despicable in all; this universal contempt of a man who infringes upon none of the laws of society, some moralists have arraigned as a popular and unjust prejudice; never considering the necessary degradations a wretch must undergo, who previously expects to grow rich by benefits, without having either natural or social claims to enforce his petitions.

But this intercourse of benefaction and acknowledgement is often injurious even to the giver as well as the receiver; a man can gain but little knowledge of himself, or of the world, amidst a circle of those whom hope or gratitude has gathered round him; their unceasing humiliations must necessarily increase his comparative magnitude, for all men measure their own abilities by those of their company; thus being taught to over-rate his merit, he in reality lessens it; increasing in confidence, but not in power, his professions end in empty boast, his undertakings in shameful disappointment.

It is perhaps one of the severest misfortunes of the great, that they are, in general, obliged to live among men whose real value is lessened by dependence, and whose minds are enslaved by obligation. The humble companion may have at first accepted patronage with generous views, but soon he feels the mortifying influence of conscious inferiority, by degrees sinks into a flatterer, and from flattery at last degenerates into stupid veneration. To remedy this the great often dismiss their old dependents, and take new. Such changes are falsely imputed to levity, falsehood, or caprice, in the patron, since they may be more justly ascribed to the client's gradual deterioration.

No, my son, a life of independence is generally a life of virtue. It is that which fits the soul for every generous flight of humanity, freedom, and friendship. To give should be our pleasure, but to receive our shame; serenity, health, and affluence attend the desire of rising by labour; misery, repentance, and disrespect that of succeeding by extorted benevolence; the man who can thank himself alone for the happiness he enjoys, is truly blest; and lovely, far more lovely the sturdy gloom of laborious indigence, than the fawning simper of thriving adulation. Adieu.

LETTER CI.—*From Lien Chi Altangi, to Fum Hoam, first President of the Ceremonial Academy, at Pekin in China.*

IN every society some men are born to teach, and others to receive instruction; some to work, and others to enjoy in idleness the fruits of their industry; some to govern, and others to obey. Every people, how free soever, must be contented to give up part of their liberty and judgment to those who govern, in exchange for their hopes of security; and the motives which first influenced their choice in the election of their governors should ever be weighed against the succeeding apparent inconsistencies of their conduct. All cannot be rulers, and men are generally best governed by a few. In making way through the intricacies of business, the smallest obstacles are apt to retard the execution of what is to be planned by a multiplicity of counsels; the judgment of one alone being always fittest for winding through the labyrinths of intrigue, and the obstructions of disappointment. A serpent, which, as the fable observes, is furnished with one head and many tails, is much more capable of subsistence and expedition, than another, which is furnished with but one tail and many heads.

Obvious as these truths are, the people of this country seem insensible of their force. Not satisfied with the advantages of internal peace and opulence, they still murmur at their governors, and interfere in the execution of their designs; as if they wanted to be something more than happy. But as the Europeans instruct by argument, and the Asiatics mostly by narration, were I to address them, I should convey my sentiments in the following story.

Takupi had long been Prime Minister of Tipartala, a fertile country that stretches along the western confines of China. During his administration, whatever advantages could be derived from arts, learning, and commerce, were seen to bless the people; nor were the necessary precautions of providing for the security of the state forgotten. It often happens, however, that when men are possessed of all they want, they then begin to find torment from imaginary afflictions, and lessen their present enjoyments, by foreboding that those enjoyments are to have an end. The people now therefore endeavoured to find out grievances; and after some search, actually began to think themselves aggrieved. A petition against the enormities of Takupi was carried to the throne in due form; and the Queen who governed the country, willing to satisfy her subjects, appointed a day, in which his accusers should be heard, and the Minister should stand upon his defence.

The day being arrived, and the Minister brought before the tribunal, a carrier, who supplied the city with fish, appeared among the number of his accusers. He exclaimed, that it was the custom, time immemorial, for carriers to bring their fish upon an horse in a hamper; which being placed on one side, and balanced by a stone on the other, was thus conveyed with ease and safety; but that the prisoner, moved either by a spirit of innovation, or perhaps bribed by the hamper-makers, had obliged all carriers to use the stone no longer, but balance one hamper with another; an order entirely repugnant to the customs of all antiquity, and those of the kingdom of Tipartala in particular.

The carrier finished; and the whole court shook their heads at the innovating Minister: when a second witness appeared. He was inspector of the city buildings, and accused the disgraced favourite of having given orders for the demolition of an ancient ruin, which obstructed the passage through one of the principal streets. He observed, that such buildings were noble monuments of barbarous antiquity; contributed finely to shew how little their ancestors understood of architecture: and for that reason such monuments should be held sacred, and suffered gradually to decay.

The last witness now appeared. This was a widow, who had laudably attempted to burn herself upon her husband's funeral pile. But the innovating Minister had prevented the execution of her design, and was insensible to her tears, protestations, and entreaties.

The Queen could have pardoned the two former offences, but this last was considered as so gross an injury to the sex, and so directly contrary to all the customs of antiquity, that it called for immediate justice. 'What, cried the Queen, not suffer a woman to burn herself when she thinks proper? The sex are to be very prettily tutored, no doubt, if they must be restrained from entertaining their female friends now and then with a fried wife, or roasted acquaintance. I sentence the criminal to be banished my presence for ever, for his injurious treatment of the sex.'

Takupi had been hitherto silent, and spoke only to shew the sincerity of his resignation. 'Great Queen, cried he, I acknowledge my crime; and since I am to be banished, I beg it may be to some ruined town, or desolate village in the country I have governed. I shall find some pleasure in improving the soil, and bringing back a spirit of industry among the inhabitants.' His request appearing reasonable, it was immediately complied with, and a courtier had orders to fix upon a place of banishment, answering the Minister's description. After some months' search, however, the enquiry proved fruitless; neither a desolate village, nor a ruined town, was found in the whole kingdom. *Alas*, said Takupi then to the Queen, *how can that country be ill governed which has neither a desolate village, nor a ruined town in it?* The Queen perceived the justice of his expostulation, and the Minister was received into more than former favour.

LETTER CII.—*From the same.*

THE ladies here are by no means such ardent gamesters as the women of Asia. In this respect I must do the English justice; for I love to praise where applause is justly merited. Nothing more common in China, than to see two women of fashion continue gaming, till one has won all the other's clothes, and stripped her quite naked; the winner thus marching off in a double suit of finery, and the loser shrinking behind in the primitive simplicity of Nature.

No doubt, you remember when *Shang*, our maiden aunt, played with a sharper. First her money went; then her trinkets were produced; her clothes followed piece by piece soon after; when she had thus played herself quite naked, being a woman of spirit, and willing to pursue *her own*, she staked her teeth; fortune was against her even here, and her teeth followed her clothes; at last she played for her left eye, and oh, hard fate, this too she lost: however, she had the consolation of biting the sharper, for he never perceived that it was made of glass till it became his own.

How happy, my friend, are the English ladies, who never rise to such an inordinance of passion! Though the sex here are naturally fond of games of chance, and are taught to manage games of skill from their infancy, yet they never pursue ill fortune with such amazing intrepidity. Indeed I may entirely acquit them of ever playing——I mean of playing for their eyes or their teeth.

It is true, they often stake their fortune, their beauty, health, and reputations at a gaming-table. It even sometimes happens, that they play their husbands into a jail; yet still they preserve a decorum unknown to our wives and daughters of China. I have been present at a rout in this country, where a woman of fashion, after losing her money, has sat writhing in all the agonies of bad luck; and yet, after all, never once attempted to strip a single petticoat, or cover the board, as her last stake, with her head-clothes.

However, though I praise their moderation at play, I must not conceal their assiduity. In China, our women, except upon some great days, are never permitted to finger a dice-box; but here every day seems to be a festival; and night itself, which gives others rest, only serves to increase the female gamester's industry. I have been told of an old lady in the country, who being given over by the physicians, played with the curate of her parish to pass the time away; having won all his money, she next proposed playing for her funeral charges; the proposal was accepted; but unfortunately the lady expired just as she had taken in her game.

There are some passions, which though differently pursued, are attended with equal consequences in every country: here they game with more perseverance, there with greater fury; here they strip their families, there they strip themselves naked. A lady in China, who indulges a passion for gaming, often becomes a drunkard; and by flourishing a dice-box in one hand, she generally comes to brandish a dram cup in the other. Far be it from me to say there are any who drink drams in England; but it is natural to suppose, that when a lady has lost everything else but her honour, she will be apt to toss that into the bargain; and grown insensible to nicer feelings, behave like the Spaniard, who, when all his money was gone, endeavoured to borrow more, by offering to pawn his whisker. Adieu.

LETTER CIII.—*From Lien Chi Altangi to * * *, Merchant in Amsterdam.*

I HAVE just received a letter from my son, in which he informs me of the fruitlessness of his endeavours to recover the lady with whom he fled from Persia. He strives to cover under the appearance of fortitude a heart torn with anxiety and disappointment. I have offered little consolation; since that but too frequently feeds the sorrow which it pretends to deplore, and strengthens the impression, which nothing but the external rubs of time and accident can thoroughly efface.

He informs me of his intentions of quitting Moscow the first opportunity, and travelling by land to Amsterdam. I must, therefore, upon his arrival, entreat the continuance of your friendship; and beg of you to provide him with proper directions for finding me in London. You can scarcely be sensible of the joy I expect upon seeing him once more: the ties between the father and the son among us of China are much more closely drawn than with you of Europe.

The remittances sent me from Argun to Moscow came in safety. I cannot sufficiently admire that spirit of honesty, which prevails through the whole country of Siberia: perhaps the savages of that desolate region are the only untutored people of the globe, that cultivate the moral virtues, even without knowing that their actions merit praise. I have been told surprising things of their goodness, benevolence, and generosity; and the uninterrupted commerce between China and Russia, serves as a collateral confirmation.

Let us, says the Chinese law-giver, *admire the rude virtues of the ignorant, but rather imitate the delicate morals of the polite.* In the country where I reside, though honesty and benevolence be not so congenial, yet Art supplies the place of Nature. Though here every vice is carried to excess; yet every virtue is practised also with unexampled superiority. A city like this is the soil for great virtues and great vices; the villain can soon improve here in the deepest mysteries of deceiving; and the practical philosopher can every day meet new incitements to mend his honest intentions. There are no pleasures, sensual or sentimental, which this city does not produce; yet I know not how, I could not be content to reside here for life. There is something so seducing in that spot in which we first had existence, that nothing but it can please; whatever vicissitudes we experience in life, however we toil, or wheresoever we wander, our fatigued wishes still recur to home for tranquillity, we long to die in that spot which gave us birth, and in that pleasing expectation opiate every calamity.

You now therefore perceive that I have some intentions of leaving this country; and yet my designed departure fills me with reluctance and regret. Though the friendships of travellers are generally more transient than vernal snows, still I feel an uneasiness at breaking the connections I have formed since my arrival; particularly I shall have no small pain in leaving my usual companion, guide, and instructor.

I shall wait for the arrival of my son before I set out. He shall be my companion in every intended journey for the future; in his company I can support the fatigues of the way with redoubled ardour, pleased at once with conveying instruction, and exacting obedience. Adieu.

LETTER CIV.—*From Lien Chi Altangi, to Fum Hoam, first President of the Ceremonial Academy at Pekin, in China.*

OUR scholars of China have a most profound veneration for forms. A first rate beauty never studied the decorums of dress with more assiduity; they may properly enough be said to be clothed with wisdom from head to foot; they have their philosophical whiskers, their philosophical slippers, and philosophical fans; there is even a philosophical standard for measuring the nails; and yet, with all this seeming wisdom, they are often found to be mere empty pretenders.

A philosophical beau is not so frequent in Europe; yet I am told that such characters are found here. I mean such as punctually support all the decorums of learning, without being really very profound, or naturally possessed of a fine understanding; who labour hard to obtain the titular honours attending literary merit; who flatter others, in order to be flattered in turn; and only study to be thought students.

A character of this kind generally receives company in his study, in all the pensive formality of slippers, night-gown, and easy chair. The table is covered with a large book, which is always keept open, and never read; his solitary hours being dedicated to dozing, mending pens, feeling his pulse, peeping through the microscope, and sometimes reading amusing books, which he condemns in company. His library is preserved with the most religious neatness; and is generally a repository of scarce books, which bear an high price, because too dull or useless to become common by the ordinary methods of publication.

Such men are generally candidates for admittance into literary clubs, academies, and institutions, where they regularly meet to give and receive a little instruction and a great deal of praise. In conversation they never betray ignorance, because they never seem to receive information. Offer a new observation, they have heard it before; pinch them in an argument, and they reply with a sneer.

Yet how trifling soever these little arts may appear, they answer one valuable purpose, of gaining the practisers the esteem they wish for. The bounds of a man's knowledge are easily concealed, if he has but prudence; but all can readily see and admire a gilt library, a set of long nails, a silver standish, or a well combed whisker, who are incapable of distinguishing a dunce.

When Father Matthew, the first European Missioner, entered

China, the court was informed, that he possessed great skill in astronomy; he was therefore sent for, and examined. The established astronomers of state undertook this task; and made their report to the Emperor, that his skill was but very superficial, and no way comparable to their own. The Missioner, however, appealed from their judgment to experience, and challenged them to calculate an eclipse of the moon, that was to happen a few nights following. 'What, said some, shall a Barbarian, without nails, pretend to vie with men in astronomy, who have made it the study of their lives, with men who know half the knowable characters of words, who wear scientifical caps and slippers, and who have gone through every literary degree with applause?' They accepted the challenge, confident of success. The eclipse began; the Chinese produced a most splendid apparatus, and were fifteen minutes wrong; the Missioner, with a single instrument, was exact to a second. This was convincing; but the court astronomers were not to be convinced; instead of acknowledging their error, they assured the Emperor, that their calculations were certainly exact, but that the stranger without nails had actually bewitched the moon. *Well then*, cries the good Emperor, smiling at their ignorance, *you shall still continue to be servants of the moon; but I constitute this man her Controller*.

China is thus replete with men, whose only pretensions to knowledge arise from external circumstances; and in Europe every country abounds with them in proportion to its ignorance. Spain and Flanders, who are behind the rest of Europe in learning, at least three centuries, have twenty literary titles and marks of distinction unknown in France or England: they have their *Clarissimi* and *Preclarissimi*, their *Accuratissimi* and *Minutissimi*; a round cap entitles one student to argue, and a square cap permits another to teach; while a cap with a tassel almost sanctifies the head it happens to cover. But where true knowledge is cultivated, these formalities begin to disappear; the ermined cowl, the solemn beard, and sweeping train are laid aside; philosophers dress, and talk, and think like other men; and lamb-skin dressers, and cap-makers, and tail-carriers, now deplore a literary age.

For my own part, my friend, I have seen enough of presuming ignorance, never to venerate wisdom but where it actually appears. I have received literary titles and distinctions myself; and, by the quantity of my own wisdom, know how very little wisdom they can confer. Adieu.

LETTER CV.—*From the same.*

THE time for the young King's coronation approaches; the great and the little world look forward with impatience. A knight from the country, who has brought up his family to see and be seen on this occasion, has taken all the lower part of the house where I lodge. His wife is laying in a large quantity of silks, which the mercer tells her are to be fashionable next season; and Miss, her daughter, has actually had her ears bored previous to the ceremony. In all this bustle of preparation I am considered as mere lumber, and have been shoved up two stories higher to make room for others my landlady seems perfectly convinced are my betters; but whom, before me, she is contented with only calling very good company.

The little beau, who has now forced himself into my intimacy, was yesterday giving me a most minute detail of the intended procession. All men are eloquent upon their favourite topic; and this seemed peculiarly adapted to the size and turn of his understanding. His whole mind was blazoned over with a variety of glittering images; coronets, escutcheons, lace, fringe, tassels, stones, bugles, and spun glass. 'Here, cried he, Garter is to walk; and there Rouge Dragon marches with the escutcheons on his back. Here Clarencieux moves forward; and there Blue Mantle disdains to be left behind. Here the Aldermen march two and two; and there the undaunted Champion of England, no way terrified at the very numerous appearance of gentlemen and ladies, rides forward in complete armour, and, with an intrepid air, throws down his glove. Ah, continues he, should any be so hardy as to take up that fatal glove, and so accept the challenge, we should see fine sport; the Champion would shew him no mercy; he would soon teach him all his passes with a witness. However, I am afraid we shall have none willing to try it with him, upon the approaching occasion, for two reasons; first, because his antagonist would stand a chance of being killed in the single combat; and secondly, because if he escapes the Champion's arm, he would certainly be hanged for treason. No, no, I fancy none will be so hardy as to dispute it with a Champion like him inured to arms; and we shall probably see him prancing unmolested away, holding his bridle thus in one hand, and brandishing his dram cup in the other.'

Some men have a manner of describing, which only wraps the subject in more than former obscurity; thus I was unable, with all my companion's volubility, to form a distinct idea of the intended procession. I was certain, that the inauguration of a king should be conducted with solemnity and religious awe; and I could not be persuaded that there was much solemnity in this description. If this be true, cried I to myself, the people of Europe surely have a strange manner of mixing solemn and fantastic images together; pictures at once replete with burlesque and the sublime. At a time when the King enters into the most solemn compact with his people, nothing surely should be admitted to diminish from the real majesty of the ceremony. A ludicrous image brought in at such a time throws an air of ridicule upon the whole. It some way resembles a picture I have seen, designed by Albert Durer, where, amidst all the solemnity of that awful scene, a Deity judging, and a trembling world awaiting the decree, he has introduced a merry mortal trundling his scolding wife to hell in a wheel-barrow.

My companion, who mistook my silence during this interval of reflection, for the rapture of astonishment, proceeded to describe those frivolous parts of the show, that mostly struck his imagination; and to assure me, that if I stayed in this country some months longer I should see fine things. 'For my own part, continued he, I know already of fifteen suits of clothes, that would stand on one end with gold lace, all designed to be first shewn there; and as for diamonds, rubies, emeralds, and pearls, we shall see them as thick as brass nails in a sedan chair. And then we are all to walk so majestically thus; this foot always behind the foot before. The ladies are to fling nosegays; the court poets to scatter verses; the spectators are to be all in full dress; Mrs. Tibbs, in a new sacque, ruffles, and frenched hair; look where you will, one thing finer than another; Mrs. Tibbs curtsies to the Duchess; her Grace returns the compliment with a bow. Largess, cries the Herald. Make room, cries the Gentleman Usher. Knock him down, cries the guard. Ah, continued he, amazed at his own description, what an astonishing scene of grandeur can art produce from the smallest circumstance, when it thus actually turns to wonder one man putting on another man's hat.'

I now found his mind was entirely set upon the fopperies of the pageant, and quite regardless of the real meaning of such costly preparations. *Pageants*, says Bacon, *are pretty things; but we should rather study to make them elegant than expensive.* Processions, cavalcades, and all that fund of gay frippery, furnished out by tailors, barbers, and tire-women, mechanically influence the mind into veneration: an Emperor, in his night-cap, would not meet with half the respect of an Emperor with a glittering crown. Politics resemble religion; attempting to divest of ceremony, is the most certain method of bringing either into contempt. The weak must have their inducements to admiration as well as the wise; and it is the business of a sensible government, to impress all ranks with a sense of subordination, whether this be effected by a diamond buckle or a virtuous edict, a sumptuary law or a glass necklace.

This interval of reflection only gave my companion spirits to begin his description afresh; and as a greater inducement to raise my curiosity, he informed me of the vast sums that were given by the spectators for places. 'That the ceremony must be fine, cries he, is very evident from the fine price that is paid for seeing it. Several ladies have assured me, they could willingly part with one eye, rather than be prevented from looking on with the other. Come, come, continues he, I have a friend, who, for my sake, will supply us with places at the most reasonable rates; I'll take care you shall not be imposed upon; and he will inform you of the use, finery, rapture, splendour, and enchantment of the whole ceremony better than I.'

Follies often repeated, lose their absurdity and assume the appearance of reason: his arguments were so often and so strongly enforced, that I had actually some thoughts of becoming a spectator. We accordingly went together to bespeak a place; but guess my surprise, when the man demanded a purse of gold for a single seat: I could hardly believe him serious upon making the demand. 'Prithee, friend, cried I, after I have paid twenty pounds for sitting here an hour or two, can I bring a part of the Coronation back?' *No, sir.* 'How long can I live upon it after I have come away?' *Not long, Sir.* 'Can a Coronation clothe, feed, or fatten me?' *Sir*, replied the man, *you seem to be under a mistake; all that you can bring away, is the pleasure of having it to say, that you saw the Coronation.* 'Blast me, cries Tibbs, if that be all, there's no need of paying for that, since I am resolved to have that pleasure, whether I am there or no!'

I am conscious, my friend, that this is but a very confused description of the intended ceremony. You may object, that I neither settle rank, precedency, nor place; that I am ignorant whether Gules walks before or behind Garter; that I have neither mentioned the dimensions of a Lord's cap, nor measured the length of a Lady's tail. I know your delight is in minute description; and this I am unhappily disqualified from furnishing; yet, upon the whole, I fancy it will be no way comparable to the magnificence of our late Emperor Whangti's procession, when he was married to the moon, at which Fum Hoam himself presided in person. Adieu.

LETTER CVI.—*To the same.*

It was formerly the custom here, when men of distinction died, for their surviving acquaintance to throw each a slight present into the grave. Several things of little value were made use of for that purpose; perfumes, reliques, spices, bitter herbs, camomile, wormwood, and verses. This custom, however, is almost discontinued; and nothing but verses alone are now lavished on such occasions; an oblation which they suppose may be interred with the dead without any injury to the living.

Upon the death of the great therefore, the poets and undertakers are sure of employment. While one provides the long cloak, black staff, and mourning coach, the other produces the pastoral or elegy, the monody or apotheosis. The nobility need be under no apprehensions, but die as fast as they think proper, the poet and undertaker are ready to supply them; these can find metaphorical tears and family escutcheons at half an hour's warning; and when the one has soberly laid the body in the grave, the other is ready to fix it figuratively among the stars.

There are several ways of being poetically sorrowful on such occasions. The bard is now some pensive youth of science, who sits deploring among the tombs; again he is Thyrsis, complaining in a circle of harmless sheep. Now Britannia sits upon her own shore, and gives a loose to maternal tenderness; at another time, Parnassus, even the mountain Parnassus, gives way to sorrow, and is bathed in tears of distress.

But the most useful manner is this: Damon meets Menalcas, who has got a most gloomy countenance. The shepherd asks his friend, whence that look of distress? to which the other replies, that Pollio is no more. If that be the case, then, cries Damon, let us retire to yonder bower at some distance off, where the cypress and the jessamine add fragrance to the breeze; and let us weep alternately for Pollio, the friend of shepherds, and the patron of every muse. Ah, returns his fellow shepherd, what think you rather of that grotto by the fountain side; the murmuring stream will help to assist our complaints, and a nightingale on a neighbouring tree will join her voice to the concert. When the place is thus settled, they begin: the brook stands still to hear their lamentations; the cows forget to graze; and the very tigers start from the forest with sympathetic concern. By the tombs of our ancestors, my dear Fum, I am quite unaffected in all this distress: the whole is liquid laudanum to my spirits; and a tiger of common sensibility has twenty times more tenderness than I.

But though I could never weep with the complaining shepherd, yet I am sometimes induced to pity the poet, whose trade is thus to make Demigods and Heroes for a dinner. There is not in Nature a more dismal figure than a man who sits down to premeditated flattery; every stanza he writes, tacitly reproaches the meanness of his occupation, till at last his stupidity becomes more stupid, and his dullness more diminutive.

I am amazed, therefore, that none have yet found out the secret of flattering the worthless, and yet of preserving a safe conscience. I have often wished for some method by which a man might do himself and his deceased patron justice, without being under the hateful reproach of self-conviction. After long lucubration, I have hit upon such an expedient; and send you the specimen of a poem upon the decease of a great man, in which the flattery is perfectly fine, and yet the poet perfectly innocent.

On the Death of the Right Honourable ***

Ye muses, pour the pitying tear
   For Pollio snatch'd away:
O had he liv'd another year!
  ——*He had not died to-day*.

O, were he born to bless mankind,
   In virtuous times of yore,
Heroes themselves had fallen behind!
  ——*Whene'er he went before*.

How sad the groves and plains appear,
   And sympathetic sheep;
Even pitying hills would drop a tear!
  ——*If hills could learn to weep*.

His bounty in exalted strain
   Each bard might well display:
Since none implor'd relief in vain!
  ——*That went reliev'd away*.

And hark! I hear the tuneful throng
   His obsequies forbid,
He still shall live, shall live as long,
  ——*As ever dead man did*.

LETTER CVII.—*To the same.*

It is the most usual method in every report, first to examine its probability, and then act as the conjuncture may require. The English, however, exert a different spirit in such circumstances; they first act, and, when too late begin to examine. From a knowledge of this disposition, there are several here who make it their business to frame new reports at every convenient interval, all tending to denounce ruin both on their contemporaries and their posterity. This denunciation is eagerly caught up by the public; away they fling to propagate the distress; sell out at one place, buy in at another, grumble at their governors, shout in mobs, and when they have thus, for some time, behaved like fools, sit down coolly to argue and talk wisdom, to puzzle each other with syllogism, and prepare for the next report that prevails, which is always attended with the same success.

Thus are they ever rising above one report only to sink into another. They resemble a dog in a well, pawing to get free. When he has raised his upper parts above water, and every spectator imagines him disengaged, his lower parts drag him down again and sink him to the nose; he makes new efforts to emerge, and every effort increasing his weakness, only tends to sink him the deeper.

There are some here, who, I am told, make a tolerable subsistence by the credulity of their countrymen: as they find the public fond of blood, wounds and death, they contrive political ruins suited to every month in the year; this month the people are to be eaten up by the French in flat-bottomed boats; the next by the soldiers, designed to beat the French back; now the people are going to jump down the gulf of luxury; and now nothing but a herring subscription can fish them up again. Time passes on; the report proves false; new circumstances produce new changes, but the people never change, they are persevering in folly.

In other countries, those boding politicians would be left to fret over their own schemes alone, and grow splenetic without hopes of infecting others. But England seems to be the very region where spleen delights to dwell; a man not only can give an unbounded scope to the disorder in himself, but may, if he pleases, propagate it over the whole kingdom, with a certainty of success. He has only to cry out, that the government, the government is all wrong, that their schemes are leading to ruin, that Britons are no more, every good member of the common-wealth thinks it his duty, in such a case, to deplore the universal decadence with sympathetic sorrow and, by fancying the constitution in a decay, absolutely to impair its vigour.

This people would laugh at my simplicity, should I advise them to be less sanguine in harbouring gloomy predictions, and examine coolly before they attempted to complain. I have just heard a story, which, though transacted in a private family, serves very well to describe the behaviour of the whole nation, in cases of threatened calamity. As there are public, so there are private incendiaries here. One of the last, either for the amusement of his friends, or to divert a fit of the spleen, lately sent a threatening letter to a worthy family in my neighbourhood, to this effect:

'SIR, knowing you to be very rich, and finding myself to be very poor, I think proper to inform you, that I have learned the secret of poisoning man, woman, and child, without danger of detection. Don't be uneasy, Sir, you may take your choice of being poisoned in a fortnight, or poisoned in a month, or poisoned in six weeks; you shall have full time to settle your affairs. Though I 'm poor, I love to do things like a gentleman. But, Sir, you must die; I have determined it within my own breast that you must die. Blood, Sir, blood is my trade; so I could wish you would this day six weeks take leave of your friends, wife, and family, for I cannot possibly allow you longer time. To convince you more certainly of the power of my art, by which you may know I speak truth; take this letter, when you have read it, tear off the seal, fold it up, and give it to your favourite Dutch mastiff that sits by the fire, he will swallow it, Sir, like a butter'd toast; in three hours four minutes after he has taken it, he will attempt to bite off his own tongue, and half an hour after burst asunder in twenty pieces. Blood, blood, blood; so no more at present from, Sir, your most obedient, most devoted humble servant to command till death.'

You may easily imagine the consternation into which this letter threw the whole good-natured family. The poor man, to whom it was addressed, was the more surprised, as not knowing how he could merit such inveterate malice. All the friends of the family were convened; it was universally agreed, that it was a most terrible affair, and that the government should be solicited to offer a reward and a pardon: a fellow of this kind would go on poisoning family after family; and it was impossible to say where the destruction would end. In pursuance of these determinations, the government was applied to; strict search was made after the incendiary, but all in vain. At last, therefore, they recollected that the experiment was not yet tried upon the dog; the Dutch mastiff was brought up, and placed in the midst of the friends and relations, the seal was torn off, the packet folded up with care, and soon they found, to the great surprise of all——that the dog would not eat the letter. Adieu.

LETTER CVIII.—*To the same.*

I HAVE frequently been amazed at the ignorance of almost all the European travellers who have penetrated any considerable way eastward into Asia. They have been influenced either by motives of commerce or piety, and their accounts are such as might reasonably be expected from men of very narrow or very prejudiced education, the dictates of superstition, or the result of ignorance. Is it not surprising that, in such a variety of adventurers, not one single philosopher should be found? for as to the travels of Gemelli, the learned are long agreed that the whole is but an imposture.

There is scarce any country, how rude or uncultivated soever, where the inhabitants are not possessed of some peculiar secrets, either in Nature or Art, which might be transplanted with success; in Siberian Tartary, for instance, the natives extract a strong spirit from milk, which is a secret probably unknown to the chemists of Europe. In the most savage parts of India, they are possessed of the secret of dyeing vegetable substances scarlet; and of refining lead into a metal which, for hardness and colour, is little inferior to silver; not one of which secrets but would in Europe make a man's fortune. The power of the Asiatics in producing winds, or bringing down rain, the Europeans are apt to treat as fabulous, because they have no instances of the like nature among themselves; but they would have treated the secrets of gunpowder and the mariner's compass, in the same manner, had they been told the Chinese used such arts before the invention was common with themselves at home.

Of all the English philosophers I most reverence *Bacon,* that great and hardy genius; he it is who allows of secrets yet unknown; who, undaunted by the seeming difficulties that oppose, prompts human curiosity to examine every part of Nature, and even exhorts man to try whether he cannot subject the tempest, the thunder, and even earthquakes to human control: O did a man of his daring spirit, of his genius, penetration, and learning travel to those countries, which have been visited only by the superstitious and mercenary, what might not mankind expect; how would he enlighten the regions to which he travelled! And what a variety of knowledge and useful improvement would he not bring back in exchange!

There is probably no country so barbarous, that would not disclose all it knew, if it received from the traveller equivalent information; and I am apt to think, that a person, who was ready to give more knowledge than he received, would be welcome wherever he came. All his care in travelling should only be to suit his intellectual banquet to the people with whom he conversed; he should not attempt to teach the unlettered Tartar astronomy, nor yet instruct the polite Chinese in the ruder arts of subsistence; he should endeavour to improve the Barbarian in the secrets of living comfortably; and the inhabitant of a more refined country in the speculative pleasures of science. How much more nobly would a philosopher thus employed spend his time, than by sitting at home earnestly intent upon adding one star more to his catalogue, or one monster more to his collection; or still, if possible, more triflingly sedulous in the incatenation of fleas, or the sculpture of a cherry-stone.

I never consider this subject, without being surprised how none of those societies, so laudably established in England for the promotion of arts and learning, have never thought of sending one of their members into the most eastern parts of Asia, to make what discoveries he was able. To be convinced of the utility of such an undertaking, let them but read the relations of their own travellers. It will be there found, that they are as often deceived themselves, as they attempt to deceive others. The merchants tell us perhaps the price of different commodities, the methods of baling them up, and the properest manner for an European to preserve his health in the country. The missioner, on the other hand, informs us, with what pleasure the country to which he was sent embraced Christianity, and the numbers he converted; what methods he took to keep Lent in a region where there was no fish, or the shifts he made to celebrate the rites of his religion, in places where there was neither bread nor wine; such accounts, with the usual appendage of marriages and funerals, inscriptions, rivers, and mountains, make up the whole of an European traveller's diary; but as to all the secrets of which the inhabitants are possessed, those are universally attributed to magic; and when the traveller can give no other account of the wonders he sees performed, he very contentedly ascribes them to the power of the devil.

It was an usual observation of *Boyle*, the English chemist, that if every artist would but discover what new observations occurred to him in the exercise of his trade, philosophy would thence gain innumerable improvements. It may be observed, with still greater justice, that if the useful knowledge of every country, howsoever barbarous, was gleaned by a judicious observer, the advantages would be inestimable. Are there not even in Europe many useful inventions known or practised, but in one place? The instrument, as an example, for cutting down corn in Germany, is much more handy and expeditious, in my opinion, than the sickle used in England. The cheap and expeditious manner of making vinegar without previous fermentation, is known only in a part of France. If such discoveries, therefore, remain still to be known at home; what funds of knowledge might not be collected, in countries yet unexplored, or only passed through by ignorant travellers in hasty caravans.

The caution with which foreigners are received in Asia may be alleged as an objection to such a design. But how readily have several European merchants found admission into regions the most suspecting, under the character of *Sanjapins*, or northern pilgrims; to such, not even China itself denies access.

To send out a traveller, properly qualified for these purposes, might be an object of national concern; it would in some measure repair the breaches made by ambition; and might shew there were still some who boasted a greater name than that of patriots, who professed themselves lovers of men. The only difficulty would remain in choosing a proper person for so arduous an enterprise. He should be a man of a philosophical turn, one apt to deduce consequences of general utility from particular occurrences, neither swollen with pride, nor hardened by prejudice, neither wedded to one particular system, nor instructed only in one particular science; neither wholly a botanist, nor quite an antiquarian; his mind should be tinctured with miscellaneous knowledge, and his manners humanized by an intercourse with men. He should be, in some measure, an enthusiast to the design; fond of travelling, from a rapid imagination, and an innate love of change; furnished with a body capable of sustaining every fatigue, and a heart not easily terrified at danger. Adieu.

LETTER CIX.—*From the same.*

One of the principal tasks I had proposed to myself on my arrival here, was to become acquainted with the names and characters of those now living, who as scholars or wits, had acquired the greatest share of reputation. In order to succeed in this design, I fancied the surest method would be to begin my enquiry among the ignorant, judging that his fame would be greatest, which was loud enough to be heard by the vulgar. Thus predisposed, I began the search, but only went in quest of disappointment and perplexity. I found every district had a peculiar famous man of its own. Here the story-telling shoe-maker had engrossed the admiration on one side of the street, while the bellman, who excelleth at a catch, was in quiet possession of the other. At one end of a lane, the sexton was regarded as the greatest man alive, but I had not travelled half its length, till I found an enthusiast teacher had divided his reputation. My landlady, perceiving my design, was kind enough to offer me her advice in this affair. It was true, she observed, that she was no judge, but she knew what pleased herself, and if I would rest upon her judgment, I should set down Tom Collins as the most ingenious man in the world, for Tom was able to take off all mankind, and imitate besides a sow and pigs to perfection.

I now perceived that, taking my standard of reputation among the vulgar, would swell my catalogue of great names above the size of a Court Calendar, I therefore discontinued this method of pursuit, and resolved to prosecute my enquiry into that usual residence of fame, a book-seller's shop. In consequence of this, I entreated the bookseller to let me know who were they who now made the greatest figure either in morals, wit, or learning. Without giving me a direct answer, he pulled a pamphlet from the shelf, *The Young Attorney's Guide*; There, Sir, cries he, there's a touch for you, fifteen hundred of these moved off in a day; I take the author of this pamphlet either for title, preface, plan, body, or index to be the completest hand in England. I found it was vain to prosecute my enquiry, where my informer appeared so incompetent a judge of merit, so paying for the *Young Attorney's Guide*, which good manners obliged me to buy, I walked off.

My pursuit after famous men now brought me into a print shop. Here, thought I, the painter only reflects the public voice. As every man who deserved it had formerly his statue placed up in the Roman forum, so here probably the pictures of none but such as merit a place in our affections are held up for public sale. But guess my surprise when I came to examine this depository of noted faces; all distinctions were levelled here, as in the grave, and I could not but regard it as the catacomb of real merit. The brickdust man took up as much room as the truncheoned hero, and the judge was elbowed by the thief-taker; quacks, pimps, and buffoons increased the group, and noted stallions only made room for more noted whores. I had read the works of some of the moderns previous to my coming to England, with delight and approbation, but I found their faces had no place here; the walls were covered with the names of authors I had never known, or had endeavoured to forget; with the little self-advertising things of a day, who had forced themselves into fashion, but not into fame; I could read at the bottom of some pictures, the names of **, and ***, and ****, all equally candidates for the vulgar shout, and foremost to propagate their unblushing faces upon brass. My uneasiness therefore at not finding my few favourite names among the number, was now changed into congratulation; I could not avoid reflecting on the fine observation of Tacitus on a similar occasion. In this cavalcade of flattery, cries the historian, neither the pictures of Brutus, Cassius, nor Cato, were to be seen, *eo clariores quia imagines eorum non deferebantur*, their absence being the strongest proof of their merit.

It is in vain, cried I, to seek for true greatness among these monuments of the unburied dead; let me go among the tombs of those who are confessedly famous, and see if any have been lately deposited there, who deserve the attention of posterity, and whose names may be transmitted to my distant friend, as an honour to the present age. Determined in my pursuit, I paid a second visit to Westminster-abbey. There I found several new monuments erected to the memory of several great men; the names of the great men I absolutely forget, but I well remember that Roubillac was the statuary who carved them. I could not help smiling at two modern epitaphs in particular; one of which praised the deceased for being *ortus ex antiqua stirpe*; the other commended the dead, because *hanc ædem suis sumptibus reædificavit*: the greatest merit of one, consisted in his being descended from an illustrious house; the chief distinction of the other, that he had propped up an old house that was falling. Alas, alas, cried I, such monuments as these confer honour, not upon the great men, but upon little Roubillac.

Hitherto disappointed in my enquiry after the great of the present age, I was resolved to mix in company, and try what I could learn among critics in coffee-houses; and here it was that I heard my favourite names talked of even with inverted fame. A gentleman of exalted merit, as a writer, was branded in general terms as a bad man; another of exquisite delicacy, as a poet, was reproached for wanting good nature; a third was accused of freethinking; and a fourth of having once been a player. Strange, cried I, how unjust are mankind in the distribution of fame; the ignorant, among whom I sought at first, were willing to grant, but incapable of distinguishing the virtues of those which deserved it; among those I now converse with, they know the proper objects of admiration, but mix envy with applause.

Disappointed so often, I was now resolved to examine those characters in person, of whom the world talked so freely; by conversing with men of real merit, I began to find out those characters which really deserved, though they strove to avoid, applause. I found the vulgar admiration entirely misplaced, and malevolence without its sting. The truly great, possessed of numerous small faults, and shining virtues, preserve a sublime in morals as in writing. They who have attained an excellence in either, commit numberless transgressions observable to the meanest understanding. The ignorant critic and dull remarker can readily spy blemishes in eloquence or morals, whose sentiments are not sufficiently elevated to observe a beauty; but such are judges neither of books nor of life; they can diminish no solid reputation by their censure, nor bestow a lasting character by their applause. In short, I found by my search, that such only can confer real fame upon others, who have merit themselves to deserve it. Adieu.

LETTER CX.—*To the same.*

THERE are numberless employments in the courts of the Eastern monarchs utterly unpractised and unknown in Europe. They have no such officers, for instance, as the Emperor's ear-tickler, or tooth-picker; they have never introduced at the courts the Mandarine appointed to bear the royal tobacco-box, or the grave director of the imperial exercitations in the seraglio. Yet I am surprised that the English have imitated us in none of these particulars, as they are generally pleased with everything that comes from China, and excessively fond of creating new and useless employments. They have filled their houses with our furniture, their public gardens with our fire-works, and their very ponds with our fish; our courtiers, my friend, are the fish and the furniture they should have imported; our courtiers would fill up the necessary ceremonies of a court better than those of Europe, would be contented with receiving large salaries for doing little, whereas some of this country are at present discontented though they receive large salaries for doing nothing.

I lately, therefore, had thoughts of publishing a proposal here, for the admission of some new Eastern offices and titles into their court register. As I consider myself in the light of a Cosmopolite, I find as much satisfaction in scheming for the countries in which I happen to reside, as for that in which I was born.

The finest apartments in the palace of Pegu are frequently infested with rats. These the religion of the country strictly forbids the people to kill. In such circumstances therefore they are obliged to have recourse to some great man of the court, who is willing to free the royal apartments even at the hazard of his salvation. After a weak monarch's reign, the quantity of court vermin in every corner of the palace is surprising, but a prudent king and a vigilant officer soon drives them from their sanctuaries behind the mats and the tapestry, and effectually frees the court. Such an officer in England would in my opinion be serviceable at this juncture; for if, as I am told, the palace be old, much vermin must undoubtedly have taken refuge behind the wainscot and hangings. A minister should therefore be invested with the title and dignities of Court-vermin killer; he should have full power either to banish, take, poison, or destroy them, with enchantments, traps, ferrets, or ratsbane. He might be permitted to brandish his besom without remorse, and brush down every part of the furniture without sparing a single cobweb however sacred by long prescription. I communicated this proposal some days ago in a company of the first distinction, and enjoying the most honourable offices of the state. Among the number were the inspector of Great Britain, Mr. Henriques the Director of the Ministry, Ben. Victor the Treasurer, John Lockman the Secretary, and the Conductor of the Imperial Magazine. They all acquiesced in the utility of my proposal, but were apprehensive it might meet with some obstructions from court upholsterers and chamber-maids, who would object to it from the demolition of the furniture, and the dangerous use of ferrets and ratsbane.

My next proposal is rather more general than the former, and might probably meet with less opposition. Though no people in the world flatter each other more than the English, I know none who understand the art less, and flatter with such little refinement. Their panegyric, like a Tartar feast, is indeed served up with profusion, but their cookery is insupportable. A client here shall dress up a fricassee for his patron, that shall offend an ordinary nose before it enters the room. A town shall send up their address to a great minister, which shall prove at once a satire on the minister and themselves. If the favourite of the day sits, or stands, or sleeps, there are poets to put it into verse, and priests to preach it in the pulpit. In order therefore to free both those who praise, and those who are praised, from a duty probably disagreeable to both, I would constitute professed flatterers here as in several courts of India. These are appointed in the courts of their princes, to instruct the people where to exclaim with admiration, and where to lay an emphasis of praise. But an officer of this kind is always in waiting when the Emperor converses in a familiar manner among his Rajahs and other nobility. At every sentence, when the monarch pauses, and smiles at what he has been saying, the Karamatman, as this officer is called, is to take it for granted, that his majesty has said a good thing. Upon which he cries out Karamat! Karamat! a miracle, a miracle, and throws up his hands and his eyes in extasy. This is echoed by the courtiers around, while the Emperor sits all this time in sullen satisfaction, enjoying the triumph of his joke, or studying a new repartee.

I would have such an officer placed at every great man's table in England. By frequent practice he might soon become a perfect master of the art, and in time would turn out pleasing to his patron, no way troublesome to himself, and might prevent the nauseous attempts of many more ignorant pretenders. The clergy here, I am convinced, would relish this proposal. It would provide places for several of them. And indeed by some of their late productions many appear to have qualified themselves as candidates for this office already.

But my last proposal I take to be of the utmost importance. Our neighbour the Empress of Russia has, you may remember, instituted an order of female knighthood. The Empress of Germany has also instituted another; the Chinese have had such an order time immemorial. I am amazed the English have never come into such an institution. When I consider what kind of men are made knights here, it appears strange, that they have never conferred this honour upon women. They make cheesemongers and pastry-cooks, Knights; then why not their wives? They have called up tallow-chandlers to maintain the hardy profession of chivalry and arms; then why not their wives? Haberdashers are sworn, as I suppose all Knights must be sworn, *never to fly in time of mellay or battle, to maintain and uphold the noble estate of Chivalry, with horse harnishe and other Knightlye habiliments*. Haberdashers, I say, are sworn to all this, then why not their wives? Certain I am their wives understand fighting and feats of mellay and battle better than they, and as for Knightlye horse and harnishe, it is probable, both know nothing more than the harness of a one horse chaise. No, no, my friend, instead of conferring any order upon the husbands, I would knight their wives. However, the state should not be troubled with a new institution upon this occasion. Some ancient exploded order might be revived, which would furnish both a motto and a name, the ladies might be permitted to choose for themselves. There are for instance, the obsolete orders of the *Dragon* in Germany, of the *Rue* in Scotland, and the *Porcupine* in France, all well-sounding names, and very applicable to my intended female institution. Adieu.

LETTER CXI.—*To the same.*

RELIGIOUS sects in England are far more numerous than in China. Every man who has interest enough to hire a conventicle here, may set up for himself and sell off a new religion. The sellers of the newest pattern at present give extreme good bargains; and let their disciples have a great deal of *confidence* for very little money.

Their shops are much frequented, and their customers every day increasing, for people are naturally fond of going to Paradise at as small expense as possible.

Yet you must not conceive this modern sect, as differing in opinion from those of the established religion: Difference of opinion indeed formerly divided their sectaries, and sometimes drew their armies to the field. White gowns and black mantles, flapped hats and cross pocket holes, were once the causes of quarrel; men then had some reason for fighting, they knew what they fought about; but at present, they are arrived at such refinement in religion-making, that they have actually formed a new sect without a new opinion; they quarrel for

opinions they both equally defend; they hate each other, and
that is all the difference between them.

But though their principles are the same, their practice is
somewhat different. Those of the established religion laugh
when they are pleased, and their groans are seldom extorted
but by pain or danger. The new sect, on the contrary, weep
for their amusement, and use little music, except a chorus of
sighs and groans, or tunes that are made to imitate groaning.
Laughter is their aversion; lovers court each other from the
Lamentations; the bridegroom approaches the nuptial couch in
sorrowful solemnity, and the bride looks more dismal than an
undertaker's shop. Dancing round the room is with them
running in a direct line to the devil; and as for gaming, though
but in jest, they would sooner play with a rattle-snake's tail,
than finger a dice-box.

By this time you perceive that I am describing a sect of
Enthusiasts, and you have already compared them with the
Faquirs, Bramins, and Talapoins of the East. Among these,
you know, are generations that have been never known to
smile, and voluntary affliction makes up all the merit they can
boast of. Enthusiasms in every country produce the same
effects; stick the Faquir with pins, or confine the Bramine to a
vermin hospital, spread the Talapoin on the ground, or load the
Sectary's brow with contrition; those worshippers who discard
the light of reason, are ever gloomy; their fears increase in
proportion to their ignorance, as men are continually under
apprehensions who walk in darkness.

Yet there is still a stronger reason for the enthusiast's being
an enemy to laughter, namely, his being himself so proper an
object of ridicule. It is remarkable that the propagators of
false doctrines have ever been averse to mirth, and always begin
by recommending gravity, when they intended to disseminate
imposture. Fohi, the idol of China, is represented as having
never laughed; Zoroaster, the leader of the Bramins, is said to
have laughed but twice, upon his coming into the world, and
upon his leaving it; and Mahomet himself, though a lover of
pleasure, was a professed opposer of gaiety. Upon a certain
occasion telling his followers, that they would all appear naked
at the resurrection, his favourite wife represented such an
assembly as immodest and unbecoming. Foolish woman, cried
the grave prophet, though the whole assembly be naked, on that
day they shall have forgotten to laugh. Men like him opposed
ridicule, because they knew it to be a most formidable antagonist,

and preached up gravity, to conceal their own want of importance.

Ridicule has ever been the most powerful enemy of enthusiasm, and properly the only antagonist that can be opposed to it with success. Persecution only serves to propagate new religions; they acquire fresh vigour beneath the executioner and the axe, and like some vivacious insects, multiply by dissection. It is also impossible to combat enthusiasm with reason, for though it makes a shew of resistance, it soon eludes the pressure, refers you to distinctions not to be understood, and feelings which it cannot explain. A man who would endeavour to fix an enthusiast by argument, might as well attempt to spread quicksilver with his fingers. The only way to conquer a visionary is to despise him; the stake, the faggot, and the disputing doctor, in some measure, ennoble the opinions they are brought to oppose; they are harmless against innovating pride; contempt alone is truly dreadful. Hunters generally know the most vulnerable part of the beasts they pursue, by the care which every animal takes to defend the side which is weakest; on what side the enthusiast is most vulnerable, may be known by the care which he takes in the beginning to work his disciples into gravity, and guard them against the power of ridicule.

When Philip the Second was King of Spain, there was a contest in Salamanca between two orders of friars for superiority. The legend of one side contained more extraordinary miracles, but the legend of the other was reckoned most authentic. They reviled each other, as is usual in disputes of divinity, the people were divided into factions, and a civil war appeared unavoidable. In order to prevent such an imminent calamity, the combatants were prevailed upon to submit their legends to the fiery trial, and that which came forth untouched by the fire, was to have the victory, and to be honoured with a double share of reverence. Whenever the people flock to see a miracle, it is an hundred to one but that they see a miracle; incredible therefore were the numbers that were gathered round upon this occasion; the friars on each side approached, and confidently threw their respective legends into the flames, when lo, to the utter disappointment of all the assembly, instead of a miracle, both legends were consumed. Nothing but this, turning both parties into contempt, could have prevented the effusion of blood. The people now laughed at their former folly, and wondered why they fell out. Adieu.

LETTER CXII.—*To the same.*

THE English are at present employed in celebrating a feast which becomes general every seventh year; the Parliament of the nation being then dissolved and another appointed to be chosen. This solemnity falls infinitely short of our feast of the lanterns in magnificence and splendour; it is also surpassed by others of the East in unanimity and pure devotion, but no festival in the world can compare it with for eating. Their eating indeed amazes me: Had I five hundred heads, and were each head furnished with brains, yet would they all be insufficient to compute the number of cows, pigs, geese, and turkeys, which upon this occasion die for the good of their country!

To say the truth, eating seems to make a grand ingredient in all English parties of zeal, business, or amusement. When a Church is to be built, or an Hospital to be endowed, the Directors assemble, and instead of consulting upon it, they eat upon it, by which means the business goes forward with success. When the Poor are to be relieved, the officers appointed to dole out public charity, assemble and eat upon it: nor has it ever been known, that they filled the bellies of the poor till they had previously satisfied their own. But in the election of magistrates the people seem to exceed all bounds; the merits of a candidate are often measured by the number of his treats; his constituents assemble, eat upon him, and lend their applause, not to his integrity or sense, but to the quantities of his beef and brandy.

And yet I could forgive this people their plentiful meals on this occasion, as it is extremely natural for every man to eat a great deal when he gets it for nothing; but what amazes me is, that all this good living no way contributes to improve their good humour. On the contrary they seem to lose their temper as they lose their appetites: every morsel they swallow, and every glass they pour down, serves to increase their animosity. Many an honest man, before as harmless as a tame rabbit, when loaded with a single election dinner, has become more dangerous than a charged culverin. Upon one of these occasions, I have actually seen a bloody-minded man milliner sally forth at the head of a mob, determined to face a desperate pastry cook, who was general of the opposite party.

But you must not suppose they are without a pretext for thus beating each other. On the contrary, no man here is so uncivilized as to beat his neighbour without producing very sufficient reasons. One candidate, for instance, treats with gin, a spirit of their own manufacture; another, always drinks brandy imported from abroad. Brandy is a wholesome liquor; gin a liquor wholly their own. This then furnishes an obvious cause of quarrel, Whether it be most reasonable to get drunk with gin, or get drunk with brandy? The mob meet upon the debate: fight themselves sober; and then draw off to get drunk again, and charge for another encounter. So that the English may now properly be said to be engaged in war; since while they are subduing their enemies abroad, they are breaking each other's heads at home.

I lately made an excursion to a neighbouring village, in order to be a spectator of the ceremonies practised upon this occasion. I left town in company with three fiddlers, nine dozen of hams, and a corporation poet, which were designed as reinforcements to the gin-drinking party. We entered the town with a very good face; the fiddlers, no way intimidated by the enemy, kept handling their arms up the principal street. By this prudent manœuvre they took peaceable possession of their head-quarters, amidst the shouts of multitudes, who seemed perfectly rejoiced at hearing their music, but above all at seeing their bacon.

I must own I could not avoid being pleased to see all ranks of people on this occasion, levelled into an equality, and the poor, in some measure, enjoying the primitive privileges of Nature. If there was any distinction shown, the lowest of the people seemed to receive it from the rich. I could perceive a cobbler with a levee at his door, and an haberdasher giving audience from behind his counter. But my reflections were soon interrupted by a mob, who demanded whether I was for the distillery or the brewery? as these were terms with which I was totally unacquainted, I chose at first to be silent; however, I know not what might have been the consequence of my reserve, had not the attention of the mob been called off to a skirmish between a brandy-drinker's cow, and a gin-drinker's mastiff, which turned out greatly to the satisfaction of the mob in favour of the mastiff.

This spectacle, which afforded high entertainment, was at last ended by the appearance of one of the candidates, who came to harangue the mob; he made a very pathetic speech upon the late excessive importation of foreign drams, and the downfall of the distillery; I could see some of the audience shed tears. He was accompanied in his procession by Mrs. Deputy and Mrs. Mayoress. Mrs. Deputy was not in the least in liquor; and for Mrs. Mayoress, one of the spectators assured me in my ear that,—she was a very fine woman before she had the small pox.

Mixing with the crowd, I was now conducted to the hall where the magistrates are chosen: but what tongue can describe this scene of confusion? The whole crowd seemed equally inspired with anger, jealousy, politics, patriotism, and punch: I remarked one figure that was carried up by two men upon this occasion. I at first began to pity his infirmities as natural, but soon found the fellow so drunk that he could not stand; another made his appearance to give his vote, but though he could stand, he actually lost the use of his tongue, and remained silent; a third, who, though excessively drunk, could both stand and speak, being asked the candidate's name for whom he voted, could be prevailed upon to make no other answer, but tobacco and brandy. In short, an election-hall seems to be a theatre where every passion is seen without disguise; a school where fools may readily become worse, and where philosophers may gather wisdom. Adieu.

LETTER CXIII.—*From the same.*

THE disputes among the learned here are now carried on in a much more compendious manner than formerly. There was a time when folio was brought to oppose folio, and a champion was often listed for life under the banners of a single sorites. At present the controversy is decided in a summary way; an epigram or an acrostic finishes the debate, and the combatant, like the incursive Tartar, advances, and retires with a single blow.

An important literary debate at present engrosses the attention of the town. It is carried on with sharpness, and a proper share of this epigrammatical fury. An author, it seems, has taken an aversion to the faces of several players, and has written verses to prove his dislike; the players fall upon the author, and assure the town he must be dull, and their faces must be good because he wants a dinner; a critic comes to the poet's assistance, asserting, that the verses were perfectly original, and so smart that he could never have written them without the assistance of friends; the friends upon this arraign the critic, and plainly prove the verses to be all the author's own. So at it they are, all four together by the ears, the friends at the critic, the critic at the players, the players at the author, and the author at the players again. It is impossible to determine how this many-sided contest will end, or which party to adhere to. The town, without siding with any, view the combat in suspense, like the fabled hero of antiquity, who beheld the earth-born brothers give and receive mutual wounds, and fall by indiscriminate destruction.

This is, in some measure, a state of the present dispute; but the combatants here differ in one respect from the champions of the fable. Every new wound only gives vigour for another blow; though they appear to strike, they are in fact mutually swelling themselves into consideration, and thus advertising each other into fame. To-day says one, my name shall be in the *Gazette*, the next day my rival's; people will naturally enquire about us; thus we shall at least make a noise in the street, though we have nothing to sell. I have read of a dispute of a similar nature, which was managed here about twenty years ago. Hildebrand Jacob, as I think he was called, and Charles Johnson were poets, both at that time possessed of great reputation, for Johnson had written eleven plays acted with great success, and Jacob, though he had written but five, had five times thanked the town for their unmerited applause. They soon became mutually enamoured of each other's talents; they wrote, they felt, they challenged the town for each other. Johnson assured the public that no poet alive had the easy simplicity of Jacob, and Jacob exhibited Johnson as a master-piece in the pathetic. Their mutual praise was not without effect, the town saw their plays, were in raptures, read, and without censuring them, forgot them. So formidable an union, however, was soon opposed by Tibbald. Tibbald asserted, that the tragedies of one had faults, and the comedies of the other substituted wit for vivacity; the combined champions flew at him like tigers, arraigned the censurer's judgment, and impeached his sincerity. It was a long time a dispute among the learned, which was in fact the greatest man, Jacob, Johnson, or Tibbald; they had all written for the stage with great success, their names were seen in almost every paper, and their works in every coffee-house. However, in the hottest of the dispute, a fourth combatant made his appearance, and swept away the three combatants, tragedy, comedy, and all into undistinguished ruin.

From this time they seemed consigned into the hands of

criticism, scarce a day passed in which they were not arraigned as detested writers. The critics, those enemies of Dryden and Pope, were their enemies. So Jacob and Johnson, instead of mending by criticism, called it envy, and because Dryden and Pope were censured, they compared themselves to Dryden and Pope.

But to return; the weapon chiefly used in the present controversy is epigram, and certainly never was a keener made use of. They have discovered surprising sharpness on both sides. The first that came out upon this occasion, was a kind of new composition in this way, and might more properly be called an epigrammatic thesis than an epigram. It consists first, of an argument in prose; next follows a motto from Roscommon; then comes the epigram; and lastly, notes serving to explain the epigram. But you shall have it with all its decorations.

An EPIGRAM

Addressed to the gentlemen reflected on in the Rosciad, a Poem, by the Author.

Worried with debts, and past all hopes of bail,
His pen he prostitutes, t'avoid a gaol.—Roscom.

Let not the *hungry* Bavius' angry stroke
Awake resentment, or your rage provoke:
But pitying his distress, let virtue [1] shine,
And giving each your bounty, [2] *let him dine*;
For thus retain'd, as learned counsel can,
Each case, however bad, he 'll new japan:
And by a quick transition, plainly show
'Twas no defect of yours, but *pocket low*,
That caus'd his *putrid kennel* to o'erflow.

The last lines are certainly executed in a very masterly manner. It is of that species of argumentation, called the perplexing. It effectually flings the antagonist into a mist; there 's no answering it: the laugh is raised against him, while he is endeavouring to find out the jest. At once he shows, that the author has a kennel, and that this kennel is putrid, and that this putrid kennel overflows. But why does it overflow? It overflows, because the author happens to have low pockets!

There was also another new attempt in this way; a prosaic epigram which came out upon this occasion. This is so full

---

[1] Charity. [2] Settled at one shilling, the price of the poem.

of matter, that a critic might split it into fifteen epigrams, each properly fitted with its sting. You shall see it.

To G. C. and R. L.

'Twas you, or I, or he, or altogether,
'Twas one, both, three of them, they know not whether.
This I believe, between us great or small,
You, I, he, wrote it not—'twas Churchill's all.

There, there's a perplex! I could have wished, to make it quite perfect, the author as in the case before, had added notes. Almost every word admits a scholium, and a long one too. I, YOU, HE! Suppose a stranger should ask, and who are you? Here are three obscure persons spoken of, that may in a short time be utterly forgotten. Their names should have consequently been mentioned in notes at the bottom. But when the reader comes to the words *great* and *small*, the maze is inextricable. Here the stranger may dive for a mystery, without ever reaching the bottom. Let him know then, that *small* is a word purely introduced to make good rhyme, and *great* was a very proper word to keep *small* company.

Yet, by being thus a spectator of others' dangers, I must own I begin to tremble in this literary contest for my own. I begin to fear that my challenge to Doctor Rock was unadvised, and has procured me more antagonists than I had at first expected. I have received private letters from several of the literati here, that fill my soul with apprehension. I may safely aver, that *I never gave any creature in this good city offence*, except only my rival Doctor Rock, yet by the letters I every day receive, and by some I have seen printed, I am arraigned at one time as being a dull fellow, at another as being pert; I am here petulant, there I am heavy; by the head of my ancestors, they treat me with more inhumanity than a flying fish. If I dive and run my nose to the bottom, there a devouring shark is ready to swallow me up; if I skim the surface, a pack of dolphins are at my trail to snap me; but when I take wing and attempt to escape them by flight, I become a prey to every ravenous bird that winnows the bosom of the deep. Adieu.

LETTER CXIV.—*To the same*.

THE formalities, delays, and disappointments, that precede a treaty of marriage here, are usually as numerous as those previous to a treaty of peace. The laws of this country are finely calculated to promote all commerce, but the commerce between the sexes. Their encouragement for propagating hemp, madder and tobacco, are indeed admirable! Marriages are the only commodity that meet with none.

Yet from the vernal softness of the air, the verdure of the fields, the transparency of the streams, and the beauty of the women, I know few countries more proper to invite to courtship. Here Love might sport among painted lawns and warbling groves, and revel upon gales, wafting at once both fragrance and harmony. Yet it seems he has forsaken the island; and when a couple are now to be married, mutual love or an union of minds is the last and most trifling consideration. If their goods and chattels can be brought to unite, their sympathetic souls are ever ready to guarantee the treaty. The gentleman's mortgaged lawn becomes enamoured of the lady's marriageable grove; the match is struck up, and both parties are piously in love—according to act of parliament.

Thus they, who have fortune, are possessed at least of something that is lovely; but I actually pity those that have none. I am told there was a time, when ladies with no other merit but youth, virtue, and beauty, had a chance for husbands, at least, among the ministers of the church, or the officers of the army. The blush and innocence of sixteen was said to have a powerful influence over these two professions. But of late, all the little traffic of blushing, ogling, dimpling, and smiling, has been forbidden by an act in that case wisely made and provided. A lady's whole cargo of smiles, sighs, and whispers, is declared utterly contraband, till she arrives in the warm latitudes of twenty-two, where commodities of this nature are too often found to decay. She is then permitted to dimple and smile, when the dimples and smiles begin to forsake her; and when perhaps grown ugly is charitably entrusted with an unlimited use of her charms. Her lovers, however, by this time have forsaken her; the captain has changed for another mistress; the priest himself leaves her in solitude, to bewail her virginity, and she dies even without the benefit of clergy.

Thus you find the Europeans discouraging love with as much earnestness, as the rudest savage of Sofala. The Genius is surely now no more. In every region I find enemies in arms to oppress him. Avarice in Europe, jealousy in Persia, ceremony in China, poverty among the Tartars, and lust in Circassia, are all prepared to oppose his power. The Genius is certainly banished from earth, though once adored under such a variety of forms. He is nowhere to be found; and all that the ladies of each country can produce, are but a few trifling reliques as instances of his former residence and favour.

The Genius of Love, says the Eastern apologue, had long resided in the happy plains of Abra, where every breeze was health, and every sound produced tranquillity. His temple at first was crowded, but every age lessened the number of his votaries, or cooled their devotion. Perceiving, therefore, his altars at length quite deserted, he was resolved to remove to some more propitious region, and he apprised the fair sex of every country, where he could hope for a proper reception, to assert their right to his presence among them. In return to this proclamation, embassies were sent from the ladies of every part of the world to invite him, and to display the superiority of their claims.

And first the beauties of China appeared. No country could compare with them for modesty, either of look, dress, or behaviour; their eyes were never lifted from the ground; their robes of the most beautiful silk, hid their hands, bosom and neck, while their faces only were left uncovered. They indulged no airs that might express loose desire, and they seemed to study only the graces of inanimate beauty. Their black teeth and plucked eye-brows were, however, alleged by the Genius against them, but he set them entirely aside, when he came to examine their little feet.

The beauties of Circassia next made their appearance. They advanced hand in hand, singing the most immodest airs, and leading up a dance in the most luxurious attitudes. Their dress was but half a covering; the neck, the left breast, and all the limbs were exposed to view, which after some time seemed rather to satiate than inflame desire. The lily and the rose contended in forming their complexions; and a soft sleepiness of eye, added irresistible poignancy to their charms; but their beauties were obtruded, not offered to their admirers; they seemed to give rather than receive courtship; and the Genius of Love dismissed them as unworthy his regard, since they exchanged the duties of love, and made themselves not the pursued, but the pursuing sex.

The kingdom of Kashmire next produced its charming deputies. This happy region seemed peculiarly sequestered by Nature for his abode. Shady mountains fenced it on one side from the scorching sun; the sea-born breezes on the other, gave peculiar luxuriance to the air. Their complexions were of a bright yellow, that appeared almost transparent, while the crimson tulip seemed to blossom on their cheeks. Their features and limbs were delicate beyond the statuary's power to express; and their teeth whiter than their own ivory. He was almost persuaded to reside among them, when unfortunately one of the ladies talked of appointing his seraglio.

In this procession the naked inhabitants of Southern America would not be left behind; their charms were found to surpass whatever the warmest imagination could conceive; and served to shew, that beauty could be perfect, even with the seeming disadvantage of a brown complexion. But their savage education rendered them utterly unqualified to make the proper use of their power, and they were rejected as being incapable of uniting mental with sensual satisfaction. In this manner the deputies of other kingdoms had their suits rejected; the black beauties of Benin, and the tawny daughters of Borneo, the women of Wida with well scarred faces, and the hideous virgins of Caffraria; the squab ladies of Lapland, three feet high, and the giant fair ones of Patagonia.

The beauties of Europe at last appeared; grace was in their steps, and sensibility sat smiling in every eye. It was the universal opinion, while they were approaching, that they would prevail; and the Genius seemed to lend them his most favourable attention. They opened their pretentions with the utmost modesty; but unfortunately as their orator proceeded, she happened to let fall the words *house in town, settlement and pin-money*. The seemingly harmless terms had instantly a surprising effect: the Genius with ungovernable rage burst from amidst the circle; and waving his youthful pinions, left this earth, and flew back to those ethereal mansions from whence he descended.

The whole assembly was struck with amazement; they now justly apprehended, that female power would be no more, since Love had forsaken them. They continued some time thus in a state of torpid despair, when it was proposed by one of the number, that since the real Genius had left them, in order to continue their power, they should set up an idol in his stead: and that the ladies of every country should furnish him with what each liked best. This proposal was instantly relished and agreed to. An idol was formed by uniting the capricious gifts of all the assembly, though no way resembling the departed Genius. The ladies of China furnished the monster with wings; those of Kashmire supplied him with horns; the dames of

Europe clapped a purse in his hand; and the virgins of Congo furnished him with a tail. Since that time, all the vows addressed to Love are in reality paid to the idol; but, as in other false religions, the adoration seems most fervent, where the heart is least sincere.   Adieu.

LETTER CXV.—*To the same.*

MANKIND have ever been prone to expatiate in the praise of human nature.   The dignity of man is a subject that has always been the favourite theme of humanity; they have declaimed with that ostentation, which usually accompanies such as are sure of having a partial audience; they have obtained victories, because there were none to oppose.   Yet from all I have ever read or seen, men appear more apt to err by having too high, than by having too despicable an opinion of their nature; and by attempting to exalt their original place in the creation, depress their real value in society.

The most ignorant nations have always been found to think most highly of themselves.   The Deity has ever been thought peculiarly concerned in their glory and preservation; to have fought their battles, and inspired their teachers: their wizards are said to be familiar with heaven; and every hero has a guard of angels as well as men to attend him.   When the Portuguese first came among the wretched inhabitants of the coast of Africa, these savage nations readily allowed the strangers more skill in navigation and war; yet still considered them, at best, but as useful servants brought to their coasts by their guardian serpent, to supply them with luxuries they could have lived without.   Though they could grant the Portuguese more riches, they will never allow them to have such a king as their Tottimondelem, who wore a bracelet of shells round his neck, and whose legs were covered with ivory.

In this manner, examine a savage in the history of his country and predecessors; you ever find his warriors able to conquer armies, and his sages acquainted with more than possible knowledge: human nature is to him an unknown country; he thinks it capable of great things, because he is ignorant of its boundaries; whatever can be conceived to be done he allows to be possible, and whatever is possible he conjectures must have been done. He never measures the actions and powers of others by what himself is able to perform, nor makes a proper estimate of the greatness of his fellows by bringing it to the standard of his own incapacity. He is satisfied to be one of a country where mighty things have been; and imagines the fancied power of others reflects a lustre on himself. Thus by degrees, he loses the idea of his own insignificance in a confused notion of the extra-ordinary powers of humanity, and is willing to grant extra-ordinary gifts to every pretender, because unacquainted with their claims.

This is the reason, why demi-gods and heroes have ever been erected in times or countries of ignorance and barbarity; they addressed a people who had high opinions of human nature, because they were ignorant how far it could extend; they addressed a people who were willing to allow that men should be gods, because they were yet imperfectly acquainted with God, and with man. These impostors knew, that all men are naturally fond of seeing something very great made from the little materials of humanity; that ignorant nations are not more proud of building a tower to reach heaven, or a pyramid to last for ages, than of raising up a demi-god of their own country and creation. The same pride that erects a colossus or a pyra-mid, installs a god or a hero; but though the adoring savage can raise his colossus to the clouds, he can exalt the hero not one inch above the standard of humanity; incapable therefore of exalting the idol, he debases himself and falls prostrate before him.

When man has thus acquired an erroneous idea of the dignity of his species, he and the gods become perfectly intimate; men are but angels, angels are but men, nay but servants that stand in waiting to execute human commands. The Persians, for instance, thus address their prophet Haly:[1] 'I salute thee, glorious Creator, of whom the sun is but the shadow. Master-piece of the Lord of human creatures, great star of justice and religion. The sea is not rich and liberal but by the gifts of thy munificent hands. The angel treasurer of heaven reaps his harvest in the fertile gardens of the purity of thy nature. The primum mobile would never dart the ball of the sun through the trunk of heaven were it not to serve the morning out of the extreme love she has for thee. The angel Gabriel, messenger of truth, every day kisses the groundsil of thy gate. Were there a place more exalted than the most high throne of God, I would affirm it to be thy place, O master of the faithful; Gabriel with all his art and knowledge, is but a mere scholar

[1] Chardin's Travels, p 402.

to thee.' Thus, my friend, men think proper to treat angels; but if indeed there be such an order of beings, with what a degree of satirical contempt must they listen to the songs of little mortals thus flattering each other. Thus to see creatures, wiser indeed than the monkey, and more active than the oyster, claiming to themselves the mastery of heaven; minims, the tenants of an atom, thus arrogating a partnership in the creation of universal Nature! Sure heaven is kind, that launches no thunder at those guilty heads; but it is kind, and regards their follies with pity, nor will destroy creatures that it loved into being.

But whatever success this practice of making demi-gods might have been attended with in barbarous nations, I do not know that any man became a god in a country, where the inhabitants were refined. Such countries generally have too close an inspection into human weakness, to think it invested with celestial power. They sometimes indeed admit the gods of strangers, or of their ancestors, which had their existence in times of obscurity; their weakness being forgotten, while nothing but their power and their miracles were remembered. The Chinese, for instance, never had a god of their own country, the idols which the vulgar worship at this day were brought from the barbarous nations around them. The Roman Emperors, who pretended to divinity, were generally taught by a poniard that they were mortal; and Alexander, though he passed among barbarous countries for a real God, could never persuade his polite countrymen into a similitude of thinking. The Lacedemonians shrewdly complied with his commands, by the following sarcastic edict:

Εἰ ᾿Αλέξανδρος βούλεται εἶναι θεὸς, θεὸς ἔστω.

Adieu.

LETTER CXVI.—*To the same.*

THERE is something irresistibly pleasing in the conversation of a fine woman; even though her tongue be silent, the eloquence of her eyes teaches wisdom. The mind sympathises with the regularity of the object in view, and struck with external grace, vibrates into respondent harmony. In this agreeable disposition, I lately found myself in company with my friend and his niece. Our conversation turned upon love, which she seemed equally capable of defending and inspiring. We were each of different opinions upon this subject; the lady insisted that it was a natural and universal passion, and produced the happiness of those who cultivated it with proper precaution. My friend denied it to be the work of Nature, but allowed it to have a real existence, and affirmed that it was of infinite service in refining society; while I, to keep up the dispute, affirmed it to be merely a name, first used by the cunning part of the fair sex, and admitted by the silly part of ours, therefore no way more natural than taking snuff or chewing opium.

'How is it possible, cried I, that such a passion can be natural, when our opinions even of beauty, which inspires it, are entirely the result of fashion and caprice? The ancients, who pretended to be connoisseurs in the art, have praised narrow foreheads, red hair, and eyebrows that joined each other over the nose. Such were the charms that once captivated Catullus, Ovid, and Anacreon. Ladies would at present be out of humour, if their lovers praised them for such graces; and should an antique beauty now revive, her face would certainly be put under the discipline of the tweezer, forehead-cloth and lead comb, before it could be seen in public company.

'But the difference between the ancients and moderns is not so great, as between the different countries of the present world. A lover of Gongora, for instance, sighs for thick lips; a Chinese lover is poetical in praise of thin. In Circassia, a straight nose is thought most consistent with beauty; cross but a mountain which separates it from the Tartars, and there flat noses, tawny skins, and eyes three inches asunder, are all the fashion. In Persia and some other countries, a man when he marries, chooses to have his bride a maid; in the Philippine Islands, if a bridegroom happens to perceive on the first night that he is put off with a virgin, the marriage is declared void to all intents and purposes, and the bride sent back with disgrace. In some parts of the East, a woman of beauty, properly fed up for sale, often amounts to one hundred crowns; in the kingdom of Loango, ladies of the very best fashion are sold for a pig, queens however sell better and sometimes amount to a cow. In short, turn even to England, do not I there see the beautiful part of the sex neglected; and none now marrying or making love but old men and old women that have saved money? Do not I see beauty from fifteen to twenty-one rendered null and void to all intents and purposes, and those six precious years of womanhood put under a statute of virginity? What! shall I call that rancid passion love, which passes between an old bachelor of fifty-six, and a widow lady of forty-nine? Never! never! What advantage is society to reap from an intercourse, where the big belly is oftenest on the man's side? Would any persuade me that such a passion was natural, unless the human race were more fit for love as they approached the decline, and, like the silk-worms, become breeders just before they expired?'

Whether love be natural or no, replied my friend, gravely, it contributes to the happiness of every society into which it is introduced. All our pleasures are short, and can only charm at intervals: love is a method of protracting our greatest pleasure: and surely that gamester who plays the greatest stake to the best advantage, will, at the end of life, rise victorious. This was the opinion of Vanini, who affirmed that *every hour was lost which was not spent in love*. His accusers were unable to comprehend his meaning, and the poor advocate for love was burned in flames, alas, no way metaphorical. But whatever advantages the individual may reap from this passion, society will certainly be refined and improved by its introduction: All laws, calculated to discourage it, tend to embrute the species, and weaken the state. Though it cannot plant morals in the human breast, it cultivates them when there: pity, generosity, and honour, receive a brighter polish from its assistance; and a single amour is sufficient entirely to brush off the clown.

But it is an exotic of the most delicate constitution; it requires the greatest art to introduce it into a state, and the smallest discouragement is sufficient to repress it again. Let us only consider with what ease it was formerly extinguished in Rome, and with what difficulty it was lately revived in Europe: it seemed to sleep for ages, and at last fought its way among us through tilts, tournaments, dragons, and all the dreams of chivalry. The rest of the world, China only excepted, are and have ever been utter strangers to its delights and advantages. In other countries, as men find themselves stronger than women, they lay a claim to a rigorous superiority; this is natural, and love, which gives up this natural advantage, must certainly be the effect of art. An art calculated to lengthen out our happier moments, and add new graces to society.

I entirely acquiesce in your sentiments, says the lady, with regard to the advantages of this passion, but cannot avoid giving it a nobler origin than you have been pleased to assign. I must think, that those countries, where it is rejected, are obliged to have recourse to art to stifle so natural a production, and those nations where it is cultivated, only make nearer advances to nature. The same efforts that are used in some places to suppress pity and other natural passions, may have been employed to extinguish love. No nation, however unpolished, is remarkable for innocence, that is not famous for passion; it has flourished in the coldest as well as the warmest regions. Even in the sultry wilds of southern America, the lover is not satisfied with possessing his mistress's person without having her mind.

> *In all my Enna's beauties blest,*
> *Amidst profusion still I pine;*
> *For tho' she gives me up her breast,*
> *Its panting tenant is not mine.*[1]

But the effects of love are too violent to be the result of an artificial passion. Nor is it in the power of fashion to force the constitution into those changes, which we every day observe. Several have died of it. Few lovers are unacquainted with the fate of the two Italian lovers, Da Corsin and Julia Bellamano, who, after a long separation, expired with pleasure in each other's arms. Such instances are too strong confirmations of the reality of the passion, and serve to shew that suppressing it, is but opposing the natural dictates of the heart. Adieu.

LETTER CXVII.—*To the same.*

THE clock just struck two, the expiring taper rises and sinks in the socket, the watchman forgets the hour in slumber, the laborious and the happy are at rest, and nothing wakes but meditation, guilt, revelry, and despair. The drunkard once more fills the destroying bowl, the robber walks his midnight round, and the suicide lifts his guilty arm against his own sacred person.

Let me no longer waste the night over the page of antiquity, or the sallies of cotemporary genius, but pursue the solitary walk, where vanity, ever changing, but a few hours past, walked before me, where she kept up the pageant, and now, like a froward child, seems hushed with her own importunities.

What a gloom hangs all around; the dying lamp feebly emits a yellow gleam, no sound is heard but of the chiming clock, or the distant watch-dog. All the bustle of human pride is forgotten, an hour like this may well display the emptiness of human vanity.

There will come a time when this temporary solitude may be

---

[1] Translation of a South American Ode.

made continual, and the city itself, like its inhabitants, fade away, and leave a desert in its room.

What cities, as great as this, have once triumphed in existence, had their victories as great, joy as just, and as unbounded, and with short-sighted presumption, promised themselves immortality.   Posterity can hardly trace the situation of some.   The sorrowful traveller wanders over the awful ruins of others; and as he beholds, he learns wisdom, and feels the transience of every sublunary possession.

Here, he cries, stood their citadel, now grown over with weeds; there their senate-house, but now the haunt of every noxious reptile; temples and theatres stood here, now only an undistinguished heap of ruin.   They are fallen, for luxury and avarice first made them feeble.   The rewards of state were conferred on amusing, and not on useful, members of society.   Their riches and opulence invited the invaders, who though at first repulsed, returned again, conquered by perseverance, and at last swept the defendants into undistinguished destruction.

How few appear in those streets, which but some few hours ago were crowded; and those who appear, now no longer wear their daily mask, nor attempt to hide their lewdness or their misery.

But who are those who make the streets their couch, and find a short repose from wretchedness at the doors of the opulent?   These are strangers, wanderers, and orphans, whose circumstances are too humble to expect redress, and whose distresses are too great even for pity.   Their wretchedness excites rather horror than pity.   Some are without the covering even of rags, and others emaciated with disease; the world has disclaimed them; society turns its back upon their distress, and has given them up to nakedness and hunger.   These poor shivering females have once seen happier days, and been flattered into beauty.   They have been prostituted to the gay luxurious villain, and are now turned out to meet the severity of winter.   Perhaps, now lying at the doors of their betrayers, they sue to wretches whose hearts are insensible, or debauchees who may curse, but will not relieve them.

Why, why was I born a man, and yet see the suffering of wretches I cannot relieve! Poor houseless creatures! the world will give you reproaches, but will not give you relief.   The slightest misfortunes of the great, the most imaginary uneasiness of the rich, are aggravated with all the power of eloquence, and held up to engage our attention and sympathetic sorrow.   The poor weep unheeded, persecuted by every subordinate species of tyranny; and every law, which gives others security, becomes an enemy to them.

Why was this heart of mine formed with so much sensibility! or why was not my fortune adapted to its impulse! Tenderness, without a capacity of relieving, only makes the man who feels it more wretched than the object which sues for assistance. Adieu.

LETTER CXVIII.—*Fum Hoam to Lien Chi Altangi, the discontented Wanderer, by the way of Moscow.*

I HAVE been just sent upon an embassy to Japan; my commission is to be dispatched in four days, and you can hardly conceive the pleasure I shall find upon revisiting my native country. I shall leave with joy this proud, barbarous, inhospitable region, where every object conspires to diminish my satisfaction, and increase my patriotism.

But though I find the inhabitants savage, yet the Dutch merchants who are permitted to trade hither, seem still more detestable. They have raised my dislike to Europe in general; by them I learn how low avarice can degrade human nature; how many indignities an European will suffer for gain.

I was present at an audience given by the Emperor to the Dutch envoy, who had sent several presents to all the courtiers some days previous to his admission; but he was obliged to attend those designed for the Emperor himself. From the accounts I had heard of this ceremony, my curiosity prompted me to be a spectator of the whole.

First went the presents, set out on beautiful enamelled tables, adorned with flowers, borne on men's shoulders, and followed by Japanese music and dancers. From so great respect paid to the gifts themselves, I had fancied the donors must have received almost divine honours. But about a quarter of an hour after the presents had been carried in triumph, the envoy and his train were brought forward. They were covered from head to foot with long black veils, which prevented their seeing, each led by a conductor, chosen from the meanest of the people. In this dishonourable manner having traversed the city of Jedo, they at length arrived at the palace gate, and after waiting half an hour, were admitted into the guard room. Here their eyes were uncovered, and in about an hour the gentleman usher introduced them into the hall of audience. The Emperor was at length shewn sitting in a kind of alcove at the upper end of the room, and the Dutch envoy was conducted towards the throne.

As soon as he had approached within a certain distance, the gentleman usher cried out with a loud voice, *Holanda Capitan*; upon these words the envoy fell flat upon the ground, and crept upon his hands and feet towards the throne. Still approaching, he reared himself upon his knees, and then bowed his forehead to the ground. These ceremonies being over, he was directed to withdraw, still grovelling on his belly, and going backward like a lobster.

Men must be excessively fond of riches, when they are earned with such circumstances of abject submission. Do the Europeans worship Heaven itself with marks of more profound respect? Do they confer those honours on the Supreme of beings, which they pay to a barbarous king, who gives them a permission to purchase trinkets and porcelain? What a glorious exchange, to forfeit their national honour, and even their title to humanity, for a screen or a snuff-box!

If these ceremonies essayed in the first audience appeared mortifying, those which are practised in the second are infinitely more so. In the second audience, the Emperor and the ladies of court were placed behind lattices in such a manner as to see without being seen. Here all the Europeans were directed to pass in review, and grovel and act the serpent as before: with this spectacle, the whole court seemed highly delighted. The strangers were asked a thousand ridiculous questions; as their names and their ages: They were ordered to write, to stand upright, to sit, to stop, to compliment each other, to be drunk, to speak the Japanese language, to talk Dutch, to sing, to eat; in short, they were ordered to do all that could satisfy the curiosity of women.

Imagine, my dear Altangi, a set of grave men thus transformed into buffoons, and acting a part every whit as honourable as that of those instructed animals which are shewn in the streets of Pekin to the mob on a holiday. Yet the ceremony did not end here, for every great lord of the court was to be visited in the same manner; and their ladies, who took the whim from their husbands, were all equally fond of seeing the strangers perform, even the children seeming highly diverted with the dancing Dutchmen.

Alas, cried I, to myself, upon returning from such a spectacle, is this the nation which assumes such dignity at the court of Pekin? Is this that people that appear so proud at home, and in every country where they have the least authority? How does a love of gain transform the gravest of mankind into the most contemptible and ridiculous? I had rather continue poor all my life, than become rich at such a rate. Perish those riches which are acquired at the expense of my honour or my humanity! Let me quit, said I, a country where there are none but such as treat all others like slaves, and more detestable still, in suffering such treatment. I have seen enough of this nation, to desire to see more of others. Let me leave a people suspicious to excess, whose morals are corrupted, and equally debased by superstition and vice; where the sciences are left uncultivated, where the Great are slaves to the Prince, and tyrants to the people, where the women are chaste only when debarred of the power of transgression; where the true disciples of Confucius are not less persecuted than those of Christianity: in a word, a country where men are forbidden to think, and consequently labour under the most miserable slavery, that of mental servitude. Adieu.

LETTER CXIX.—*From Lien Chi Altangi, to Fum Hoam, first President of the Ceremonial Academy at Pekin, in China.*

THE misfortunes of the great, my friend, are held up to engage our attention, are enlarged upon in tones of declamation, and the world is called upon to gaze at the noble sufferers; they have at once the comfort of admiration and pity.

Yet where is the magnanimity of bearing misfortunes when the whole world is looking on? Men in such circumstances can act bravely even from motives of vanity. He only who, in the vale of obscurity, can brave adversity, who without friends to encourage, acquaintances to pity, or even without hope to alleviate his distresses, can behave with tranquillity and indifference, is truly great: whether peasant or courtier, he deserves admiration, and should be held up for our imitation and respect.

The miseries of the poor are however entirely disregarded; though some undergo more real hardships in one day, than the great in their whole lives. It is indeed inconceivable what difficulties the meanest English sailor or soldier endures without murmuring or regret. Every day is to him a day of misery, and yet he bears his hard fate without repining.

With what indignation do I hear the heroes of tragedy complain of misfortunes and hardships, whose greatest calamity s founded in arrogance and pride. Their severest distresses are pleasures, compared to what many of the adventuring poor every day sustain, without murmuring. These may eat, drink, and sleep, have slaves to attend them, and are sure of subsistence for life, while many of their fellow-creatures are obliged to wander, without a friend to comfort or to assist them, find enmity in every law, and are too poor to obtain even justice.

I have been led into these reflections, from accidentally meeting some days ago a poor fellow begging at one of the outlets of this town, with a wooden leg. I was curious to learn what had reduced him to his present situation; and after giving him what I thought proper, desired to know the history of his life and misfortunes, and the manner in which he was reduced to his present distress. The disabled soldier, for such he was, with an intrepidity truly British, leaning on his crutch, put himself into an attitude to comply with my request, and gave me his history as follows:

'As for misfortunes, Sir, I cannot pretend to have gone through more than others. Except the loss of my limb, and my being obliged to beg, I don't know any reason, thank heaven, that I have to complain; there are some who have lost both legs and an eye; but, thank heaven, it is not quite so bad with me.

'My father was a labourer in the country, and died when I was five years old; so I was put upon the parish. As he had been a wandering sort of a man, the parishioners were not able to tell to what parish I belonged, or where I was born; so they sent me to another parish, and that parish sent me to a third, till at last it was thought I belonged to no parish at all. At length, however, they fixed me. I had some disposition to be a scholar, and had actually learned my letters; but the master of the workhouse put me to business, as soon as I was able to handle a mallet.

'Here I lived an easy kind of a life for five years. I only wrought ten hours in the day, and had my meat and drink provided for my labour. It is true, I was not suffered to stir far from the house, for fear I should run away: but what of that? I had the liberty of the whole house, and the yard before the door, and that was enough for me.

'I was next bound out to a farmer, where I was up both early and late, but I eat and drank well, and liked my business well enough, till he died. Being then obliged to provide for myself, I was resolved to go and seek my fortune. Thus I lived, and went from town to town, working when I could get employment, and starving when I could get none, and might have lived so still. But happening one day to go through a field belonging to a magistrate, I spy'd a hare crossing the path just before me. I believe the devil put it in my head to fling my stick at it: well, what will you have on 't? I kill'd the hare, and was bringing it away in triumph, when the justice himself met me: he called me a villain, and collaring me, desired I would give an account of myself. I began immediately to give a full account of all that I knew of my breed, seed, and generation; but though I gave a very long account, the justice said, I could give no account of myself; so I was indicted, and found guilty of being poor, and sent to Newgate, in order to be transported to the plantations.

'People may say this and that of being in jail; but for my part, I found Newgate as agreeable a place as ever I was in, in all my life. I had my belly full to eat and drink, and did no work; but alas, this kind of life was too good to last for ever! I was taken out of prison, after five months, put on board of a ship, and sent off with two hundred more. Our passage was but indifferent, for we were all confined in the hold, and died very fast for want of sweet air and provisions; but for my part, I did not want meat, because I had a fever all the way; Providence was kind when provisions grew short, it took away my desire of eating. When we came ashore, we were sold to the planters. I was bound for seven years, and as I was no scholar, for I had forgotten my letters, I was obliged to work among the negroes; and served out my time, as in duty bound to do.

'When my time was expired, I worked my passage home, and glad I was to see Old England again, because I loved my country. O liberty, liberty, liberty, that is the property of every Englishman, and I will die in its defence: I was afraid, however, that I should be indicted for a vagabond once more, so did not much care to go into the country, but kept about town, and did little jobs when I could get them. I was very happy in this manner for some time; till one evening, coming home from work, two men knocked me down, and then desired me to stand still. They belonged to a press gang: I was carried before the justice, and as I could give no account of myself (that was the thing that always hobbled me) I had my choice left, whether to go on board a man of war, or list for a soldier; I chose to be a soldier, and in this post of a gentleman, I served two campaigns, was at the battles in Flanders, and received but one wound through the breast, which is troublesome to this day.

'When the peace came on, I was discharged: and as I could

not work, because my wound was sometimes painful, I listed for a landman in the East-India company's service. I here fought the French in six pitched battles; and verily believe, that if I could read or write, our captain would have given me promotion, and made me a corporal. But that was not my good fortune, I soon fell sick, and when I became good for nothing, got leave to return home again with forty pounds in my pocket, which I saved in the service. This was at the beginning of the present war, so I hoped to be set on shore, and to have the pleasure of spending my money; but the government wanted men, and I was pressed again, before ever I could set foot on shore.

'The boatswain found me, as he said, an obstinate fellow: he swore that I understood my business perfectly well, but that I pretended sickness merely to be idle: God knows, I knew nothing of sea-business. He beat me without considering what he was about. But still my forty pounds was some comfort to me under every beating; the money was my comfort, and the money I might have had to this day; but that our ship was taken by the French, and so I lost it all!

'Our crew was carried into a French prison, and many of them died, because they were not used to live in a jail; but for my part it was nothing to me, for I was seasoned. One night, however, as I was sleeping on the bed of boards, with a warm blanket about me (for I always loved to lie well), I was awaked by the boatswain, who had a dark lantern by his hand. "Jack, says he to me, will you knock out the French sentry's brains?" "I don't care, says I, striving to keep myself awake, if I lend a hand." "Then follow me, says he, and I hope we shall do business." So up I got, and tied my blanket, which was all the clothes I had, about my middle, and went with him to fight the Frenchman: we had no arms; but one Englishman is able to beat five French at any time; so we went down to the door, where both sentries were posted, and rushing upon them, seized their arms in a moment, and knocked them down. From thence, nine of us ran together to the quay, and seizing the first boat we met, got out of the harbour, and put to sea: we had not been here three days, before we were taken up by an English privateer, who was glad of so many good hands; and we consented to run our chance. However, we had not so much luck as we expected. In three days we fell in with a French man of war of forty guns, while we had but twenty-three; so to it we went. The fight lasted for three hours, and I verily believe we should have taken the Frenchman, but unfortunately, we lost almost all our men, just as we were going to get the victory. I was once more in the power of the French, and I believe it would have gone hard with me, had I been brought back to my old jail in Brest; but by good fortune, we were retaken and carried to England once more.

'I had almost forgot to tell you, that in this last engagement, I was wounded in two places; I lost four fingers of the left hand, and my leg was shot off. Had I the good fortune to have lost my leg and use of my hand on board a king's ship, and not a privateer, I should have been entitled to clothing and maintenance during the rest of my life, but that was not my chance; one man is born with a silver spoon in his mouth, and another with a wooden ladle. However, blessed be God, I enjoy good health, and have no enemy in this world that I know of, but the French, and the Justice of Peace.'

Thus saying, he limped off, leaving my friend and me in admiration of his intrepidity and content; nor could we avoid acknowledging, that an habitual acquaintance with misery is the truest school of fortitude and philosophy. Adieu.

LETTER CXX.—*From the same.*

THE titles of European Princes are rather more numerous than ours of Asia, but by no means so sublime. The king of Visapour or Pegu, not satisfied with claiming the globe and all its appurtenances to him and his heirs, asserts a property even in the firmament, and extends his orders to the milky way. The monarchs of Europe, with more modesty, confine their titles to earth, but make up by number, what is wanting in their sublimity. Such is their passion for a long list of these splendid trifles, that I have known a German Prince with more titles than subjects, and a Spanish nobleman with more names than shirts.

Contrary to this, 'The English monarchs, says a writer of the last century, disdain to accept of such titles, which tend only to increase their pride, without improving their glory; they are above depending on the feeble helps of heraldry for respect, perfectly satisfied with the consciousness of acknowledged power.' At present, however, these maxims are laid aside; the English monarchs have of late assumed new titles, and have impressed their coins with the names and arms of obscure dukedoms, petty states, and subordinate employments. Their design in this, I make no doubt, was laudably to add new lustre to the British throne, but in reality, paltry claims only serve to diminish that respect they are designed to secure.

There is, in the honours assumed by Kings, as in the decorations of architecture, a majestic simplicity, which best conduces to inspire our reverence and respect; numerous and trifling ornaments in either, are strong indications of meanness in the designer, or of concealed deformity: should, for instance, the Emperor of China, among other titles, assume that of Deputy Mandarine of Maccan, or the Monarch of Great Britain, France, and Ireland, desire to be acknowledged as Duke of Brentford, Lunenburg, or Lincoln, the observer revolts at this mixture of important and paltry claims, and forgets the Emperor in his familiarity with the Duke or the Deputy.

I remember a similar instance of this inverted ambition, in the illustrious King of Manacabo, upon his first treaty with the Portuguese. Among the presents that were made him by the ambassador of that nation, was a sword with a brass hilt, which he seemed to set a peculiar value upon. This he thought too great an acquisition to his glory, to be forgotten among the number of his titles. He therefore gave orders that his subjects should style him for the future, *Talipot, the immortal Potentate of Manacabo, Messenger of Morning, Enlightener of the Sun, Possessor of the whole Earth, and mighty Monarch of the Brass-handled Sword.*

This method of mixing majestic and paltry titles, of quartering the arms of a great empire and an obscure province, upon the same medal here, had its rise in the virtuous partiality of their late monarchs. Willing to testify an affection to their native country, they gave its name and ensigns a place upon their coins, and thus in some measure ennobled its obscurity. It was indeed but just, that a people which had given England up their King, should receive some honorary equivalent in return; but at present these motives are no more: England has now a Monarch wholly British, and it has some reason to hope for British titles upon British coins.

However, were the money of England designed to circulate in Germany, there would be no flagrant impropriety in impressing it with German names and arms; but though this might have been so upon former occasions, I am told there is no danger of it for the future; as England therefore designs to keep back its gold, I candidly think Lunenburg, Oldenburgh, and the rest of them, may very well keep back their titles.

It is a mistaken prejudice in princes, to think that a number of loud sounding names can give new claims to respect. The truly great have ever disdained them. When Timur the Lame had conquered Asia, an orator by profession came to compliment him upon the occasion. He began his harangue, by styling him the most omnipotent, and the most glorious object of the creation; the Emperor seemed displeased with his paltry adulation, yet still he went on, complimenting him, as the most mighty, the most valiant, and the most perfect of beings: Hold there, my friend, cries the lame Emperor, hold there, till I have got another leg. In fact, the feeble or the despotic alone find pleasure in multiplying these pageants of vanity, but strength and freedom have nobler aims, and often find the finest adulation in majestic simplicity.

The young Monarch of this country has already testified a proper contempt for several unmeaning appendages on royalty; cooks and scullions have been obliged to quit their fires; gentlemen's gentlemen, and the whole tribe of *necessary people*, who did nothing, have been dismissed from further services. A youth, who can thus bring back simplicity and frugality to a court, will soon probably have a true respect for his own glory, and while he has dismissed all useless employments, may disdain to accept of empty or degrading titles. Adieu.

LETTER CXXI.—*From the Same.*

WHENEVER I attempt to characterise the English in general, some unforeseen difficulties constantly occur to disconcert my design; I hesitate between censure and praise; when I consider them as a reasoning philosophical people, they have my applause; but when I reverse the medal, and observe their inconstancy and irresolution, I can scarcely persuade myself that I am observing the same people.

Yet upon examination, this very inconstancy, so remarkable here, flows from no other source than their love of reasoning. The man who examines a complicated subject on every side, and calls in reason to his assistance, will frequently change; will find himself distracted by opposing probabilities and contending proofs; every alteration of place will diversify the prospect, will give some latent argument new force, and contribute to maintain an anarchy in the mind.

On the contrary, they who never examine with their own

reason, act with more simplicity. Ignorance is positive, instinct perseveres, and the human being moves in safety within the narrow circle of brutal uniformity. What is true with regard to individuals, is not less so when applied to states. A reasoning government like this, is in continual fluctation, while those kingdoms where men are taught not to controvert but obey, continue always the same. In Asia, for instance, where the monarch's authority is supported by force, and acknowledged through fear, a change of government is entirely unknown. All the inhabitants seem to wear the same mental complexion, and remain contented with hereditary oppression. The sovereign's pleasure is the ultimate rule of duty, every branch of the administration is a perfect epitome of the whole; and if one tyrant is deposed, another starts up in his room to govern as his predecessor. The English, on the contrary, instead of being led by power, endeavour to guide themselves by reason; instead of appealing to the pleasure of the prince, appeal to the original rights of mankind. What one rank of men assert is denied by others, as the reasons on opposite sides happen to come home with greater or less conviction. The people of Asia are directed by precedent, which never alters; the English by reason, which is ever changing its appearance.

The disadvantages of an Asiatic government acting in this manner by precedent are evident; original errors are thus continued, without hopes of redress, and all marks of genius are levelled down to one standard, since no superiority of thinking can be allowed its exertion in mending obvious defects. But to recompense those defects, their governments undergo no new alterations, they have no new evils to fear, nor no fermentations in the constitution that continue: the struggle for power is soon over, and all becomes tranquil as before; they are habituated to subordination, and men are taught to form no other desires, than those which they are allowed to satisfy.

The disadvantages of a government acting from the immediate influence of reason, like that of England, are not less than those of the former. It is extremely difficult to induce a number of free beings to co-operate for their mutual benefit; every possible advantage will necessarily be sought, and every attempt to procure it must be attended with a new fermentation; various reasons will lead different ways, and equity and advantage will often be out-balanced by a combination of clamour and prejudice. But though such a people may be thus in the wrong, they have been influenced by an happy delusion, their errors are seldom seen till they are felt; each man is himself the tyrant he has obeyed and such a master he can easily forgive. The disadvantages he feels, may in reality be equal to what is felt in the most despotic government; but man will bear every calamity with patience, when he knows himself to be the author of his own misfortunes. Adieu.

LETTER CXXII.—*From the same.*

My long residence here begins to fatigue me as every object ceases to be new, it no longer continues to be pleasing; some minds are so fond of variety, that pleasure itself, if permanent, would be insupportable, and we are thus obliged to solicit new happiness even by courting distress: I only, therefore, wait the arrival of my son to vary this trifling scene, and borrow new pleasure from danger and fatigue. A life, I own, thus spent in wandering from place to place is at best but empty dissipation. But to pursue trifles is the lot of humanity; and whether we bustle in a pantomime or strut at a coronation; whether we shout at a bonfire or harangue in a senate-house; whatever object we follow, it will at last surely conduct us to futility and disappointment. The wise bustle and laugh as they walk in the pageant, but fools bustle and are important; and this probably is all the difference between them.

This may be an apology for the levity of my former correspondence; I talked of trifles, and I knew that they were trifles; to make the things of this life ridiculous, it was only sufficient to call them by their names.

In other respects, I have omitted several striking circumstances in the description of this country, as supposing them either already known to you, or as not being thoroughly known to myself. But there is one omission for which I expect no forgiveness, namely, my being totally silent upon their buildings, roads, rivers, and mountains. This is a branch of science, on which all other travellers are so very prolix, that my deficiency will appear the more glaring. With what pleasure, for instance, do some read of a traveller in Egypt, measuring a fallen column with his cane, and finding it exactly five feet nine inches long; of his creeping through the mouth of a catacomb, and coming out by a different hole from that he entered; of his stealing the finger of an antique statue, in spite of the janizary that watched him; or his adding a new conjecture to the hundred and fourteen conjectures, already published upon the names of *Osiris* and *Isis*.

Methinks I hear some of my friends in China, demanding a similar account of London and the adjacent villages: and if I remain here much longer, it is probable I may gratify their curiosity. I intend, when run dry on other topics, to take a serious survey of the City-wall; to describe that beautiful building the Mansion-house; I will enumerate the magnificent squares, in which the nobility chiefly reside, and the royal palace appointed for the reception of the English monarch; nor will I forget the beauties of Shoe-lane, in which I myself have resided since my arrival. You shall find me no way inferior to many of my brother travellers in the arts of description. At present, however, as a specimen of this way of writing, I send you a few hasty remarks, collected in a late journey I made to Kentish-town, *and this in the manner of modern voyagers.*

'Having heard much of Kentish-town, I conceived a strong desire to see that celebrated place. I could have wished, indeed, to satisfy my curiosity without going thither; but that was impracticable, and therefore I resolved to go. Travellers have two methods of going to Kentish-town; they take coach which costs ninepence, or they go a foot, which costs nothing; in my opinion, a coach is by far the most eligible convenience, but I was resolved to go on foot, having considered with myself, that going in that manner would be the cheapest way.

'As you set out from Dog-house Bar, you enter upon a fine levelled road, railed in on both sides, commanding on the right a fine prospect of groves, and fields enamelled with flowers, which would wonderfully charm the sense of smelling, were it not for a dunghill on the left, which mixes its effluvia with their odours. This dunghill is of much greater antiquity than the road; and I must not omit a piece of injustice I was going to commit upon this occasion. My indignation was levelled against the makers of the dunghill, for having brought it so near the road, whereas, it should have fallen upon the makers of the road, for having brought that so near the dunghill.

'After proceeding in this manner for some time, a building resembling somewhat a triumphal arch salutes the traveller's view. This structure, however, is peculiar to this country, and vulgarly called a turnpike gate: I could perceive a long inscription in large characters on the front, probably upon the occasion of some triumph, but being in haste, I left it to be made out by some subsequent adventurer, who may happen to travel this way; so continuing my course to the west, I soon arrived at an unwalled town called Islington.

'Islington is a pretty neat town, mostly built of brick, with a church and bells. It has a small lake or rather pond in the midst; though at present very much neglected. I am told it is dry in summer; if this be the case, it can be no very proper receptacle for fish, of which the inhabitants themselves seem sensible, by bringing all that is eaten there from London.

'After having surveyed the curiosities of this fair and beautiful town, I proceeded forward, leaving a fair stone building called the White Conduit House on my right; here the inhabitants of London often assemble to celebrate a feast of hot rolls and butter; seeing such numbers, each with their little tables before them, employed on this occasion, must no doubt be a very amusing sight to the looker on, but still more so to those who perform in the solemnity.

'From hence I parted with reluctance to *Pancrass* as it is written, or *Pancridge* as it is pronounced; but which should be both pronounced and written *Pangrace*. This emendation I will venture meo arbitrio; Παν in the Greek language signifies *all*, which added to the English word *grace*, maketh *all grace*, or *Pangrace*, and indeed this is a very proper appellation to a place of so much sanctity, as Pangrace is universally esteemed. However this be, if you except the parish church and its fine bells, there is little in Pangrace worth the attention of the curious observer.

'From Pangrace to Kentish-town is an easy journey of one mile and a quarter. The road lies through a fine champaign country, well watered with beautiful drains, and enamelled with flowers of all kinds, which might contribute to charm every sense, were it not that the odoriferous gales are often more impregnated with dust than perfume.

'As you enter Kentish-town, the eye is at once presented with the shops of artificers, such as vendors of candles, small coal, and hair-brooms; there are also several august buildings of red brick, with numberless sign-posts, or rather pillars, in a peculiar order of architecture; I send you a drawing of several, vide A. B. C. This pretty town probably borrows its name from its vicinity to the county of Kent; and indeed it is not unnatural that it should, as there are only London and the adjacent villages that lie between them. Be this as it will, perceiving night approach, I made a hasty repast on roasted mutton, and a certain dried fruit called potatoes, resolving to protract my remarks upon my return; and this I would very willingly have done; but was prevented by a circumstance which in truth I had for some time foreseen, for night coming on, it was impossible to take a proper survey of the country, as I was to return home in the dark.'   Adieu.

LETTER CXXIII.—*To the same.*

AFTER a variety of disappointments, my wishes are at length fully satisfied. My son, so long expected, is arrived, at once, by his presence, banishing my anxiety, and opening a new scene of unexpected pleasure. His improvements in mind and person have far surpassed even the sanguine expectations of a father. I left him a boy, but he is returned a man; pleasing in his person, hardened by travel, and polished by adversity. His disappointment in love, however, had infused an air of melancholy into his conversation, which seemed at intervals to interrupt our mutual satisfaction. I expected that this could find a cure only from time; but Fortune, as if willing to load us with her favours, has, in a moment, repaid every uneasiness with rapture.

Two days after his arrival, the man in black, with his beautiful niece, came to congratulate us upon this occasion; but guess our surprise, when my friend's lovely kinswoman was found to be the very captive my son had rescued from Persia, and who had been wrecked on the Wolga, and was carried by the Russian peasants to the port of Archangel. Were I to hold the pen of a novelist, I might be prolix in describing their feelings at so unexpected an interview; but you may conceive their joy, without my assistance; words were unable to express their transports, then how can words describe it?

When two young persons are sincerely enamoured of each other, nothing can give me such pleasure as seeing them married: whether I know the parties or not, I am happy at thus binding one link more in the universal chain. Nature has, in some measure, formed me for a match-maker, and given me a soul to sympathise with every mode of human felicity. I instantly, therefore, consulted the man in black, whether we might not crown their mutual wishes by marriage; his soul seems formed of similar materials with mine, he instantly gave his consent, and the next day was appointed for the solemnisation of their nuptials.

All the acquaintances which I had made since my arrival, were present at this gay solemnity. The little beau was constituted master of the ceremonies, and his wife Mrs. Tibbs conducted the entertainment with proper decorum. The man in black and the pawnbroker's widow, were very sprightly and tender upon this occasion. The widow was dressed up under the direction of Mrs. Tibbs; and as for her lover, his face was set off by the assistance of a pig-tail wig, which was lent by the little beau, to fit him for making love with proper formality. The whole company easily perceived, that it would be a double wedding before all was over, and indeed my friend and the widow seemed to make no secret of their passion; he even called me aside, in order to know my candid opinion, whether I did not think him a little too old to be married. As for my own part, continued he, I know I am going to play the fool, but all my friends will praise my wisdom, and produce me as the very pattern of discretion to others.

At dinner, every thing seemed to run on with good humour, harmony, and satisfaction. Every creature in company thought themselves pretty, and every jest was laughed at: the man in black sat next his mistress, helped her plate, chimed her glass, and jogging her knees and her elbow, he whispered something arch in her ear, on which she patted his cheek; never was antiquated passion so playful, so harmless, and amusing, as between this reverend couple.

The second course was now called for, and among a variety of other dishes, a fine turkey was placed before the widow. The Europeans, you know, carve as they eat; my friend therefore begged his mistress to help him to a part of the turkey. The widow, pleased with an opportunity of shewing her skill in carving; an art, upon which, it seems, she piqued herself; began to cut it up by first taking off the leg. *Madam*, cried my friend, *if I may be permitted to advise, I would begin by cutting off the wing, and then the leg will come off more easily*. Sir, replies the widow, give me leave to understand cutting up a fowl, I always begin with the leg. *Yes, madam*, replies the lover, *but if the wing be the most convenient manner, I would begin with the wing*. Sir, interrupts the lady, when you have fowls of your own, begin with the wing if you please; but give me leave to take off the leg. I hope I am not to be taught at this time of the day. *Madam*, interrupts he, *we are never too old to be instructed*. Old, Sir! interrupts the other, who is old, Sir? when I die of age I know of some that will quake for fear; if the leg does not come off, take the turkey to yourself. *Madam,* replied the man in black, *I don't care a farthing whether the leg or the wing comes off; if you care for the leg first, why you shall have the argument, even though it be as I say.* As for the matter of that, cries the widow, I don't care a fig whether you are for the leg off or on; and friend, for the future, keep your distance. *O,* replied the other, *that is easily done, it is only moving to the other end of the table, and so, madam, your most obedient humble servant.*

Thus was this courtship of an age destroyed in one moment; for this dialogue effectually broke off the match between this respectable couple, that had been but just concluded. The smallest accidents disappoint the most important treaties. However, though it in some measure interrupted the general satisfaction, it no ways lessened the happiness of the youthful couple; and by the young lady's looks, I could perceive she was not entirely displeased with the interruption.

In a few hours the whole transaction seemed entirely forgotten, and we have all since enjoyed those satisfactions which result from a consciousness of making each other happy. My son and his fair partner are fixed here for life; the man in black has given them up a small estate in the country, which added to what I was able to bestow, will be capable of supplying all the real, but not the fictitious demands of happiness. As for myself, the world being but one city to me, I don't much care in which of the streets I happen to reside; I shall therefore spend the remainder of life in examining the manners of different countries, and have prevailed upon the man in black to be my companion. *They must often change,* says Confucius, *who would be constant in happiness or wisdom.* Adieu.

THE BEE

No. I.—SATURDAY, OCTOBER 6, 1759

Introduction

THERE is not, perhaps, a more whimsically dismal figure in nature, than a man of real modesty, who assumes an air of impudence—who, while his heart beats with anxiety, studies ease, and affects good-humour. In this situation, however, a periodical writer often finds himself, upon his first attempt to address the public in form. All his power of pleasing is damped by solicitude, and his cheerfulness dashed with apprehension. Impressed with the terrors of the tribunal before which he is going to appear, his natural humour turns to pertness, and for real wit he is obliged to substitute vivacity. His first publication draws a crowd; they part dissatisfied; and the author, never more to be indulged a favourable hearing, is left to condemn the indelicacy of his own address, or their want of discernment.

For my part, as I was never distinguished for address, and have often even blundered in making my bow, such bodings as these had like to have totally repressed my ambition. I was at a loss whether to give the public specious promises, or give none; whether to be merry or sad on this solemn occasion. If I should modestly decline all merit, it was too probable the hasty reader might have taken me at my word. If, on the other hand, like labourers in the Magazine trade, I had, with modest impudence, humbly presumed to promise an epitome of all the good things that ever were said or written, this might have disgusted those readers I most desire to please. Had I been merry, I might have been censured as *vastly low*; and had I been sorrowful, I might have been left to mourn in solitude and silence: in short, whichever way I turned, nothing presented but prospects of terror, despair, chandlers' shops, and waste paper.

In this debate between fear and ambition, my publisher happening to arrive, interrupted for a while my anxiety. Perceiving my embarrassment about making my first appearance, he instantly offered his assistance and advice. 'You must know, Sir,' says he, 'that the republic of letters is at present divided into three classes. One writer, for instance, excels at a plan, or a title-page, another works away at the body of the book, and a third is a dab at an index. Thus a Magazine is not the result of any single man's industry, but goes through as many hands as a new pin, before it is fit for the public. I fancy, Sir,' continues he, 'I can provide an eminent hand, and upon moderate terms, to draw up a promising plan to smooth up our readers a little, and pay them as Colonel Charteris paid his seraglio, at the rate of three halfpence in hand, and three shillings more in promises.'

He was proceeding in his advice, which, however. I thought proper to decline, by assuring him, that as I intended to pursue no fixed method, so it was impossible to form any regular plan; determined never to be tedious in order to be logical, wherever pleasure presented, I was resolved to follow. Like the Bee, which I had taken for the title of my paper, I would rove from flower to flower, with seeming inattention, but concealed choice, expatiate over all the beauties of the season, and make my industry my amusement.

This reply may also serve as an apology to the reader, who expects, before he sits down, a bill of his future entertainment. It would be improper to pall his curiosity by lessening his surprise, or anticipate any pleasure I am able to procure him, by saying what shall come next. Thus much, however, he may be assured of, that neither war nor scandal shall make any part of it. Homer finely imagines his deity turning away with horror from the prospect of a field of battle, and seeking tranquillity among a nation noted for peace and simplicity. Happy, could any effort of mine, but for a moment, repress that savage pleasure some men find in the daily accounts of human misery! How gladly would I lead them from scenes of blood and altercation, to prospects of innocence and ease, where every breeze breathes health, and every sound is but the echo of tranquillity.

But whatever the merit of his intentions may be, every writer is now convinced that he must be chiefly indebted to good fortune for finding readers willing to allow him any degree of reputation. It has been remarked, that almost every character which has excited either attention or praise, has owed part of its success to merit, and part to an happy concurrence of circumstances in its favour. Had Cæsar or Cromwell exchanged countries, the one might have been a sergeant, and the other an exciseman. So it is with wit, which generally succeeds more from being happily addressed, than from its native poignancy. A *bon mot*, for instance, that might be relished at White's, may

lose all its flavour when delivered at the Cat and Bagpipes in
St. Giles's. A jest calculated to spread at a gaming table, may
be received with a perfect neutrality of face, should it happen
to drop in a mackerel boat. We have all seen dunces triumph
in some companies, where men of real humour were disregarded
by a general combination in favour of stupidity. To drive the
observation as far as it will go, should the labours of a writer
who designs his performances for readers of a more refined
appetite, fall into the hands of a devourer of compilations,
what can he expect but contempt and confusion? If his merits
are to be determined by judges who estimate the value of a
book from its bulk, or its frontispiece, every rival must acquire
an easy superiority, who, with persuasive eloquence, promises
four extraordinary pages of letterpress, or three beautiful prints,
curiously coloured from nature.

But to proceed: Though I cannot promise as much entertainment, or as much elegance, as others have done, yet the reader
may be assured, he shall have as much of both as I can. He
shall, at least, find me alive while I study his entertainment;
for I solemnly assure him, I was never yet possessed of the
secret at once of writing and sleeping.

During the course of this paper, therefore, all the wit and
learning I have are heartily at his service; which, if, after
so candid a confession, he should, notwithstanding, still find
intolerably dull, low, or sad stuff, this, I protest, is more than
I know. I have a clear conscience, and am entirely out of
the secret.

Yet I would not have him, upon the perusal of a single paper,
pronounce me incorrigible; he may try a second, which, as there
is a studied difference in subject and style, may be more suited
to his taste; if this also fails, I must refer him to a third, or even
to a fourth, in case of extremity. If he should still continue
refractory, and find me dull to the last, I must inform him, with
Bayes, in the Rehearsal, that I think him a very odd kind of
a fellow, and desire no more of his acquaintance.

It is with such reflections as these I endeavour to fortify
myself against the future contempt or neglect of some readers,
and am prepared for their dislike by mutual recrimination.
If such should impute dealing neither in battles nor scandal
to me as a fault, instead of acquiescing in their censure, I must
beg leave to tell them a story.

A traveller, in his way to Italy, happening to pass at the
foot of the Alps, found himself at last in a country where the

inhabitants had each a large excrescence depending from the chin, like the pouch of a monkey. This deformity, as it was endemic, and the people little used to strangers, it had been the custom, time immemorial, to look upon as the greatest ornament of the human visage. Ladies grew toasts from the size of their chins, and none were regarded as pretty fellows, but such whose faces were broadest at the bottom.—It was Sunday; a country church was at hand, and our traveller was willing to perform the duties of the day. Upon his first appearance at the church door, the eyes of all were naturally fixed upon the stranger; but what was their amazement, when they found that he actually wanted that emblem of beauty, a pursed chin! This was a defect that not a single creature had sufficient gravity (though they were noted for being grave) to withstand. Stifled bursts of laughter, winks, and whispers, circulated from visage to visage, and the prismatic figure of the stranger's face was a fund of infinite gaiety; even the parson, equally remarkable for his gravity and chin, could hardly refrain joining in the good-humour. Our traveller could no longer patiently continue an object for deformity to point at. 'Good folks,' said he, 'I perceive that I am the unfortunate cause of all this good-humour. It is true, I may have faults in abundance, but I shall never be induced to reckon my want of a swelled face among the number.'

REMARKS ON OUR THEATRES

Our theatres are now opened, and all Grub Street is preparing its advice to the managers. We shall undoubtedly hear learned disquisitions on the structure of one actor's legs, and another's eyebrows. We shall be told much of enunciations, tones, and attitudes; and shall have our lightest pleasures commented upon by didactic dulness. We shall, it is feared, be told that Garrick is a fine actor; but then as a manager, so avaricious! That Palmer is a most promising genius, and Holland likely to do well in a particular cast of character. We shall have them giving Shuter instructions to amuse us by rule, and deploring over the ruins of desolated majesty at Covent Garden. As I love to be advising too—for advice is easily given, and bears a shew of wisdom and superiority—I must be permitted to offer a few observations upon our theatres and actors, without, on this trivial occasion, throwing my thoughts into the formality of method.

There is something in the deportment of all our players infinitely more stiff and formal than among the actors of other nations. Their action sits uneasy upon them; for as the English use very little gesture in ordinary conversation, our English bred actors are obliged to supply stage gestures by their imagination alone. A French comedian finds proper models of action in every company, and in every coffee-house he enters. An Englishman is obliged to take his models from the stage itself; he is obliged to imitate nature from an imitation of nature. I know of no set of men more likely to be improved by travelling than those of the theatrical profession. The inhabitants of the Continent are less reserved than here; they may be seen through upon a first acquaintance: such are the proper models to draw from; they are at once striking, and are found in great abundance.

Though it would be inexcusable in a comedian to add anything of his own to the poet's dialogue, yet, as to action, he is entirely at liberty. By this he may show the fertility of his genius, the poignancy of his humour, and the exactness of his judgment; we scarce see a coxcomb or a fool in common life, that has not some peculiar oddity in his action. These peculiarities it is not in the power of words to represent, and depend solely upon the actor. They give a relish to the humour of the poet, and make the appearance of nature more illusive. The Italians, it is true, mask some characters, and endeavour to preserve the peculiar humour by the make of the mask; but I have seen others still preserve a great fund of humour in the face without a mask; one actor, particularly, by a squint which he threw into some characters of low life, assumed a look of infinite solidity. This, though upon reflection we might condemn, yet immediately, upon representation, we could not avoid being pleased with.

To illustrate what I have been saying by the plays I have of late gone to see: In the Miser, which was played a few nights ago at Covent Garden, Lovegold appears through the whole in circumstances of exaggerated avarice; all the player's action, therefore, should conspire with the poet's design, and represent him as an epitome of penury. The French comedian, in this character, in the midst of one of his most violent passions, while he appears in an ungovernable rage, feels the demon of avarice still upon him, and stoops down to pick up a pin, which he quilts into the flap of his coat-pocket with great assiduity. Two candles are lighted up for his wedding; he flies and turns one of

them into the socket: it is, however, lighted up again; he then
steals to it, and privately crams it into his pocket. The Mock
Doctor was lately played at the other house. Here again the
comedian had an opportunity of heightening the ridicule by
action. The French player sits in a chair with a high back, and
then begins to shew away by talking nonsense, which he would
have thought Latin by those whom he knows do not understand
a syllable of the matter. At last he grows enthusiastic, enjoys
the admiration of the company, tosses his legs and arms about,
and, in the midst of his raptures and vociferation, he and the
chair fall back together. All this appears dull enough in the
recital, but the gravity of Cato could not stand it in the representation. In short, there is hardly a character in comedy to
which a player of any real humour might not add strokes of
vivacity that could not fail of applause. But, instead of this,
we too often see our fine gentlemen do nothing, through a whole
part, but strut and open their snuff-box; our pretty fellows sit
indecently with their legs across, and our clowns pull up their
breeches. These, if once, or even twice, repeated, might do
well enough; but to see them served up in every scene, argues
the actor almost as barren as the character he would expose.

The magnificence of our theatres is far superior to any others
in Europe, where plays only are acted. The great care our
performers take in painting for a part, their exactness in all the
minutiæ of dress, and other little scenical properties, have been
taken notice of by Riccoboni, a gentleman of Italy, who travelled
Europe with no other design but to remark upon the stage; but
there are several apparent improprieties still continued, or lately
come into fashion. As, for instance, spreading a carpet punctually at the beginning of the death scene, in order to prevent our
actors from spoiling their clothes; this immediately apprises us
of the tragedy to follow; for laying the cloth is not a more sure
indication of dinner, than laying the carpet of bloody work at
Drury Lane. Our little pages, also, with unmeaning faces,
that bear up the train of a weeping princess, and our awkward
lords in waiting, take off much from her distress. Mutes of
every kind divide our attention, and lessen our sensibility; but
here it is entirely ridiculous, as we see them seriously employed
in doing nothing. If we must have dirty-shirted guards upon
the theatres, they should be taught to keep their eyes fixed on
the actors, and not roll them round upon the audience, as if they
were ogling the boxes.

Beauty, methinks, seems a requisite qualification in an actress.

This seems scrupulously observed elsewhere, and, for my part, I could wish to see it observed at home. I can never conceive a hero dying for love of a lady totally destitute of beauty. I must think the part unnatural; for I cannot bear to hear him call that face angelic, when even paint cannot hide its wrinkles. I must condemn him of stupidity; and the person whom I can accuse for want of taste, will seldom become the object of my affections or admiration. But if this be a defect, what must be the entire perversion of scenical decorum, when, for instance, we see an actress that might act the Wapping Landlady without a bolster, pining in the character of Jane Shore, and, while unwieldy with fat, endeavouring to convince the audience that she is dying with hunger!

For the future, then, I could wish that the parts of the young or beautiful were given to performers of suitable figures; for I must own, I could rather see the stage filled with agreeable objects, though they might sometimes bungle a little, than see it crowded with withered or misshapen figures, be their emphasis, as I think it is called, ever so proper. The first may have the awkward appearance of new-raised troops; but in viewing the last, I cannot avoid the mortification of fancying myself placed in a hospital of invalids.

The Story of Alcander and Septimius

Translated from a Byzantine Historian

Athens, long after the decline of the Roman empire, still continued the seat of learning, politeness, and wisdom. Theodoric, the Ostrogoth, repaired the schools which barbarity was suffering to fall into decay, and continued those pensions to men of learning which avaricious governors had monopolised.

In this city, and about this period, Alcander and Septimius were fellow-students together. The one the most subtile reasoner of all the Lyceum; the other the most eloquent speaker in the Academic grove. Mutual admiration soon begot a friendship. Their fortunes were nearly equal, and they were natives of the two most celebrated cities in the world; for Alcander was of Athens, Septimius came from Rome.

In this state of harmony they lived for some time together, when Alcander, after passing the first part of his youth in the indolence of philosophy, thought at length of entering into the busy world; and, as a step previous to this, placed his affections on Hypatia, a lady of exquisite beauty. The day of their intended nuptials was fixed; the previous ceremonies were performed; and nothing now remained but her being conducted in triumph to the apartment of the intended bridegroom.

Alcander's exultation in his own happiness, or being unable to enjoy any satisfaction without making his friend Septimius a partner, prevailed upon him to introduce Hypatia to his fellow-student; which he did with all the gaiety of a man who found himself equally happy in friendship and love. But this was an interview fatal to the future peace of both; for Septimius no sooner saw her, but he was smitten with an involuntary passion; and though he used every effort to suppress desires at once so imprudent and unjust, the emotions of his mind in a short time became so strong, that they brought on a fever which the physicians judged incurable.

During this illness, Alcander watched him with all the anxiety of fondness, and brought his mistress to join in those amiable offices of friendship. The sagacity of the physicians, by these means, soon discovered that the cause of their patient's disorder was love; and Alcander, being apprised of their discovery, at length extorted a confession from the reluctant dying lover.

It would but delay the narrative to describe the conflict between love and friendship in the breast of Alcander on this occasion; it is enough to say that the Athenians were at that time arrived at such refinement in morals, that every virtue was carried to excess. In short, forgetful of his own felicity, he gave up his intended bride, in all her charms, to the young Roman. They were married privately by his connivance; and this unlooked-for change of fortune wrought as unexpected a change in the constitution of the now happy Septimius. In a few days he was perfectly recovered, and set out with his fair partner for Rome. Here, by an exertion of those talents which he was so eminently possessed of, Septimius in a few years arrived at the highest dignities of the state, and was constituted the city judge, or prætor.

In the meantime Alcander not only felt the pain of being separated from his friend and his mistress, but a prosecution was also commenced against him by the relations of Hypatia, for having basely given up his bride, as was suggested, for money. His innocence of the crime laid to his charge, and even his eloquence in his own defence, were not able to withstand the influence of a powerful party. He was cast and condemned to pay an enormous fine. However, being unable to raise so large a sum at the time appointed, his possessions were confiscated, he himself was stripped of the habit of freedom, exposed as slave in the market-place, and sold to the highest bidder.

A merchant of Thrace becoming his purchaser, Alcander, with some other companions of distress, was carried into that region of desolation and sterility. His stated employment was to follow the herds of an imperious master; and his success in hunting was all that was allowed him to supply his precarious subsistence. Every morning waked him to a renewal of famine or toil, and every change of season served but to aggravate his unsheltered distress. After some years of bondage, however, an opportunity of escaping offered; he embraced it with ardour, so that travelling by night, and lodging in caverns by day, to shorten a long story, he at last arrived in Rome. The same day on which Alcander arrived, Septimius sat administering justice in the forum, whither our wanderer came, expecting to be instantly known, and publicly acknowledged by his former friend. Here he stood the whole day amongst the crowd, watching the eyes of the judge, and expecting to be taken notice of; but he was so much altered by a long succession of hardships, that he continued unnoted among the rest; and, in the evening, when he was going up to the prætor's chair, he was brutally repulsed by the attending lictors. The attention of the poor is generally driven from one ungrateful object to another; for night coming on, he now found himself under a necessity of seeking a place to lie in, and yet knew not where to apply. All emaciated and in rags as he was, none of the citizens would harbour so much wretchedness; and sleeping in the streets might be attended with interruption or danger: in short, he was obliged to take up his lodging in one of the tombs without the city, the usual retreat of guilt, poverty, and despair. In this mansion of horror, laying his head upon an inverted urn, he forgot his miseries for a while in sleep; and found, on his flinty couch, more ease than beds of down can supply to the guilty.

As he continued here, about midnight, two robbers came to make this their retreat; but happening to disagree about the division of their plunder, one of them stabbed the other to the heart, and left him weltering in blood at the entrance. In these circumstances he was found next morning dead at the mouth of the vault. This naturally induced a further enquiry; an alarm was spread; the cave was examined; and Alcander being found was immediately apprehended and accused of robbery and murder. The circumstances against him were strong, and the wretchedness of his appearance confirmed suspicion. Misfortune and he were now so long acquainted that he at last became regardless of life. He detested a world where he had found only ingratitude, falsehood, and cruelty; he was determined to make no defence; and thus, lowering with resolution, he was dragged, bound with cords, before the tribunal of Septimius. As the proofs were positive against him, and he offered nothing in his own vindication, the judge was proceeding to doom him to a most cruel and ignominious death, when the attention of the multitude was soon divided by another object. The robber who had been really guilty, was apprehended selling his plunder, and, struck with a panic, had confessed his crime. He was brought bound to the same tribunal, and acquitted every other person of any partnership in his guilt. Alcander's innocence, therefore, appeared, but the sullen rashness of his conduct remained a wonder to the surrounding multitude; but their astonishment was still further increased when they saw their judge start from his tribunal to embrace the supposed criminal: Septimius recollected his friend and former benefactor, and hung upon his neck with tears of pity and of joy. Need the sequel be related? Alcander was acquitted; shared the friendship and honours of the principal citizens of Rome; lived afterwards in happiness and ease; and left it to be engraved on his tomb, that,—No circumstances are so desperate which Providence may not relieve.

A Letter from a Traveller

(The sequel of this correspondence to be continued occasionally. I shall alter nothing either in the style or substance of these letters, and the reader may depend on their being genuine.)

CRACOW, *August* 2, 1758.

My dear Will,—You see, by the date of my letter, that I am arrived in Poland. When will my wanderings be at an end? When will my restless disposition give me leave to enjoy the present hour? When at Lyons, I thought all happiness lay beyond the Alps; when in Italy, I found myself still in want of something, and expected to leave solicitude behind me by going into Roumelia; and now you find me turning back, still expecting ease everywhere but where I am. It is now seven years since I saw the face of a single creature who cared a farthing whether I was dead or alive. Secluded from all the comforts of confidence, friendship, or society, I feel the solitude of a hermit, but not his ease.

The Prince of * * * has taken me in his train, so that I am in no danger of starving for this bout. The Prince's governor is a rude ignorant pedant, and his tutor a battered rake; thus, between two such characters, you may imagine he is finely instructed. I made some attempts to display all the little knowledge I had acquired by reading or observation; but I find myself regarded as an ignorant intruder. The truth is, I shall never be able to acquire a power of expressing myself with ease in any language but my own; and, out of my own country, the highest character I can ever acquire, is that of being a philosophic vagabond.

When I consider myself in the country which was once so formidable in war, and spread terror and desolation over the whole Roman empire, I can hardly account for the present wretchedness and pusillanimity of its inhabitants: a prey to every invader; their cities plundered without an enemy; their magistrates seeking redress by complaints, and not by vigour. Everything conspires to raise my compassion for their miseries, were not my thoughts too busily engaged by my own. The whole kingdom is in strange disorder: when our equipage, which consists of the Prince and thirteen attendants, had arrived at some towns, there were no conveniences to be found, and we were obliged to have girls to conduct us to the next. I have seen a woman travel thus on horseback before us for thirty miles, and think herself highly paid, and make twenty reverences, upon receiving, with ecstasy, about twopence for her trouble. In general, we were better served by the women than the men, on those occasions. The men seemed directed by a low sordid interest alone; they seemed mere machines, and all their thoughts were employed in the care of their horses. If we gently desired them to make more speed, they took not the least notice; kind language was what they had by no means been used to. It was proper to speak to them in the tones of anger, and sometimes it was even necessary to use blows, to excite them to their duty. How different these from the common people of England, whom a blow might induce to return the affront sevenfold. These poor people, however, from being brought up to vile usage, lose all the respect which they should have for themselves. They have contracted a habit of regarding constraint as the great rule of their duty. When they were treated with mildness, they no longer continued to perceive a superiority. They fancied themselves our equals, and a continuance of our humanity might probably have rendered them insolent; but the imperious tone, menaces, and blows, at once changed their sensations and their ideas; their ears and their shoulders taught their souls to shrink back into servitude, from which they had for some moments fancied themselves disengaged.

The enthusiasm of liberty an Englishman feels is never so strong, as when presented by such prospects as these. I must own, in all my indigence, it is one of my comforts, (perhaps, indeed, it is my only boast,) that I am of that happy country; though I scorn to starve there; though I do not choose to lead a life of wretched dependence, or be an object for my former acquaintance to point at. While you enjoy all the ease and elegance of prudence and virtue, your old friend wanders over the world, without a single anchor to hold by, or a friend, except you, to confide in.

Yours, &c.

A Short Account of the Late Mr. Maupertuis

Mr. Maupertuis, lately deceased, was the first to whom the English philosophers owed their being particularly admired by the rest of Europe. The romantic system of Des Cartes was adapted to the taste of the superficial and the indolent; the foreign universities had embraced it with ardour, and such are seldom convinced of their errors till all others give up such false opinions as untenable. The philosophy of Newton and the metaphysics of Locke appeared; but, like all new truths, they were at once received with opposition and contempt. The English, it is true, studied, understood, and, consequently, admired them; it was very different on the Continent. Fontenelle, who seemed to preside over the republic of letters, unwilling to acknowledge that all his life had been spent in erroneous philosophy, joined in the universal disapprobation, and the English philosophers seemed entirely unknown.

Maupertuis, however, made them his study; he thought he might oppose the physics of his country, and yet still be a good citizen; he defended our countrymen, wrote in their favour, and, at last, as he had truth on his side, carried his cause. Almost all the learning of the English, till very lately, was conveyed in the language of France. The writings of Maupertuis spread the reputation of his master, Newton, and, by a happy fortune, have united his fame with that of our human prodigy.

The first of his performances, openly in vindication of the Newtonian system, is his treatise, entitled, 'Sur la figure des Astres', if I remember right; a work at once expressive of a deep geometrical knowledge, and the most happy manner of delivering abstruse science with ease. This met with violent opposition from a people, though fond of novelty in everything else, yet, however, in matters of science, attached to ancient opinions with bigotry. As the old and obstinate fell away, the youth of France embraced the new opinions, and now seem more eager to defend Newton than even his countrymen.

The oddity of character which great men are sometimes remarkable for, Maupertuis was not entirely free from. If we can believe Voltaire, he once attempted to castrate himself; but whether this be true or no, it is certain he was extremely whimsical. Though born to a large fortune, when employed in mathematical inquiries, he disregarded his person to such a degree, and loved retirement so much, that he has been more than once put on the list of modest beggars by the curates of Paris, when he retired to some private quarter of the town, in order to enjoy his meditations without interruption. The character given of him by one of Voltaire's antagonists, if it can be depended upon, is much to his honour. 'You,' says this writer to Mr. Voltaire, 'you were entertained by the King of Prussia as a buffoon, but Maupertuis as a philosopher.' It is certain, that the preference which this royal scholar gave to Maupertuis was the cause of Voltaire's disagreement with him. Voltaire could not bear to see a man, whose talents he had no great opinion of, preferred before him as president of the Royal Academy. His 'Micromegas' was designed to ridicule Maupertuis; and, probably, it has brought more disgrace on the author than the subject. Whatever absurdities men of letters have indulged, and how fantastical soever the modes of science have been, their anger is still more subject to ridicule.

No. II.—SATURDAY, OCTOBER 13, 1759

ON DRESS

FOREIGNERS observe, that there are no ladies in the world more beautiful, or more ill-dressed, than those of England. Our countrywomen have been compared to those pictures, where the face is the work of a Raphael, but the draperies thrown out by some empty pretender, destitute of taste, and unacquainted with design.

If I were a poet, I might observe, on this occasion, that so much beauty set off with all the advantages of dress, would be too powerful an antagonist for the opposite sex; and, therefore, it was wisely ordered that our ladies should want taste, lest their admirers should entirely want reason.

But to confess a truth, I do not find they have a greater aversion to fine clothes than the women of any other country whatsoever. I can't fancy that a shop-keeper's wife in Cheapside has a greater tenderness for the fortune of her husband than a citizen's wife in Paris; or, that Miss in a boarding-school is more an economist in dress than Mademoiselle in a nunnery.

Although Paris may be accounted the soil in which almost every fashion takes its rise, its influence is never so general there as with us. They study there the happy method of uniting grace and fashion, and never excuse a woman for being awkwardly dressed, by saying her clothes are in the mode. A French woman is a perfect architect in dress; she never, with Gothic ignorance, mixes the orders; she never tricks out a squabby Doric shape with Corinthian finery; or, to speak without metaphor, she conforms to a general fashion only when it happens not to be repugnant to private beauty.

The English ladies, on the contrary, seem to have no other standard of grace but the run of the town. If fashion gives the word, every distinction of beauty, complexion, or stature, ceases. Sweeping trains, Prussian bonnets, and trollopees, as like each other as if cut from same piece, level all to one standard. The Mall, the gardens, and play-houses, are filled with ladies in uniform: and their whole appearance shows as little variety or taste, as if their clothes were bespoke by the colonel of a marching regiment, or fancied by the artist who dresses the three battalions of guards.

But not only the ladies of every shape and complexion, but of every age too, are possessed of this unaccountable passion levelling all distinction in dress. The lady of no quality travels fast behind the lady of some quality, and a woman of sixty is as gaudy as her granddaughter. A friend of mine, a good-natured old man, amused me the other day, with an account of his journey to the Mall. It seems, in his walk thither, he, for some time, followed a lady who, as he thought by her dress, was a girl of fifteen. It was airy, elegant, and youthful. My old friend had called up all his poetry on this occasion, and fancied twenty Cupids prepared for execution in every folding of her white negligée. He had prepared his imagination for an angel's face;

but what was his mortification to find that the imaginary goddess was no other than his cousin Hannah, some years older than himself !

But to give it in his own words: 'After the transports of our first salute,' said he, 'were over, I could not avoid running my eye over her whole appearance. Her gown was of cambric, cut short before, in order to discover a high-heeled shoe, which was buckled almost at the toe. Her cap consisted of a few bits of cambric, and flowers of painted paper stuck on one side of her head. Her bosom, that had felt no hand, but the hand of time, these twenty years, rose suing to be pressed. I could, indeed, have wished her more than a handkerchief of Paris net to shade her beauties; for, as Tasso says of the rosebud, "Quanto si mostra men tanto è più bella," a female breast is generally thought more beautiful as it is more sparingly discovered.

'As my cousin had not put on all this finery for nothing, she was at that time sallying out to the Park, when I had overtaken her. Perceiving, however, that I had on my best wig, she offered, if I would 'squire her there, to send home the footman. Though I trembled for our reception in public, yet I could not, with any civility, refuse; so, to be as gallant as possible, I took her hand in my arm, and thus we marched on together.

'When we made our entry at the Park, two antiquated figures, so polite and so tender, soon attracted the eyes of the company. As we made our way among crowds who were out to show their finery as well as we, wherever we came I perceived we brought good-humour with us. The polite could not forbear smiling, and the vulgar burst out into a horse-laugh at our grotesque figures. Cousin Hannah, who was perfectly conscious of the rectitude of her own appearance, attributed all this mirth to the oddity of mine; while I as cordially placed the whole to her account. Thus, from being two of the best-natured creatures alive, before we got half way up the Mall, we both began to grow peevish, and, like two mice on a string, endeavoured to revenge the impertinence of the spectators upon each other. "I am amazed, cousin Jeffrey," says Miss, "that I can never get you to dress like a Christian. I knew we should have the eyes of the Park upon us, with your great wig, so frizzled, and yet so beggarly, and your monstrous muff. I hate those odious muffs!" I could have patiently borne a criticism on all the rest of my equipage; but as I had had always a peculiar veneration for my muff, I could not forbear being piqued a little; and, throwing my eyes with a spiteful air on her bosom, "I could heartily wish,

Madam," replied I, "that for your sake my muff was cut into a tippet."

'As my cousin, by this time, was grown heartily ashamed of her gentleman-usher, and as I was never very fond of any kind of exhibition myself, it was mutually agreed to retire for a while to one of the seats, and from that retreat remark on others as freely as they had remarked on us.

'When seated, we continued silent for some time, employed in very different speculations. I regarded the whole company, now passing in review before me, as drawn out merely for my amusement. For my entertainment the beauty had all that morning been improving her charms; the beau had put on lace, and the young doctor a big wig, merely to please me. But quite different were the sentiments of cousin Hannah: she regarded every well-dressed woman as a victorious rival, hated every face that seemed dressed in good-humour, or wore the appearance of greater happiness than her own. I perceived her uneasiness, and attempted to lessen it, by observing that there was no company in the Park to-day. To this she readily assented; "and yet," says she, "it is full enough of scrubs of one kind or another." My smiling at this observation gave her spirits to pursue the bent of her inclination, and now she began to exhibit her skill in secret history, as she found me disposed to listen. "Observe," says she to me, "that old woman in tawdry silk, and dressed out beyond the fashion. That is Miss Biddy Evergreen. Miss Biddy, it seems, has money; and as she considers that money was never so scarce as it is now, she seems resolved to keep what she has to herself. She is ugly enough, you see; yet, I assure you, she has refused several offers to my own knowledge within this twelve-month. Let me see, three gentlemen from Ireland who study the law; two waiting captains; a doctor; and a Scotch preacher, who had liked to have carried her off. All her time is passed between sickness and finery. Thus, she spends the whole week in a close chamber, with no other company but her monkey, her apothecary, and cat; and comes dressed out to the Park every Sunday, to show her airs, to get new lovers, to catch a new cold, and to make new work for the doctor.

'"There goes Mrs. Roundabout,—I mean the fat lady in the lutestring trollopee. Between you and I, she is but a cutler's wife. See how she 's dressed, as fine as hands and pins can make her, while her two marriageable daughters, like bunters, in stiff gowns, are now taking sixpenny worth of tea at the White

Conduit House. Odious puss! how she waddles along, with a train two yards behind her! She puts me in mind of my Lord Bantam's Indian sheep, which are obliged to have their monstrous tails trundled along in a go-cart. For all her airs, it goes to her husband's heart to see four yards of good lute-string wearing against the ground, like one of his knives on a grindstone. To speak my mind, cousin Jeffrey, I never liked those tails; for suppose a young fellow should be rude, and the lady should offer to step back in the fright, instead of retiring, she treads upon her train, and falls fairly on her back; and then, you know, cousin,—her clothes may be spoiled.

'"Ah! Miss Mazzard! I knew we should not miss her in the Park; she in the monstrous Prussian bonnet. Miss, though so very fine, was bred a milliner; and might have had home custom if she had minded her business, but the girl was fond of finery, and instead of dressing her customers, laid out all her goods in adorning herself. Every new gown she put on impaired her credit; she still, however, went on improving her appearance, and lessening her little fortune, and is now, you see, become a belle and a bankrupt."

'My cousin was proceeding in her remarks, which were interrupted by the approach of the very lady she had been so freely describing; Miss had perceived her at a distance, and approached to salute her. I found, by the warmth of the two ladies' protestations, that they had been long intimate esteemed friends and acquaintance. Both were so pleased at this happy rencounter, that they were resolved not to part for the day. So we all crossed the Park together, and I saw them into a hackney coach at St. James's.'

SOME PARTICULARS RELATIVE TO CHARLES XII
NOT COMMONLY KNOWN

STOCKHOLM.

SIR,—I cannot resist your solicitations, though it is possible I shall be unable to satisfy your curiosity. The polite of every country seem to have but one character. A gentleman of Sweden differs but little, except in trifles, from one of any other country. It is among the vulgar we are to find those distinctions which characterise a people, and from them it is that I take my picture of the Swedes.

Though the Swedes, in general, appear to languish under oppression, which often renders others wicked, or of malignant dispositions, it has not, however, the same influence upon them, as they are faithful, civil, and incapable of atrocious crimes. Would you believe that in Sweden highway robberies are not so much as heard of? For my part, I have not in the whole country seen a gibbet or a gallows. They pay an infinite respect to their ecclesiastics, whom they suppose to be the privy-councillors of Providence; who, on their part, turn this credulity to their own advantage, and manage their parishioners as they please. In general, however, they seldom abuse their sovereign authority. Hearkened to as oracles, regarded as the dispensers of eternal rewards and punishments, they readily influence their hearers into justice, and make them practical philosophers without the pains of study.

As to their persons, they are perfectly well made, and the men particularly have a very engaging air. The greatest part of the boys which I saw in the country had very white hair. They were as beautiful as Cupids, and there was something open and entirely happy in their little chubby faces. The girls, on the contrary, have neither such fair nor such even complexions, and their features are much less delicate, which is a circumstance different from that of almost every other country. Besides this, it is observed, that the women are generally afflicted with the itch, for which Scania is particularly remarkable. I had an instance of this in one of the inns on the road. The hostess was one of the most beautiful women I have ever seen; she had so fine a complexion, that I could not avoid admiring it. But what was my surprise, when she opened her bosom in order to suckle her child, to perceive that seat of delight all covered with this disagreeable distemper. The careless manner in which she exposed to our eyes so disgusting an object, sufficiently testifies that they regard it as no very extraordinary malady, and seem to take no pains to conceal it. Such are the remarks, which probably you may think trifling enough, I have made in my journey to Stockholm; which, to take it altogether, is a large, beautiful, and even populous city.

The arsenal appears to me one of its greatest curiosities: it is an handsome, spacious building, but, however, illy stored with the implements of war. To recompense this defect, they have almost filled it with trophies, and other marks of their former military glory. I saw there several chambers filled with Danish, Saxon, Polish, and Russian standards. There was at least enough to suffice half-a-dozen armies; but new standards are more easily made than new armies can be enlisted. I saw, besides, some very rich furniture, and some of the crown jewels, of great value; but what principally engaged my attention, and touched me with passing melancholy, were the bloody, yet precious spoils of the two greatest heroes the North ever produced. What I mean are the clothes in which the great Gustavus Adolphus, and the intrepid Charles XII died, by a fate not unusual to kings. The first, if I remember, is a sort of a buff waistcoat, made antique fashion, very plain, and without the least ornaments; the second, which was even more remarkable, consisted only of a coarse blue cloth coat, a large hat of less value, a shirt of coarse linen, large boots, and buff gloves made to cover a great part of the arm. His saddle, his pistols, and his sword, have nothing in them remarkable; the meanest soldier was in this respect no way inferior to his gallant monarch. I shall use this opportunity to give you some particulars of the life of a man already so well known, which I had from persons who knew him when a child, and who now, by a fate not unusual to courtiers, spend a life of poverty and retirement, and talk over in raptures all the actions of their old victorious king, companion, and master.

Courage and inflexible constancy formed the basis of this monarch's character. In his tenderest years he gave instances of both. When he was yet scarce seven years old, being at dinner with the queen his mother, intending to give a bit of bread to a great dog he was fond of, this hungry animal snapped too greedily at the morsel, and bit his hand in a terrible manner. The wound bled copiously, but our young hero, without offering to cry, or taking the least notice of his misfortune, endeavoured to conceal what had happened, lest his dog should be brought into trouble, and wrapped his bloody hand in the napkin. The queen, perceiving that he did not eat, asked him the reason. He contented himself with replying, that he thanked her, he was not hungry. They thought he was taken ill, and so repeated their solicitations: but all was in vain, though the poor child was already grown pale with the loss of blood. An officer who attended at table at last perceived it; for Charles would sooner have died than betrayed his dog, who, he knew, intended no injury.

At another time, when in the small-pox, and his case appeared dangerous, he grew one day very uneasy in his bed, and a gentleman who watched him, desirous of covering him up close, received from the patient a violent box on his ear. Some hours after, observing the prince more calm, he entreated to know how he had incurred his displeasure, or what he had done to have merited a blow. 'A blow?' replied Charles, 'I don't remember anything of it: I remember, indeed, that I thought myself in the battle of Arbela, fighting for Darius, where I gave Alexander a blow which brought him to the ground.'

What great effects might not these two qualities of courage and constancy have produced, had they at first received a just direction. Charles, with proper instructions, thus naturally disposed, would have been the delight and the glory of his age. Happy those princes, who are educated by men who are at once virtuous and wise, and have been for some time in the school of affliction; who weigh happiness against glory, and teach their royal pupils the real value of fame; who are ever showing the superior dignity of man to that of royalty—that a peasant who does his duty is a nobler character than a king of even middling reputation! Happy, I say, were princes, could such men be found to instruct them; but those to whom such an education is generally entrusted, are men who themselves have acted in a sphere too high to know mankind. Puffed up themselves with ideas of false grandeur, and measuring merit by adventitious circumstances of greatness, they generally communicate those fatal prejudices to their pupils, confirm their pride by adulation, or increase their ignorance by teaching them to despise that wisdom which is found among the poor.

But not to moralize when I only intend a story,—what is related of the journeys of this prince is no less astonishing. He has sometimes been on horseback for four-and-twenty hours succesively, and thus traversed the greatest part of his kingdom. At last, none of the officers were found capable of following him; he thus consequently rode the greatest part of these journeys quite alone, without taking a moment's repose, and without any other subsistence but a bit of bread. In one of these rapid courses he underwent an adventure singular enough. Riding thus post one day, all alone, he had the misfortune to have his horse fall dead under him. This might have embarrassed an ordinary man, but it gave Charles no sort of uneasiness. Sure of finding another horse, but not equally so of meeting with a good saddle and pistols, he ungirds his horse, claps the whole equipage on his own back, and, thus accoutred, marches on to the next inn, which by good fortune was not far off. Entering the stable, he here found a horse entirely to his mind; so, without further ceremony, he clapped on his saddle and housing with great composure, and was just going to mount, when the gentleman who owned the horse was apprised of a stranger's going to steal his property out of the stable. Upon asking the king, whom he had never seen, bluntly, how he presumed to meddle with his horse, Charles coolly replied, squeezing in his lips, which was his usual custom, that he took the horse because he wanted one; 'for you see,' continued he, 'if I have none, I shall be obliged to carry the saddle myself.' This answer did not seem at all satisfactory to the gentleman, who instantly drew his sword. In this the king was not much behindhand with him, and to it they were going, when the guards by this time came up, and testified that surprise which was natural to see arms in the hand of a subject against his king. Imagine whether the gentleman was less surprised than they at his unpremeditated disobedience. His astonishment, however, was soon dissipated by the king, who, taking him by the hand, assured him he was a brave fellow, and himself would take care he should be provided for. This promise was afterwards fulfilled, and I have been assured the king made him a captain.

I am, Sir, &c.

HAPPINESS, IN A GREAT MEASURE, DEPENDENT ON CONSTITUTION

When I reflect on the unambitious retirement in which I passed the earlier part of my life in the country, I cannot avoid feeling some pain in thinking that those happy days are never to return. In that retreat all nature seemed capable of affording pleasure: I then made no refinements on happiness, but could be pleased with the most awkward efforts of rustic mirth; thought cross-purposes the highest stretch of human wit; and questions and commands the most rational way of spending the evening. Happy could so charming an illusion still continue! I find that age and knowledge only contribute to sour our dispositions. My present enjoyments may be more refined, but they are infinitely less pleasing. The pleasure the best actor gives can no way compare to that I have received from a country wag who imitated a quaker's sermon. The music of the finest singer is dissonance to what I felt when our old dairymaid sung me into tears with Johnny Armstrong's Last Good Night or the cruelty of Barbara Allen.

Writers of every age have endeavoured to show that pleasure is in us, and not in the objects offered for our amusement. If the soul be happily disposed, every thing becomes capable of affording entertainment; and distress will almost want a name. Every occurrence passes in review like the figures of a procession: some may be awkward, others ill dressed; but none but a fool is for this enraged with the master of the ceremonies.

I remember to have once seen a slave in a fortification in Flanders, who appeared no way touched with his situation. He was maimed, deformed, and chained; obliged to toil from the appearance of day till nightfall, and condemned to this for life; yet with all these circumstances of apparent wretchedness, he sung, would have danced, but that he wanted a leg, and appeared the merriest, happiest man of all the garrison. What a practical philosopher was here! a happy constitution supplied philosophy, and though seemingly destitute of wisdom, he was really wise. No reading or study had contributed to disenchant the fairy-land around him. Every thing furnished him with an opportunity of mirth; and though some thought him, from his insensibility, a fool, he was such an idiot as philosophers should wish to imitate; for all philosophy is only forcing the trade of happiness, when nature seems to deny the means.

They who, like our slave, can place themselves on that side of the world in which everything appears in a pleasing light, will find something in every occurrence to excite their good humour. The most calamitous events, either to themselves or others, can bring no new affliction: the whole world is to them a theatre, on which comedies are only acted. All the bustle of heroism, or the rants of ambition, serve only to heighten the absurdity of the scene, and make the humour more poignant. They feel, in short, as little anguish at their own distress, or the complaints of others, as the undertaker, though dressed in black, feels sorrow at a funeral.

Of all the men I ever read of, the famous Cardinal de Retz possessed this happiness of temper in the highest degree. As he was a man of gallantry, and despised all that wore the pedantic appearance of philosophy, wherever pleasure was to be sold, he was generally foremost to raise the auction. Being an universal admirer of the fair sex, when he found one lady cruel, he generally fell in love with another, from whom he expected a more favourable reception: if she too rejected his addresses, he never thought of retiring into deserts, or pining in hopeless distress. He persuaded himself, that instead of loving the lady, he only fancied he had loved her, and so all was well again. When fortune wore her angriest look, and he at last fell into the power of his most deadly enemy, Cardinal Mazarin, (being confined a close prisoner in the Castle of Valenciennes,) he never attempted to support his distress by wisdom or philosophy, for he pretended to neither. He only laughed at himself and his persecutor, and seemed infinitely pleased at his new situation. In this mansion of distress, though secluded from his friends, though denied all the amusements, and even the conveniences of life, he still retained his good humour; laughed at all the little spite of his enemies; and carried the jest so far as to be revenged, by writing the life of his gaoler.

All that the wisdom of the proud can teach, is to be stubborn or sullen under misfortunes. The Cardinal's example will instruct us to be merry in circumstances of the highest affliction. It matters not whether our good humour be construed by others into insensibility, or even idiotism; it is happiness to ourselves, and none but a fool would measure his satisfaction by what the world thinks of it: for my own part I never pass by one of our prisons for debt, that I do not envy that felicity which is still going forward among those people, who forget the cares of the world by being shut out from its ambition.

The happiest silly fellow I ever knew, was of the number of those good-natured creatures that are said to do no harm to any but themselves. Whenever he fell into any misery, he usually called it 'seeing life'. If his head was broke by a chairman, or his pocket picked by a sharper, he comforted himself by imitating the Hibernian dialect of the one, or the more fashionable cant of the other. Nothing came amiss to him. His inattention to money matters had incensed his father to such a degree, that all the intercession of friends in his favour was fruitless. The old gentleman was on his death-bed. The whole family, and Dick among the number, gathered around him. 'I leave my second son, Andrew,' said the expiring miser, 'my whole estate, and desire him to be frugal.' Andrew, in a sorrowful tone, as is usual on these occasions, prayed heaven to prolong his life and health to enjoy it himself,—'I recommend Simon, my third son, to the care of his elder brother, and leave him beside four thousand pounds.'—'Ah, father!' cried Simon, (in great affliction to be sure,) 'may heaven give you life and health to enjoy it yourself!' At last, turning to poor Dick, 'As for you, you have always been a sad dog—you'll never come to good; you'll never be rich; I'll leave you a shilling to buy an halter.'—'Ah, father!' cries Dick, without any emotion, 'may heaven give you life and health to enjoy it yourself!' This was all the trouble the loss of fortune gave this thoughtless, imprudent creature. However, the tenderness of an uncle recompensed the neglect of a father; and my friend is now not only excessively good-humoured, but competently rich.

Yes, let the world cry-out at a bankrupt who appears at a ball; at an author who laughs at the public which pronounces him a dunce; at a general who smiles at the reproach of the vulgar; or the lady who keeps her good humour in spite of scandal; but such is the wisest behaviour that any of us can possibly assume; it is certainly a better way to oppose calamity by dissipation, than to take up the arms of reason or resolution to oppose it: by the first method we forget our miseries; by the last we only conceal them from others. By struggling with misfortunes, we are sure to receive some wounds in the conflict; but a sure method to come off victorious, is by running away.

On our Theatres

Mademoiselle Clairon, a celebrated actress at Paris, seems to me the most perfect female figure I have ever seen upon any stage. Not perhaps that nature has been more liberal of personal beauty to her, than some to be seen upon our theatres at home. There are actresses here who have as much of what connoisseurs call statuary grace, by which is meant elegance unconnected with motion, as she; but they all fall infinitely short of her, when the soul comes to give expression to the limbs, and animates every feature.

Her first appearance is excessively engaging; she never comes in staring round upon the company, as if she intended to count the benefits of the house, or at least to see, as well as be seen. Her eyes are always, at first, intently fixed upon the persons of the drama, and she lifts them, by degrees, with enchanting diffidence, upon the spectators. Her first speech, or at least the first part of it, is delivered with scarcely any motion of the arm; her hands and her tongue never set out together; but the one prepares us for the other. She sometimes begins with a mute, eloquent attitude; but never goes forward all at once with hands, eyes, head, and voice. This observation, though it may appear of no importance, should certainly be adverted to; nor do I see any one performer (Garrick only excepted) among us, that is not, in this particular, apt to offend. By this simple beginning she gives herself a power of rising in the passion of the scene. As she proceeds, every gesture, every look, acquires new violence, till at last, transported, she fills the whole vehemence of the part, and all the idea of the poet.

Her hands are not alternately stretched out, and then drawn in again, as with the singing women at Sadler's Wells: they are employed with graceful variety, and every moment please with new and unexpected eloquence. Add to this, that their motion is generally from the shoulder; she never flourishes her hands while the upper part of her arm is motionless, nor has she the ridiculous appearance as if her elbows were pinned to her hips.

But, of all the cautions to be given our rising actresses, I would particularly recommend it to them never to take notice of the audience upon any occasion whatsoever; let the spectators applaud never so loudly, their praises should pass, except at the end of the epilogue, with seeming inattention. I can never pardon a lady on the stage, who, when she draws the admiration of the whole audience, turns about to make them a low curtsy for their applause. Such a figure no longer continues Belvidera, but at once drops into Mrs. Cibber. Suppose a sober tradesman, who once a-year takes his shilling's worth at Drury Lane, in order to be delighted with the figure of a queen—the queen of Sheba, for instance, or any other queen—this honest man has no other idea of the great but from their superior pride and impertinence: suppose such a man placed among the spectators, the first figure that presents on the stage is the queen herself, curtsying and cringing to all the company, how can he fancy her the haughty favourite of King Solomon the Wise, who appears actually more submissive than the wife of his bosom? We are all tradesmen of a nicer relish in this respect, and such conduct must disgust every spectator who loves to have the illusion of nature strong upon him.

Yet, while I recommend to our actresses a skilful attention to gesture, I would not have them study it in the looking-glass. This, without some precaution, will render their action formal; by too great an intimacy with this, they become stiff and affected. People seldom improve when they have no other model but themselves to copy after. I remember to have known a notable performer of the other sex, who made great use of this flattering monitor, and yet was one of the stiffest figures I ever saw. I am told his apartment was hung round with looking-glass, that he might see his person twenty times reflected upon entering the room; and I will make bold to say he saw twenty very ugly fellows whenever he did so.

No. III.—SATURDAY, OCTOBER 20, 1759

ON THE USE OF LANGUAGE

IT is usually said by grammarians, that the use of language is to express our wants and desires; but men who know the world hold, and I think with some show of reason, that he who best knows how to keep his necessities private is the most likely person to have them redressed; and that the true use of speech is not so much to express our wants, as to conceal them.

When we reflect on the manner in which mankind generally confer their favours, there appears something so attractive in riches, that the large heap generally collects from the smaller; and the poor find as much pleasure in increasing the enormous mass of the rich, as the miser, who owns it, sees happiness in its increase. Nor is there in this any thing repugnant to the laws of morality. Seneca himself allows, that in conferring benefits, the present should always be suited to the dignity of the receiver. Thus the rich receive large presents, and are thanked for accepting them; men of middling stations are obliged to be content with presents something less; while the beggar, who may be truly said to want indeed, is well paid if a farthing rewards his warmest solicitations.

Every man who has seen the world, and has had his ups and downs in life, as the expression is, must have frequently experienced the truth of this doctrine, and must know, that to have much, or to seem to have it, is the only way to have more. Ovid finely compares a man of broken fortune to a falling column; the lower it sinks, the greater is that weight it is obliged to sustain. Thus, when a man's circumstances are such that he has no occasion to borrow, he finds numbers willing to lend him; but should his wants be such that he sues for a trifle, it is two to one whether he may be trusted with the smallest sum. A certain young fellow whom I knew, whenever he had occasion to ask his friend for a guinea, used to prelude his request as if he wanted two hundred; and talked so familiarly of large sums, that none could ever think he wanted a small one. The same gentleman, whenever he wanted credit for a suit of clothes, always made the proposal in a laced coat; for he found by experience, that if he appeared shabby on these occasions, his tailor had taken an oath against trusting; or what was every whit as bad, his foreman was out of the way, and should not be at home for some time.

There can be no inducements to reveal our wants, except to find pity, and by this means relief; but before a poor man opens his mind in such circumstances, he should first consider whether he is contented to lose the esteem of the person he solicits, and whether he is willing to give up friendship to excite compassion. Pity and friendship are passions incompatible with each other; and it is impossible that both can reside in any breast for the smallest space, without impairing each other. Friendship is made up of esteem and pleasure; pity is composed of sorrow and contempt: the mind may for some time fluctuate between them, but it never can entertain both at once.

In fact pity, though it may often relieve, is but at best a short-lived passion, and seldom affords distress more than transitory assistance; with some it scarce lasts from the first impulse till the hand can be put into the pocket; with others it may continue for twice that space; and on some of extraordinary sensibility I have seen it operate for half an hour together: but still, last as it may, it generally produces but beggarly effects; and where, from this motive, we give five farthings, from others we give pounds; whatever be our feelings from the first impulse of distress, when the same distress solicits a second time, we then feel with diminished sensibility; and, like the repetition of an echo, every stroke becomes weaker; till, at last, our sensations lose all mixture of sorrow, and degenerate into downright contempt.

These speculations bring to my mind the fate of a very good-natured fellow who is now no more. He was bred in a counting-house, and his father dying just as he was out of his time, left him an handsome fortune, and many friends to advise with. The restraint in which my friend had been brought up had thrown a gloom upon his temper, which some regarded as prudence; and, from such considerations, he had every day repeated offers of friendship. Such as had money, were ready to offer him their assistance that way; and they who had daughters, frequently, in the warmth of affection, advised him to marry. My friend, however, was in good circumstances; he wanted neither money, friends, nor a wife, and therefore modestly declined their proposals.

Some errors, however, in the management of his affairs, and several losses in trade, soon brought him to a different way of thinking; and he at last considered that it was his best way to let his friends know that their offers were at length acceptable. His first address was to a scrivener, who had formerly made him frequent offers of money and friendship, at a time when, perhaps, he knew those offers would have been refused. As a man, therefore, confident of not being refused, he requested the use of a hundred guineas for a few days, as he just then had occasion for money. 'And pray, Sir,' replied the scrivener, 'do you want all this money?'—'Want it, Sir,' says the other, 'if I did not want it, I should not have asked it.'—'I am sorry for that,' says the friend; 'for those who want money when they borrow, will always want money when they should come to pay. To say the truth, Sir, money is money now; and I believe it is all sunk in the bottom of the sea, for my part; and he that has got a little, is a fool if he does not keep what he has got.'

Not quite disconcerted by this refusal, our adventurer was resolved to apply to another, whom he knew was the very best friend he had in the world. The gentleman whom he now addressed, received his proposal with all the affability that could be expected from generous friendship. 'Let me see,—you want a hundred guineas; and, pray, dear Jack, would not fifty answer?' —'If you have but fifty to spare, Sir, I must be contented.'— 'Fifty to spare! I do not say that, for I believe I have but twenty about me.'—'Then I must borrow the other thirty from some other friend.'—'And pray,' replied the friend, 'would it not be the best way to borrow the whole money from that other friend, and then one note will serve for all, you know? You know, my dear Sir, that you need make no ceremony with me at any time; you know I'm your friend, when you choose a bit of dinner or so—You, Tom, see the gentleman down. You won't forget to dine with us now and then? Your very humble servant.'

Distressed, but not discouraged, at this treatment, he was at last resolved to find that assistance from love, which he could not have from friendship. A young lady, a distant relation by the mother's side, had a fortune in her own hands; and, as she had already made all the advances that her sex's modesty would permit, he made his proposal with confidence. He soon, however, perceived, that *No bankrupt ever found the fair one kind.* She had lately fallen deeply in love with another, who had more money, and the whole neighbourhood thought it would be a match.

Every day now began to strip my poor friend of his former finery: his clothes flew piece by piece to the pawnbroker's, and he seemed at length equipped in the genuine livery of misfortune. But still he thought himself secure from actual necessity; the numberless invitations he had received to dine, even after his losses, were yet unanswered; he was, therefore, now resolved to accept of a dinner, because he wanted one; and in this manner he actually lived among his friends a whole week without being openly affronted. The last place I saw him in was at a reverend divine's. He had, as he fancied, just nicked the time of dinner, for he came in as the cloth was laying. He took a chair without being desired, and talked for some time without being attended to. He assured the company that nothing procured so good an appetite as a walk in the Park, where he had been that morning. He went on, and praised the figure of the damask table-cloth; talked of a feast where he had been the day before, but that the venison was overdone. But all this procured him no invitation: finding, therefore, the gentleman of the house insensible to all his fetches, he thought proper, at last, to retire, and mend his appetite by a second walk in the Park.

You then, O ye beggars of my acquaintance, whether in rags or lace—whether in Kent Street, or the Mall—whether at the Smyrna or St. Giles's,—might I be permitted to advise as a friend, never seem to want the favour which you solicit. Apply to every passion but human pity for redress. You may find permanent relief from vanity, from self-interest, or from avarice, but from compassion—never. The very eloquence of a poor man is disgusting; and that mouth which is opened even by wisdom, is seldom expected to close without the horrors of a petition.

To ward off the gripe of poverty, you must pretend to be a stranger to her, and she will at least use you with ceremony. If you be caught dining upon a halfpenny porringer of pease-soup and potatoes, praise the wholesomeness of your frugal repast. You may observe that Dr. Cheyne has prescribed pease-broth for the gravel; hint that you are not one of those who are always making a deity of your belly. If, again, you are obliged to wear flimsy stuff in the midst of winter, be the first to remark that stuffs are very much worn at Paris; or, if there be found some irreparable defects in any part of your equipage, which cannot be concealed by all the arts of sitting cross-legged, coaxing, or darning, say that neither you nor Samson Gideon were ever very fond of dress. If you be a philosopher, hint that Plato or Seneca are the tailors you choose to employ; assure the company, that man ought to be content with a bare covering, since what is now so much his pride, was formerly his shame.

In short, however caught, never give out; but ascribe to the frugality of your disposition, what others might be apt to attribute to the narrowness of your circumstances. To be poor, and to seem poor, is a certain method never to rise: pride in the great is hateful; in the wise it is ridiculous; but beggarly pride is a rational vanity which I have been taught to applaud and excuse.

The History of Hypatia

Man, when secluded from society, is not a more solitary being than the woman who leaves the duties of her own sex to invade the privileges of ours. She seems, in such circumstances, like one in banishment; she appears like a neutral being between the sexes; and, though she may have the admiration of both, she finds true happiness from neither.

Of all the ladies of antiquity, I have read of none who was ever more justly celebrated than the beautiful Hypatia, the daughter of Theon the philosopher. This most accomplished of women was born at Alexandria, in the reign of Theodosius the younger. Nature was never more lavish of its gifts than it had been to her, endued as she was with the most exalted understanding, and the happiest turn to science. Education completed what nature had begun, and made her the prodigy not only of her age, but the glory of her sex.

From her father she learned geometry and astronomy; she collected from the conversation and schools of the other philosophers, for which Alexandria was at that time famous, the principles of the rest of the sciences.

What cannot be conquered by natural penetration and a passion for study! The boundless knowledge which, at that period of time, was required to form the character of a philosopher no way discouraged her; she delivered herself up to the study of Aristotle and Plato, and soon not one in all Alexandria understood so perfectly as she all the difficulties of these two philosophers.

But not their systems alone, but those of every other sect, were quite familiar to her; and, to this knowledge, she added that of polite learning, and the art of oratory. All the learning which it was possible for the human mind to contain, being joined to a most enchanting eloquence, rendered this lady the wonder not only of the populace, who easily admire, but of philosophers themselves, who are seldom fond of admiration.

The city of Alexandria was every day crowded with strangers, who came from all parts of Greece and Asia to see and hear her.

As for the charms of her person, they might not probably have been mentioned, did she not join to a beauty the most striking, a virtue that might repress the most assuming; and though, in the whole capital famed for charms, there was not one who could equal her in beauty, though in a city the resort of all the learning then existing in the world, there was not one who could equal her in knowledge; yet, with such accomplishments, Hypatia was the most modest of her sex.   Her reputation for virtue was not less than her virtues; and, though in a city divided between two factions, though visited by the wits and the philosophers of the age, calumny never dared to suspect her morals, or attempt her character.   Both the Christians and the Heathen who have transmitted her history and her misfortunes, have but one voice, when they speak of her beauty, her knowledge, and her virtue.   Nay, so much harmony reigns in their accounts of this prodigy of perfection, that, in spite of the opposition of their faith, we should never have been able to judge of what religion was Hypatia, were we not informed, from other circumstances, that she was a heathen.   Providence had taken so much pains in forming her, that we are almost induced to complain of its not having endeavoured to make her a Christian; but from this complaint we are deterred by a thousand contrary observations, which lead us to reverence its inscrutable mysteries.

This great reputation, which she so justly was possessed of, was, at last, however, the occasion of her ruin.

The person who then possessed the patriarchate of Alexandria, was equally remarkable for his violence, cruelty, and pride.   Conducted by an ill-grounded zeal for the Christian religion, or, perhaps, desirous of augmenting his authority in the city, he had long meditated the banishment of the Jews. A difference arising between them and the Christians, with respect to some public games, seemed to him a proper juncture for putting his ambitious designs into execution.   He found no difficulty in exciting the people, naturally disposed to revolt. The prefect who, at that time, commanded the city, interposed on this occasion, and thought it just to put one of the chief creatures of the patriarch to the torture, in order to discover the first promoter of the conspiracy.   The patriarch, enraged at the injustice he thought offered to his character and dignity, and piqued at the protection which was offered to the Jews, sent for the chiefs of the synagogue, and enjoined them to renounce their designs, upon pain of incurring his highest displeasure.

The Jews, far from fearing his menaces, excited new tumults, in which several citizens had the misfortune to fall. The patriarch could no longer contain: at the head of a numerous body of Christians, he flew to the synagogues, which he demolished, and drove the Jews from a city, of which they had been possessed since the times of Alexander the Great. It may be easily imagined, that the prefect could not behold, without pain, his jurisdiction thus insulted, and the city deprived of a number of its most industrious inhabitants.

The affair was, therefore, brought before the emperor. The patriarch complained of the excesses of the Jews, and the prefect, of the outrages of the patriarch. At this very juncture, five hundred monks of Mount Nitria, imagining the life of their chief to be in danger, and that their religion was threatened in his fall, flew into the city with ungovernable rage, attacked the prefect in the streets, and, not content with loading him with reproaches, wounded him in several places.

The citizens had by this time notice of the fury of the monks; they therefore assembled in a body, put the monks to flight, seized on him who had been found throwing a stone, and delivered him to the prefect, who caused him to be put to death without farther delay.

The patriarch immediately ordered the dead body, which had been exposed to view, to be taken down, procured for it all the pomp and rites of burial, and went even so far as himself to pronounce the funeral oration, in which he classed a seditious monk among the martyrs. This conduct was by no means generally approved of; the most moderate even among the Christians perceived and blamed his indiscretion; but he was now too far advanced to retire. He had made several overtures towards a reconciliation with the prefect, which not succeeding, he bore all those an implacable hatred whom he imagined to have any hand in traversing his designs; but Hypatia was particularly destined to ruin. She could not find pardon, as she was known to have a most refined friendship for the prefect; wherefore the populace were incited against her. Peter, a reader of the principal church, one of those vile slaves by which men in power are too frequently attended—wretches ever ready to commit any crime which they hope may render them agreeable to their employer,—this fellow, I say, attended by a crowd of villains, waited for Hypatia, as she was returning from a visit, at her own door, seized her as she was going in, and dragged her to one of the churches called Cesarea, where, stripping her in a most inhuman manner, they exercised the most inhuman cruelties upon her, cut her into pieces, and burnt her remains to ashes. Such was the end of Hypatia, the glory of her own sex, and the astonishment of ours.

On Justice and Generosity

Lysippus is a man whose greatness of soul the whole world admires. His generosity is such that it prevents a demand, and saves the receiver the trouble and the confusion of a request. His liberality also does not oblige more by its greatness than by his inimitable grace in giving. Sometimes he even distributes his bounties to strangers, and has been known to do good offices to those who professed themselves his enemies. All the world are unanimous in the praise of his generosity; there is only one sort of people who complain of his conduct,—Lysippus does not pay his debts.

It is no difficult matter to account for a conduct so seemingly incompatible with itself. There is greatness in being generous, and there is only simple justice in his satisfying creditors. Generosity is the part of a soul raised above the vulgar. There is in it something of what we admire in heroes, and praise with a degree of rapture. Justice, on the contrary, is a mere mechanic virtue, only fit for tradesmen, and what is practised by every broker in 'Change Alley.

In paying his debts a man barely does his duty, and it is an action attended with no sort of glory. Should Lysippus satisfy his creditors, who would be at the pains of telling it to the world? Generosity is a virtue of a very different complexion. It is raised above duty, and from its elevation, attracts the attention and the praises of us little mortals below.

In this manner do men generally reason upon justice and generosity. The first is despised, though a virtue essential to the good of society; and the other attracts our esteem, which too frequently proceeds from an impetuosity of temper, rather directed by vanity than reason. Lysippus is told that his banker asks a debt of forty pounds, and that a distressed acquaintance petitions for the same sum. He gives it without hesitating to the latter; for he demands as a favour what the former requires as a debt.

Mankind in general are not sufficiently acquainted with the import of the word *justice*: it is commonly believed to consist only in a performance of those duties to which the laws of society can oblige us. This, I allow, is sometimes the import of the word, and in this sense justice is distinguished from equity; but there is a justice still more extensive, and which can be shown to embrace all the virtues united.

Justice may be defined, [as] that virtue which impels us to give to every person what is his due. In this extended sense of the word, it comprehends the practice of every virtue which reason prescribes, or society should expect. Our duty to our Maker, to each other, and to ourselves, are fully answered, if we give them what we owe them. Thus justice, properly speaking, is the only virtue; and all the rest have their origin in it.

The qualities of candour, fortitude, charity, and generosity, for instance, are not, in their own nature, virtues; and if ever they deserve the title, it is owing only to justice, which impels and directs them. Without such a moderator, candour might become indiscretion, fortitude obstinacy, charity imprudence, and generosity mistaken profusion.

A disinterested action, if it be not conducted by justice, is at best indifferent in its nature, and not unfrequently even turns to vice. The expenses of society, of presents, of entertainments, and the other helps of cheerfulness, are actions merely indifferent, when not repugnant to a better method of disposing of our superfluities; but they become vicious when they obstruct or exhaust our abilities from a more virtuous disposition of our circumstances.

True generosity is a duty as indispensably necessary as those imposed upon us by law. It is a rule imposed upon us by reason, which should be the sovereign law of a rational being. But this generosity does not consist in obeying every impulse of humanity, in following blind passion for our guide, and impairing our circumstances by present benefactions, so as to render us incapable of future ones.

Misers are generally characterised as men without honour, or without humanity, who live only to accumulate, and to this passion sacrifice every other happiness. They have been described as madmen, who, in the midst of abundance, banish every pleasure, and make, from imaginary wants, real necessities. But few, very few, correspond to this exaggerated picture; and perhaps there is not one in whom all these circumstances are found united. Instead of this, we find the sober and the industrious branded by the vain and the idle with this odious appellation; men who, by frugality and labour, raise themselves above their equals, and contribute their share of industry to the common stock.

Whatever the vain or the ignorant may say, well were it for society had we more of these characters amongst us. In general, these close men are found at last the true benefactors of society. With an avaricious man we seldom lose in our dealings; but too frequently in our commerce with prodigality.

A French priest, whose name was Godinot, went for a long time by the name of the Griper. He refused to relieve the most apparent wretchedness, and, by a skilful management of his vineyard, had the good fortune to acquire immense sums of money. The inhabitants of Rheims, who were his fellow-citizens, detested him; and the populace, who seldom love a miser, wherever he went followed him with shouts of contempt. He still, however, continued his former simplicity of life, his amazing and unremitted frugality. He had long perceived the wants of the poor in the city, particularly in having no water but what they were obliged to buy at an advanced price; wherefore, that whole fortune which he had been amassing, he laid out in an aqueduct; by which he did the poor more useful and lasting service, than if he had distributed his whole income in charity every day at his door.

Among men long conversant with books, we too frequently find those misplaced virtues of which I have been now complaining. We find the studious animated with a strong passion for the great virtues, as they are mistakenly called, and utterly forgetful of the ordinary ones. The declamations of philosophy are generally rather exhausted on those supererogatory duties, than such as are indispensably necessary. A man, therefore, who has taken his ideas of mankind from study alone, generally comes into the world with a heart melting at every fictitious distress. Thus he is induced, by misplaced liberality, to put himself into the indigent circumstances of the person he relieves.

I shall conclude this paper with the advice of one of the ancients, to a young man whom he saw giving away all his substance to pretended distress. 'It is possible that the person you relieve may [not] be an honest man; and I know that you who relieve him are such. You see, then, by your generosity, you rob a man who is certainly deserving, to bestow it on one who may possibly be a rogue; and, while you are unjust in rewarding uncertain merit, you are doubly guilty by stripping yourself.'

Some Particulars relating to Father Freijo

Primus mortales tollere contra
Est oculos ausus, primusque assurgere contra.—Lucr.

The Spanish nation has, for many centuries past, been remarkable for the grossest ignorance in polite literature, especially in point of natural philosophy—a science so useful to mankind, that her neighbours have ever esteemed it a matter of the greatest importance to endeavour, by repeated experiments, to strike a light out of the chaos in which truth seemed to be confounded. Their curiosity in this respect was so indifferent, that though they had discovered new worlds, they were at a loss to explain the phenomena of their own, and their pride so unaccountable, that they disdained to borrow from others that instruction which their natural indolence permitted them not to acquire.

It gives me, however, a secret satisfaction to behold an extraordinary genius now existing in that nation, whose studious endeavours seem calculated to undeceive the superstitious, and instruct the ignorant,—I mean the celebrated Padre Freijo. In unravelling the mysteries of nature, and explaining physical experiments, he takes an opportunity of displaying the concurrence of second causes, in those very wonders which the vulgar ascribe to supernatural influence.

An example of this kind happened a few years ago in a small town of the kingdom of Valencia. Passing through at the hour of mass, he alighted from his mule, and proceeded to the parish church, which he found extremely crowded, and there appeared on the faces of the faithful a more than usual alacrity. The sun, it seems, which had been for some minutes under a cloud, had begun to shine on a large crucifix, that stood on the middle of the altar, studded with several precious stones. The reflection from these, and from the diamond eyes of some silver saints, so dazzled the multitude, that they unanimously cried out, 'A miracle! a miracle!' whilst the priest at the altar, with seeming consternation, continued his heavenly conversation. Padre Freijo soon dissipated the charm, by tying his handkerchief round the head of one of the statues, for which he was arraigned by the Inquisition; whose flames, however, he has had the good fortune hitherto to escape.

No. IV.—SATURDAY, OCTOBER 27, 1759

MISCELLANEOUS

WERE I to measure the merit of my present undertaking by its success, or the rapidity of its sale, I might be led to form conclusions by no means favourable to the pride of an author. Should I estimate my fame by its extent, every newspaper and every magazine would leave me far behind. Their fame is diffused in a very wide circle, that of some as far as Islington, and some yet farther still; while mine, I sincerely believe, has hardly travelled beyond the sound of Bow-bell; and while the works of others fly like unpinioned swans, I find my own move as heavily as a new-plucked goose.

Still, however, I have as much pride as they who have ten times as many readers. It is impossible to repeat all the agreeable delusions in which a disappointed author is apt to find comfort. I conclude, that what my reputation wants in extent, is made up by its solidity. *Minus juvat gloria lata quam magna.* I have great satisfaction in considering the delicacy and discernment of those readers I have, and in ascribing my want of popularity to the ignorance or inattention of those I have not. All the world may forsake an author, but vanity will never forsake him.

Yet, notwithstanding so sincere a confession, I was once induced to show my indignation against the public, by discontinuing my endeavours to please; and was bravely resolved, like Raleigh, to vex them by burning my manuscript in a passion. Upon recollection, however, I considered what set or body of people would be displeased at my rashness. The sun, after so sad an accident, might shine next morning as bright as usual; men might laugh and sing the next day, and transact business as before, and not a single creature feel any regret but myself.

I reflected upon the story of a minister, who, in the reign of Charles II, upon a certain occasion, resigned all his posts, and retired into the country in a fit of resentment. But, as he had not given the world entirely up with his ambition, he sent a messenger to town, to see how the courtiers would bear his resignation. Upon the messenger's return he was asked, whether there appeared any commotion at court? To which he replied, there were very great ones. 'Ay,' says the minister, 'I knew my friends would make a bustle; all petitioning the

King for my restoration, I presume?'—'No, Sir,' replied the messenger, 'they are only petitioning His Majesty to be put in your place.' In the same manner, should I retire in indignation, instead of having Apollo in mourning, or the Muses in a fit of the spleen; instead of having the learned world apostrophizing at my untimely decease,—perhaps all Grub Street might laugh at my fall, and self-approving dignity might never be able to shield me from ridicule. In short, I am resolved to write on, if it were only to spite them. If the present generation will not hear my voice, hearken, O Posterity, to you I call, and from you I expect redress! What rapture will it not give to have the Scaligers, Daciers, and Warburtons of future times, commenting with admiration upon every line I now write, working away those ignorant creatures who offer to arraign my merit, with all the virulence of learned reproach. Ay, my friends, let them feel it: call names, never spare them; they deserve it all, and ten times more. I have been told of a critic, who was crucified, at the command of another, to the reputation of Homer. That, no doubt, was more than poetical justice, and I shall be perfectly content if those who criticise me are only clapped in the pillory, kept fifteen days upon bread and water, and obliged to run the gantlope through Paternoster Row. The truth is, I can expect happiness from Posterity either way. If I write ill, happy in being forgotten; if well, happy in being remembered with respect.

Yet, considering things in a prudential light, perhaps I was mistaken in designing my paper as an agreeable relaxation to the studious, or a help to conversation among the gay; instead of addressing it to such, I should have written down to the taste and apprehension of the many, and sought for reputation on the broad road. Literary fame, I now find, like religious, generally begins among the vulgar. As for the polite, they are so very polite as never to applaud upon any account. One of these, with a face screwed up into affectation, tells you, that fools may *admire*, but men of sense only *approve*. Thus, lest he should rise into rapture at any thing new, he keeps down every passion but pride and self-importance; approves with phlegm, and the poor author is damned in the taking a pinch of snuff. Another has written a book himself, and being condemned for a dunce, he turns a sort of king's evidence in criticism, and now becomes the terror of every offender. A third, possessed of full-grown reputation, shades off every beam of favour from those who endeavour to grow beneath him, and keeps down that merit, which, but for his influence, might rise into equal eminence. While others, still worse, peruse old books for their amusement, and new books only to condemn; so that the public seem heartily sick of all but the business of the day, and read every thing new with as little attention as they examine the faces of the passing crowd.

From these considerations, I was once determined to throw off all connections with taste, and fairly address my country-men in the same engaging style and manner with other periodical pamphlets, much more in vogue than probably mine shall ever be. To effect this, I had thoughts of changing the title into that of the ROYAL BEE, the ANTIGALLICAN BEE, or the BEE's MAGAZINE. I had laid in a proper stock of popular topics, such as encomiums on the King of Prussia, invectives against the Queen of Hungary and the French, the necessity of a militia, our undoubted sovereignty of the seas, reflections upon the pre-sent state of affairs, a dissertation upon liberty, some season-able thoughts upon the intended bridge of Blackfriars, and an address to Britons; the history of an old woman, whose teeth grew three inches long, an ode upon our victories, a rebus, an acrostic upon Miss Peggy P., and a journal of the weather. All this, together with four extraordinary pages of *letterpress*, a beautiful map of England, and two prints curiously coloured from nature, I fancied might touch their very souls. I was actually beginning an address to the people, when my pride at last overcame my prudence, and determined me to endeavour to please by the goodness of my entertainment, rather than by the magnificence of my sign.

The Spectator, and many succeeding essayists, frequently inform us of the numerous compliments paid them in the course of their lucubrations—of the frequent encouragements they meet to inspire them with ardour, and increase their eagerness to please. I have received *my letters* as well as they; but, alas! not congratulatory ones—not assuring me of success and favour —but pregnant with bodings that might shake even fortitude itself.

One gentleman assures me, he intends to throw away no more threepences in purchasing the BEE; and, what is still more dismal, he will not recommend me as a poor author wanting encourage-ment to his neighbourhood, which, it seems, is very numerous. Were my soul set upon threepences, what anxiety might not such a denunciation produce! But such does not happen to be the present motive of publication: I write partly to show my good nature, and partly to show my vanity; nor will I lay down the pen till I am satisfied one way or another.

Others have disliked the title and the motto of my paper; point out a mistake in the one, and assure me the other has been consigned to dulness by anticipation. All this may be true; *but what is that to me?* Titles and mottoes to books are like escutcheons and dignities in the hands of a king: the wise sometimes condescend to accept of them; but none but a fool will imagine them of any real importance. We ought to depend upon intrinsic merit, and not the slender helps of title. *Nam quæ non fecimus ipsi, vix ea nostra voco.*

For my part I am ever ready to mistrust a promising title, and have, at some expense, been instructed not to hearken to the voice of an advertisement, let it plead never so loudly, or never so long. A countryman coming one day to Smithfield, in order to take a slice of Bartholomew Fair, found a perfect show before every booth. The drummer, the fire-eater, the wire-walker, and the salt-box, were all employed to invite him in. 'Just a-going; the court of the King of Prussia in all his glory: pray, gentlemen, walk in and see.' From the people who generously gave so much away, the clown expected a monstrous bargain for his money when he got in. He steps up, pays his sixpence, the curtain is drawn; when, too late, he finds that he had the best part of the show for nothing at the door.

A FLEMISH TRADITION

Every country has its traditions, which, either too minute, or not sufficiently authentic to receive historical sanction, are handed down among the vulgar, and serve at once to instruct and amuse them. Of this number, the adventures of Robin Hood, the hunting of Chevy Chase, and the bravery of Johnny Armstrong, among the English; of Kaul Dereg, among the Irish; and Creighton, among the Scots, are instances. Of all the traditions, however, I remember to have heard, I do not recollect any more remarkable than one still current in Flanders; a story generally the first the peasants tell their children, when they bid them behave like Bidderman the Wise. It is by no means, however, a model to be set before a polite people for imitation; since if, on the one hand, we perceive in it the steady influence of patriotism, we, on the other, find as strong a desire of revenge. But, to waive introduction, let us to the story.

When the Saracens overran Europe with their armies, and penetrated as far even as Antwerp, Bidderman was lord of a city, which time has since swept into destruction. As the inhabitants of this country were divided under separate leaders, the Saracens found an easy conquest, and the city of Bidderman, among the rest, became a prey to the victors.

Thus dispossessed of his paternal city, our unfortunate governor was obliged to seek refuge from the neighbouring princes, who were as yet unsubdued, and he for some time lived in a state of wretched dependence among them.

Soon, however, his love to his native country brought him back to his own city, resolved to rescue it from the enemy, or fall in the attempt. Thus, in disguise, he went among the inhabitants, and endeavoured, but in vain, to excite them to a revolt. Former misfortunes lay so heavily on their minds, that they rather chose to suffer the most cruel bondage, than attempt to vindicate their former freedom.

As he was thus one day employed, whether by information or from suspicion is not known, he was apprehended by a Saracen soldier as a spy, and brought before the very tribunal at which he once presided. The account he gave of himself was by no means satisfactory. He could produce no friends to vindicate his character; wherefore, as the Saracens knew not their prisoner, and as they had no direct proofs against him, they were content with condemning him to be publicly whipt as a vagabond.

The execution of this sentence was accordingly performed with the utmost rigour. Bidderman was bound to the post, the executioner seeming disposed to add to the cruelty of the sentence, as he received no bribe for lenity. Whenever Bidderman groaned under the scourge, the other, redoubling his blows, cried out, 'Does the villain murmur?' If Bidderman entreated but a moment's respite from torture, the other only repeated his former exclamation, 'Does the villain murmur?'

From this period, revenge, as well as patriotism, took entire possession of his soul. His fury stooped so low as to follow the executioner with unremitting resentment. But, conceiving that the best method to attain these ends was to acquire some eminence in the city, he laid himself out to oblige its new masters, studied every art, and practised every meanness, that serve to promote the needy, or render the poor pleasing; and, by these means, in a few years, he came to be of some note in the city, which justly belonged entirely to him.

The executioner was, therefore, the first object of his resentment, and he even practised the lowest fraud to gratify the revenge he owed him. A piece of plate, which Bidderman had previously stolen from the Saracen governor, he privately conveyed into the executioner's house, and then gave information of the theft. They who are any way acquainted with the rigour of the Arabian laws, know that theft is punished with immediate death. The proof was direct in this case; the executioner had nothing to offer in his own defence, and he was therefore condemned to be beheaded upon a scaffold in the public market-place. As there was no executioner in the city but the very man who was now to suffer, Bidderman himself undertook this, to him, most agreeable office. The criminal was conducted from the judgment seat bound with cords; the scaffold was erected, and he placed in such a manner as he might lie most convenient for the blow.

But his death alone was not sufficient to satisfy the resentment of this extraordinary man, unless it was aggravated with every circumstance of cruelty. Wherefore, coming up the scaffold, and disposing everything in readiness for the intended blow, with the sword in his hand he approached the criminal, and, whispering in a low voice, assured him that he himself was the very person that had once been used with so much cruelty; that, to his knowledge, he died very innocently, for the plate had been stolen by himself, and privately conveyed into the house of the other.

'Oh, my countrymen!' cried the criminal, 'do you hear what this man says?'—'Does the villain murmur?' replied Bidderman, and immediately, at one blow, severed his head from his body.

Still, however, he was not content, till he had ample vengeance of the governors of the city, who condemned him. To effect this, he hired a small house adjoining to the town wall, under which he every day dug, and carried out the earth in a basket. In this unremitting labour he continued several years, every day digging a little, and carrying the earth unsuspected away. By this means, he at last made a secret communication from the country into the city, and only wanted the appearance of an enemy in order to betray it. This opportunity at length offered; the French army came into the neighbourhood, but had no thoughts of sitting down before a town which they considered as impregnable. Bidderman, however, soon altered their resolutions, and, upon communicating his plan to the general, he embraced it with ardour. Through the private passage above mentioned, he introduced a large body of the most resolute soldiers, who soon opened the gates for the rest, and the whole army rushing in, put every Saracen that was found to the sword.

THE SAGACITY OF SOME INSECTS

To the Author of the Bee

SIR,—Animals, in general, are sagacious, in proportion as they cultivate society. The elephant and the beaver show the greatest signs of this when united; but when men intrudes into their communities, they lose all their spirit of industry, and testify but a very small share of that sagacity, for which, when they are in a social state, they are so remarkable.

Among insects, the labours of the bee and the ant have employed the attention and admiration of the naturalist; but their whole sagacity is lost upon separation, and a single bee or ant seems destitute of every degree of industry, is the most stupid insect imaginable, languishes for a time in solitude, and soon dies.

Of all the solitary insects I have ever remarked, the spider is the most sagacious; and its actions, to me, who have attentively considered them, seem almost to exceed belief. This insect is formed by nature for a state of war, not only upon other insects, but upon each other. For this state nature seems perfectly well to have formed it. Its head and breast are covered with a strong natural coat of mail, which is impenetrable to the attempts of every other insect, and its belly is enveloped in a soft pliant skin, which eludes the sting even of a wasp. Its legs are terminated by strong claws, not unlike those of a lobster, and their vast length, like spears, serves to keep every assailant at a distance.

Not worse furnished for observation than for an attack or a defence, it has several eyes, large, transparent, and covered with a horny substance, which, however, does not impede its vision. Besides this, it is furnished with a forceps above the mouth, which serves to kill or secure the prey already caught in its claws or its net.

Such are the implements of war with which the body is immediately furnished; but its net to entangle the enemy seems what it chiefly trusts to, and what it takes most pains to render as complete as possible. Nature has furnished the body of this little creature with a glutinous liquid, which, proceeding from the anus, it spins into a thread, coarser or finer as it chooses to contract or dilate its sphincter. In order to fix its thread, when it begins to weave it emits a small drop of its liquid against the wall, which, hardening by degrees, serves to hold the thread very firmly. Then receding from the first point, as it recedes the thread lengthens; and, when the spider has come to the place where the other end of the thread should be fixed, gathering up with its claws the thread which would otherwise be too slack, it is stretched tightly, and fixed in the same manner to the wall as before.

In this manner, it spins and fixes several threads parallel to each other, which, so to speak, serve as the warp to the intended web. To form the woof, it spins in the same manner its thread, transversely fixing one end to the first thread that was spun, and which is always the strongest of the whole web, and the other to the wall. All these threads, being newly spun, are glutinous, and therefore stick to each other whenever they happen to touch; and, in those parts of the web most exposed to be torn, our natural artist strengthens them, by doubling the threads sometimes six-fold.

Thus far naturalists have gone in the description of this animal; what follows, is the result of my own observation upon that species of the insect called an house spider. I perceived, about four years ago, a large spider in one corner of my room, making its web; and, though the maid frequently levelled her fatal broom against the labours of the little animal, I had the good fortune then to prevent its destruction; and, I may say, it more than paid me by the entertainment it afforded.

In three days the web was, with incredible diligence, completed; nor could I avoid thinking, that the insect seemed to exult in its new abode. It frequently traversed it round, examined the strength of every part of it, retired into its hole, and came out very frequently. The first enemy, however, it had to encounter was another and a much larger spider, which, having no web of its own, and having probably exhausted all its stock in former labours of this kind, came to invade the property of its neighbour. Soon, then, a terrible encounter ensued, in which the invader seemed to have the victory, and the laborious spider was obliged to take refuge in its hole. Upon this I perceived the victor using every art to draw the enemy from his stronghold. He seemed to go off, but quickly returned; and when he found all arts vain, began to demolish the new web without mercy. This brought on another battle, and, contrary to my expectations, the laborious spider became conqueror, and fairly killed his antagonist.

Now, then, in peaceable possession of what was justly its own, it waited three days with the utmost patience, repairing the breaches of its web, and taking no sustenance that I could perceive. At last, however, a large blue fly fell into the snare, and struggled hard to get loose. The spider gave it leave to entangle itself as much as possible, but it seemed to be too strong for the cobweb. I must own I was greatly surprised when I saw the spider immediately sally out, and in less than a minute weave a new net round its captive, by which the motion of its wings was stopped; and when it was fairly hampered in this manner, it was seized, and dragged into the hole.

In this manner it lived, in a precarious state; and nature seemed to have fitted it for such a life, for upon a single fly it subsisted for more than a week. I once put a wasp into the net; but when the spider came out in order to seize it as usual, upon perceiving what kind of an enemy it had to deal with, it instantly broke all the bands that held it fast, and contributed all that lay in its power to disengage so formidable an antagonist. When the wasp was at liberty, I expected the spider would have set about repairing the breaches that were made in its net, but those it seems were irreparable; wherefore the cobweb was now entirely forsaken, and a new one begun, which was completed in the usual time.

I had now a mind to try how many cobwebs a single spider could furnish; wherefore I destroyed this, and the insect set about another. When I destroyed the other also, its whole stock seemed entirely exhausted, and it could spin no more. The arts it made use of to support itself, now deprived of its great means of subsistence, were indeed surprising. I have seen it roll up its legs like a ball, and lie motionless for hours together, but cautiously watching all the time; when a fly happened to approach sufficiently near, it would dart out all at once, and often seize its prey.

Of this life, however, it soon began to grow weary, and resolved to invade the possession of some other spider, since it could not make a web of its own. It formed an attack upon a neighbouring fortification with great vigour, and at first was as vigorously repulsed. Not daunted, however, with one defeat, in this manner it continued to lay siege to another's web for three days, and at length, having killed the defendant, actually took possession. When smaller flies happen to fall into the snare, the spider does not sally out at once, but very patiently waits till it is sure of them; for, upon his immediately approaching, the terror of his appearance might give the captive strength sufficient to get loose: the manner then is to wait patiently, till, by ineffectual and impotent struggles, the captive has wasted all its strength, and then he becomes a certain and an easy conquest.

The insect I am now describing lived three years; every year it changed its skin, and got a new set of legs. I have sometimes plucked off a leg, which grew again in two or three days. At first it dreaded my approach to its web, but at last it became so familiar as to take a fly out of my hand, and, upon my touching any part of the web, would immediately leave its hole, prepared either for a defence or an attack.

To complete this description, it may be observed, that the male spiders are much less than the females, and that the latter are oviparous. When they come to lay, they spread a part of their web under the eggs, and then roll them up carefully, as we roll up things in a cloth, and thus hatch them in their hole. If disturbed in their holes, they never attempt to escape without carrying this young brood in their forceps away with them, and thus frequently are sacrificed to their parental affection.

As soon as ever the young ones leave their artificial covering they begin to spin, and almost sensibly seem to grow bigger. If they have the good fortune, when even but a day old, to catch a fly, they fall-to with good appetites; but they live sometimes three or four days without any sort of sustenance, and yet still continue to grow larger, so as every day to double their former size. As they grow old, however, they do not still continue to increase, but their legs only continue to grow longer; and when a spider becomes entirely stiff with age, and unable to seize its prey, it dies at length of hunger.

THE CHARACTERISTICS OF GREATNESS

In every duty, in every science in which we would wish to arrive at perfection, we should propose for the object of our pursuit some certain station even beyond our abilities—some imaginary excellence, which may amuse and serve to animate our inquiry. In deviating from others, in following an unbeaten road, though we perhaps may never arrive at the wished-for object, yet it is possible we may meet several discoveries by the way; and the certainty of small advantages, even while we travel with security, is not so amusing as the hopes of great rewards, which inspire the adventurer. *Evenit nonnunquam*, says Quintilian, *ut aliquid grande inveniat qui semper quærit quod nimium est.*

This enterprising spirit is, however, by no means the character of the present age: every person who should now leave received opinions, who should attempt to be more than a commentator upon philosophy, or an imitator in polite learning, might be regarded as a chimerical projector. Hundreds would be ready not only to point out his errors, but to load him with reproach. Our probable opinions are now regarded as certainties; the difficulties hitherto undiscovered as utterly inscrutable; and the writers of the last age inimitable, and therefore the properest models of imitation.

One might be almost induced to deplore the philosophic spirit of the age, which, in proportion as it enlightens the mind, increases its timidity, and represses the vigour of every undertaking. Men are now content with being prudently in the right; which, though not the way to make new acquisitions, it must be owned, is the best method of securing what we have. Yet this is certain, that the writer who never deviates, who never hazards a new thought, or a new expression, though his friends may compliment him upon his sagacity, though criticism lifts her feeble voice in his praise, will seldom arrive at any degree of perfection. The way to acquire lasting esteem, is not by the fewness of a writer's faults, but the greatness of his beauties; and our noblest works are generally most replete with both.

An author who would be sublime, often runs his thoughts into burlesque: yet I can readily pardon his mistaking ten times for once succeeding. True genius walks along a line: and perhaps our greatest pleasure is in seeing it so often near falling, without being actually down.

Every science has its hitherto undiscovered mysteries, after which men should travel, undiscouraged by the failure of former adventurers. Every new attempt serves, perhaps, to facilitate its future invention. We may not find the Philosopher's stone, but we shall probably hit upon new inventions in pursuing it. We shall perhaps never be able to discover the longitude, yet perhaps we may arrive at new truths in the investigation.

Were any of those sagacious minds among us (and surely no nation, or no period, could ever compare with us in this particular), were any of those minds, I say, who now sit down contented with exploring the intricacies of another's system, bravely to shake off admiration, and, undazzled with the splendour of another's reputation, to chalk out a path to fame for themselves, and boldly cultivate untried experiment, what might not be the result of their inquiries, should the same study that has made them wise make them enterprising also? What could not such qualities united produce? But such is not the character of the English; while our neighbours of the Continent launch out into the oceans of science, without proper stores for the voyage, we fear shipwreck in every breeze, and consume in port those powers which might probably have weathered every storm.

Projectors in a state are generally rewarded above their deserts; projectors in the republic of letters, never. If wrong, every inferior dunce thinks himself entitled to laugh at their disappointment; if right, men of superior talents think their honour engaged to oppose, since every new discovery is a tacit diminution of their own pre-eminence.

To aim at excellence, our reputation, our friends, and our all must be ventured; by aiming only at mediocrity, we run no risk, and we do little service. Prudence and greatness are ever persuading us to contrary pursuits. The one instructs us to be content with our station, and to find happiness in bounding every wish; the other impels us to superiority, and calls nothing happiness but rapture. The one directs to follow mankind, and to act and think with the rest of the world: the other drives us from the crowd, and exposes us as a mark to all the shafts of envy or ignorance: 'Nec minus periculum ex magna fama quam ex mala.'—TACIT.

The rewards of mediocrity are immediately paid, those attending excellence generally paid in reversion. In a word, the little mind who loves itself, will write and think with the vulgar, but the great mind will be bravely eccentric, and scorn the beaten road, from universal benevolence.

No. V.—SATURDAY, NOVEMBER 3, 1759

Upon Political Frugality

FRUGALITY has ever been esteemed a virtue as well among Pagans as Christians: there have been even heroes who have practised it. However, we must acknowledge, that it is too modest a virtue, or if you will, too obscure a one, to be essential to heroism; few heroes have been able to attain to such an height. Frugality agrees much better with politics; it seems to be the base, the support, and, in a word, seems to be the inseparable companion of a just administration.

However this be, there is not, perhaps, in the world a people less fond of this virtue than the English; and of consequence, there is not a nation more restless, more exposed to the uneasiness of life, or less capable of providing for particular happiness. We are taught to despise this virtue from our childhood; our education is improperly directed, and a man who has gone through the politest institutions, is generally the person who is least acquainted with the wholesome precepts of frugality. We every day hear the elegance of taste, the magnificence of some, and the generosity of others, made the subject of our admiration and applause. All this we see represented, not as the end and recompense of labour and desert, but as the actual result of genius, as the mark of a noble and exalted mind.

In the midst of these praises bestowed on luxury, for which elegance and taste are but another name, perhaps it may be thought improper to plead the cause of frugality. It may be thought low, or vainly declamatory, to exhort our youth from the follies of dress, and of every other superfluity; to accustom themselves even with mechanic meanness, to the simple necessaries of life. Such sort of instructions may appear antiquated; yet, however, they seem the foundations of all our virtues, and the most efficacious method of making mankind useful members of society. Unhappily, however, such discourses are not fashionable among us, and the fashion seems every day growing still more obsolete, since the press, and every other method of exhortation, seems disposed to talk of the luxuries of life as harmless enjoyments. I remember, when a boy, to have remarked, that those who in school wore the finest clothes, were pointed at as being conceited and proud. At present, our little masters are taught to consider dress betimes, and they are regarded, even at school, with contempt, who do not appear as genteel as the rest. Education should teach us to become useful, sober, disinterested, and laborious members of society; but does it not at present point out a different path? It teaches us to multiply our wants, by which means we become more eager to possess, in order to dissipate, a greater charge to ourselves, and more useless or obnoxious to society.

If a youth happens to be possessed of more genius than fortune, he is early informed, that he ought to think of his advancement in the world; that he should labour to make himself pleasing to his superiors; that he should shun low company (by which is meant the company of his equals), that he should rather live a little above than below his fortune; that he should think of becoming great; but he finds none to admonish him to become frugal, to persevere in one single design, to avoid every pleasure and all flattery, which however seeming to conciliate the favours of his superiors, never conciliate their esteem. There are none to teach him that the best way of becoming happy in himself, and useful to others, is to continue in the state in which fortune at first placed him, without making too hasty strides to advancement; that greatness may be attained, but should not be expected; and that they who most impatiently expect advancement, are seldom possessed of their wishes. He has few, I say, to teach him this lesson, or to moderate his youthful passions; yet, this experience may say, that a young man, who, but for six years of the early part of his life, could seem divested of all his passions, would certainly make, or considerably increase, his fortune, and might indulge several of his favourite inclinations in manhood with the utmost security.

The efficaciousness of these means is sufficiently known and acknowledged; but as we are apt to connect a low idea with all our notions of frugality, the person who would persuade us to it might be accused of preaching up avarice.

Of all vices, however, against which morality dissuades, there is not one more undetermined than this of avarice. Misers are described by some as men divested of honour, sentiment, or humanity: but this is only an ideal picture, or the resemblance at least is found but in a few. In truth, they who are generally called misers, are some of the very best members of society. The sober, the laborious, the attentive, the frugal, are thus styled by the gay, giddy, thoughtless, and extravagant. The first set of men do society all the good, and the latter all the evil, that is felt. Even the excesses of the first no way injure the commonwealth; those of the latter are the most injurious that can be conceived.

The ancient Romans, more rational than we in this particular, were very far from thus misplacing their admiration or praise: instead of regarding the practice of parsimony as low or vicious, they made it synonymous even with probity. They esteemed those virtues so inseparable, that the known expression *Vir frugi* signified, at one and the same time, a sober and managing man, an honest man, and a man of substance.

The Scriptures, in a thousand places, praise economy; and it is everywhere distinguished from avarice. But, in spite of all its sacred dictates, a taste for vain pleasures and foolish expense is the ruling passion of the present times. Passion, did I call it? rather the madness which at once possesses the great and the little, the rich and the poor: even, some are so intent upon acquiring the superfluities of life, that they sacrifice its necessaries in this foolish pursuit.

To attempt the entire abolition of luxury, as it would be impossible, so it is not my intent. The generality of mankind are too weak, too much slaves to custom and opinion, to resist the torrent of bad example. But if it be impossible to convert the multitude, those who have received a more extended education, who are enlightened and judicious, may find some hints on this subject useful. They may see some abuses, the suppression of which would by no means endanger public liberty; they may be directed to the abolition of some unnecessary expenses, which have no tendency to promote happiness or virtue, and which might be directed to better purposes. Our fire-works, our public feasts and entertainments, our entries of ambassadors, &c.—what mummery all this! what childish pageants! what millions are sacrificed in paying tribute to custom! what an unnecessary charge at times when we are pressed with real want, which cannot be satisfied without burthening the poor!

Were such suppressed entirely, not a single creature in the state would have the least cause to mourn their suppression, and many might be eased of a load they now feel lying heavily upon them. If this were put in practice, it would agree with the advice of a sensible writer of Sweden, who, in the *Gazette de France*, 1753, thus expressed himself on that subject: 'It were sincerely to be wished,' says he, 'that the custom were established amongst us, that in all events which cause a public joy, we made our exultations conspicuous only by acts useful to society. We should then quickly see many useful monuments of our reason, which would much better perpetuate the memory of things worthy of being transmitted to posterity, and would be much more glorious to humanity, than all these tumultuous preparations of feasts, entertainments, and other rejoicings used upon such occasions.'

The same proposal was long before confirmed by a Chinese emperor, who lived in the last century, who, upon an occasion of extraordinary joy, forbade his subjects to make the usual illuminations, either with a design of sparing their substance, or of turning them to some more durable indications of joy, more glorious for him, and more advantageous to his people.

After such instances of political frugality, can we then continue to blame the Dutch ambassador at a certain court, who, receiving at his departure the portrait of the king, enriched with diamonds, asked what this fine thing might be worth? Being told that it might amount to about two thousand pounds,—'And why,' cries he, 'cannot his majesty keep the picture, and give me the money?' This simplicity may be ridiculed at first: but when we come to examine it more closely, men of sense will at once confess that he had reason in what he said, and that a purse of two thousand guineas is much more serviceable than a picture.

Should we follow the same method of state frugality in other respects, what numberless savings might not be the result! How many possibilities of saving in the administration of justice, which now burdens the subject, and enriches some members of society, who are useful only from its corruption!

It were to be wished, that they who govern kingdoms would imitate artisans. When at London a new stuff has been invented, it is immediately counterfeited in France. How happy were it for society, if a first minister would be equally solicitous to transplant the useful laws of other countries into his own. We are arrived at a perfect imitation of porcelain; let us endeavour to imitate the good to society that our neighbours are found to practise, and let our neighbours also imitate those parts of duty in which we excel.

There are some men, who, in their garden, attempt to raise those fruits which nature has adapted only to the sultry climates beneath the line. We have at our very doors a thousand laws and customs infinitely useful; these are the fruits we should endeavour to transplant; these the exotics that would speedily become naturalized to the soil. They might grow in every climate, and benefit every possessor.

The best and the most useful laws I have ever seen, are generally practised in Holland. When two men are determined to go to law with each other, they are first obliged to go before the reconciling judges, called the *peace-makers*. If the parties come attended with an advocate, or a solicitor, they are obliged to retire, as we take fuel from the fire we are desirous of extinguishing.

The peace-makers then begin advising the parties, by assuring them that it is the height of folly to waste their substance, and make themselves mutually miserable, by having recourse to the tribunals of justice: 'Follow but our direction, and we will accommodate matters without any expense to either.' If the rage of debate is too strong upon either party, they are remitted back for another day, in order that time may soften their tempers, and produce a reconciliation. They are thus sent for twice or thrice; if their folly happens to be incurable, they are permitted to go to law, and, as we give up to amputation such members as cannot be cured by art, justice is permitted to take its course.

It is unnecessary to make here long declamations, or calculate what society would save, were this law adopted. I am sensible, that the man who advises any reformation, only serves to make himself ridiculous. What! mankind will be apt to say, adopt the customs of countries that have not so much real liberty as our own!—our present customs, what are they to any man? we are very happy under them! This must be a very pleasant fellow, who attempts to make us happier than we already are! Does he not know that abuses are the patrimony of a great part of the nation? Why deprive us of a malady by which such numbers find their account! This, I must own, is an argument to which I have nothing to reply.

What numberless savings might there not be made in both arts and commerce, particularly in the liberty of exercising trade, without the necessary prerequisites of freedom! Such useless obstructions have crept into every state, from a spirit of monopoly, a narrow selfish spirit of gain, without the least attention to general society. Such a clog upon industry frequently drives the poor from labour, and reduces them by degrees to a state of hopeless indigence. We have already a more than sufficient repugnance to labour; we should by no means increase the obstacles, or make excuses in a state for idleness. Such faults have ever crept into a state, under wrong or needy administrations.

Exclusive of the masters, there are numberless faulty expenses among the workmen; clubs, garnishes, freedoms, and such-like impositions, which are not too minute even for law to take notice of, and which should be abolished without mercy, since they are ever the inlets to excess and idleness, and are the parent of all those outrages which naturally fall upon the more useful part of society. In the towns and countries I have seen, I never saw a city or village yet, whose miseries were not in proportion to the number of its public-houses. In Rotterdam, you may go through eight or ten streets without finding a public-house. In Antwerp, almost every second house seems an ale-house. In the one city, all wears the appearance of happiness and warm affluence; in the other, the young fellows walk about the streets in shabby finery, their fathers sit at the door darning or knitting stockings, while their ports are filled with dunghills.

Alehouses are ever an occasion of debauchery and excess, and, either in a religious or political light, it would be our highest interest to have the greatest part of them suppressed. They should be put under laws of not continuing open beyond a certain hour, and harbouring only proper persons. These rules, it may be said, will diminish the necessary taxes; but this is false reasoning, since what was consumed in debauchery abroad, would, if such a regulation took place, be more justly, and perhaps more equitably for the workman's family, spent at home; and this cheaper to them, and without loss of time. On the other hand, our alehouses being ever open, interrupt business; the workman is never certain who frequents them, nor can the master be sure of having what was begun finished at the convenient time.

An habit of frugality among the lower orders of mankind is much more beneficial to society than the unreflecting might imagine. The pawnbroker, the attorney, and other pests of society, might, by proper management, be turned into service-able members; and, were their trades abolished, it is possible the same avarice that conducts the one, or the same chicanery that characterises the other, might, by proper regulations, be converted into frugality and commendable prudence.

But some have made the eulogium of luxury, have represented it as the natural consequence of every country that is become rich. Did we not employ our extraordinary wealth in super-fluities, say they, what other means would there be to employ it in? To which it may be answered, if frugality were established in the state, if our expenses were laid out rather in the necessaries than the superfluities of life, there might be fewer wants, and even fewer pleasures, but infinitely more happiness. The rich and the great would be better able to satisfy their creditors; they would be better able to marry their children, and, instead of one marriage at present, there might be two, if such regulations took place.

The imaginary calls of vanity, which, in reality, contribute nothing to our real felicity, would not then be attended to, while the real calls of nature might be always and universally supplied. The difference of employment in the subject is what, in reality, produces the good of society. If the subject be engaged in providing only the luxuries, the necessaries must be deficient in proportion. If, neglecting the produce of our own country, our minds are set upon the productions of another, we increase our wants, but not our means; and every new imported delicacy for our tables, or ornament in our equipage, is a tax upon the poor.

The true interest of every government is to cultivate the necessaries, by which is always meant, every happiness our own country can produce; and suppress all the luxuries, by which is meant, on the other hand, every happiness imported from abroad. Commerce has, therefore, its bounds; and every new import, instead of receiving encouragement, should be first examined whether it be conducive to the interest of society.

Among the many publications with which the press is every day burdened, I have often wondered why we never had, as in other countries, an Economical Journal, which might at once direct to all the useful discoveries in other countries, and spread those of our own. As other journals serve to amuse the learned, or, what is more often the case, to make them quarrel, while they only serve to give us the history of the mischievous world, for so I call our warriors, or the idle world, for so may the learned be called, they never trouble their heads about the most useful part of mankind, our peasants and our artizans. Were such a work carried into execution, with proper management and just direction, it might serve as a repository for every useful improvement, and increase that knowledge which learning often serves to confound.

Sweden seems the only country where the science of economy seems to have fixed its empire. In other countries, it is cultivated only by a few admirers, or by societies which have not

received sufficient sanction to become completely useful; but
here there is founded a Royal Academy, destined to this purpose only, composed of the most learned and powerful members
of the state; an academy which declines everything which only
terminates in amusement, erudition, or curiosity, and admits
only of observations tending to illustrate husbandry, agriculture,
and every real physical improvement. In this country, nothing
is left to private rapacity, but every improvement is immediately diffused and its inventor immediately recompensed by the
state. Happy were it so in other countries! By this means, every
impostor would be prevented from ruining or deceiving the
public with pretended discoveries or nostrums, and every real
inventor would not, by this means, suffer the inconveniences
of suspicion.

In short, true economy, equally unknown to the prodigal and
avaricious, seems to be a just mean between both extremes;
and to a transgression of this at present decried virtue it is
that we are to attribute a great part of the evils which infest
society. A taste for superfluity, amusement, and pleasure
brings effeminacy, idleness, and expense in their train. But a
thirst of riches is always proportioned to our debauchery,
and the greatest prodigal is too frequently found to be the
greatest miser; so that the vices which seem the most opposite,
are frequently found to produce each other; and, to avoid both,
it is only necessary to be frugal.

Virtus est medium vitiorum et utrinque reductum.—HOR.

A REVERIE

Scarce a day passes in which we do not hear compliments
paid to Dryden, Pope, and other writers of the last age, while
not a month comes forward that is not loaded with invective
against the writers of this. Strange, that our critics should be
fond of giving their favours to those who are insensible of the
obligation, and their dislike to these who, of all mankind, are
most apt to retaliate the injury.

Even though our present writers had not equal merit with
their predecessors, it would be politic to use them with ceremony.
Every compliment paid them would be more agreeable, in proportion as they least deserved it. Tell a lady with a handsome
face that she is pretty, she only thinks it her due; it is what
she has heard a thousand times before from others, and dis-
regards the compliment: but assure a lady, the cut of whose

visage is something more plain, that she looks killing to-day, she instantly bridles up, and feels the force of the well-timed flattery the whole day after. Compliments which we think are deserved we only accept as debts, with indifference; but those which conscience informs us we do not merit, we receive with the same gratitude that we do favours given away.

Our gentlemen, however, who preside at the distribution of literary fame, seem resolved to part with praise neither from motives of justice or generosity; one would think, when they take pen in hand, that it was only to blot reputations, and to put their seals to the packet which consigns every new-born effort to oblivion.

Yet, notwithstanding the republic of letters hangs at present so feebly together; though those friendships which once promoted literary fame seem now to be discontinued; though every writer who now draws the quill seems to aim at profit, as well as applause, many among them are probably laying in stores for immortality, and are provided with a sufficient stock of reputation to last the whole journey.

As I was indulging these reflections, in order to eke out the present page, I could not avoid pursuing the metaphor of going a journey in my imagination, and formed the following Reverie, too wild for allegory, and too regular for a dream:—

I fancied myself placed in the yard of a large inn, in which there were an infinite number of waggons and stage-coaches, attended by fellows who either invited the company to take their places, or were busied in packing their baggage. Each vehicle had its inscription, showing the place of its destination. On one I could read, 'The Pleasure Stage Coach'; on another, 'The Waggon of Industry'; on a third, 'The Vanity Whim'; and on a fourth, 'The Landau of Riches.' I had some inclination to step into each of these, one after another; but, I know not by what means, I passed them by, and at last fixed my eye upon a small carriage, Berlin fashion, which seemed the most convenient vehicle at a distance in the world; and, upon my nearer approach, found it to be 'The Fame Machine.'

I instantly made up to the coachman, whom I found to be an affable and seemingly good-natured fellow. He informed me, that he had but a few days ago returned from the Temple of Fame, to which he had been carrying Addison, Swift, Pope, Steele, Congreve, and Colley Cibber; that they made but indifferent company by the way; and that he once or twice was going to empty his berlin of the whole cargo: 'however,' says he,

'I got them all safe home, with no other damage than a black eye, which Colley gave Mr. Pope, and am now returned for another coachful.'—'If that be all, friend,' said I, 'and if you are in want of company, I'll make one with all my heart. Open the door; I hope the machine rides easy.'—'Oh, for that, Sir, extremely easy.' But, still keeping the door shut, and measuring me with his eye, 'Pray, Sir, have you no luggage? You seem to be a good-natured sort of gentlemen; but I don't find you have got any luggage, and I never permit any to travel with me but such as have something valuable to pay for coach hire.' Examining my pockets, I own I was not a little disconcerted at this unexpected rebuff, but considering that I carried a number of the BEE under my arm, I was resolved to open it in his eyes, and dazzle him with the splendour of the page. He read the title and contents, however, without any emotion, and assured me he had never heard of it before. 'In short, friend,' said he, now losing all his former respect, 'you must not come in: I expect better passengers; but as you seem a harmless creature, perhaps, if there be room left, I may let you ride awhile for charity.'

I now took my stand by the coachman at the door; and since I could not command a seat, was resolved to be as useful as possible, and earn by my assiduity what I could not by my merit.

The next thing that presented for a place was a most whimsical figure indeed. He was hung round with papers of his own composing, not unlike those who sing ballads in the streets, and came dancing up to the door with all the confidence of instant admittance. The volubility of his motion and address prevented my being able to read more of his cargo than the word 'Inspector,' which was written in great letters at the top of some of the papers. He opened the coach-door himself without any ceremony, and was just slipping in, when the coachman, with as little ceremony, pulled him back. Our figure seemed perfectly angry at this repulse, and demanded gentleman's satisfaction. 'Lord, Sir!' replied the coachman, 'instead of proper luggage, by your bulk you seem loaded for a West-India voyage. You are big enough, with all your papers, to crack twenty stage-coaches. Excuse me, indeed, Sir, for you must not enter.' Our figure now began to expostulate: he assured the coachman that though his baggage seemed so bulky, it was perfectly light, and that he would be contented with the smallest corner of room. But Jehu was inflexible, and the carrier of the Inspectors was sent to dance back again, with all his papers fluttering in the wind. We expected to have no more trouble from this quarter, when, in a few minutes, the same figure changed his appearance, like harlequin upon the stage, and with the same confidence again made his approaches, dressed in lace and carrying nothing but a nosegay. Upon coming near, he thrust the nosegay to the coachman's nose, grasped the brass, and seemed now resolved to enter by violence. I found the struggle soon begin to grow hot, and the coachman, who was a little old, unable to continue the contest; so, in order to ingratiate myself, I stept in to his assistance, and our united efforts sent our literary Proteus, though worsted, unconquered still, clear off, dancing a rigadoon, and smelling to his own nosegay.

The person who after him appeared as candidate for a place in the stage, came up with an air not quite so confident, but somewhat, however, theatrical; and, instead of entering, made the coachman a very low bow, which the other returned, and desired to see his baggage; upon which he instantly produced some farces, a tragedy, and other miscellany productions. The coachman, casting his eye upon the cargo, assured him, at present he could not possibly have a place, but hoped in time he might aspire to one, as he seemed to have read in the book of nature, without a careful perusal of which none ever found entrance at the Temple of Fame. 'What!' replied the disappointed poet, 'shall my tragedy, in which I have vindicated the cause of liberty and virtue!——' 'Follow nature,' returned the other, 'and never expect to find lasting fame by topics which only please from their popularity. Had you been first in the cause of freedom, or praised in virtue more than an empty name, it is possible you might have gained admittance; but at present I beg, Sir, you will stand aside for another gentleman whom I see approaching.'

This was a very grave personage, whom at some distance I took for one of the most reserved, and even disagreeable figures I had seen; but as he approached, his appearance improved, and when I could distinguish him thoroughly, I perceived that, in spite of the severity of his brow, he had one of the most good-natured countenances that could be imagined. Upon coming to open the stage door, he lifted a parcel of folios into the seat before him, but our inquisitorial coachman at once shoved them out again. 'What! not take in my Dictionary?' exclaimed the other in a rage. 'Be patient, Sir,' replied the coachman, 'I have drove a coach, man and boy, these two thousand years; but I do not remember to have carried above one dictionary during the whole time. That little book which

I perceive peeping from one of your pockets, may I presume to ask what it contains?' 'A mere trifle,' replied the author; 'it is called the *Rambler*.'—'*The Rambler!*' says the coachman, 'I beg, Sir, you'll take your place; I have heard our ladies in the court of Apollo frequently mention it with rapture; and Clio, who happens to be a little grave, has been heard to prefer it to the *Spectator*, though others have observed, that the reflections, by being refined, sometimes become minute.'

This grave gentleman was scarce seated, when another, whose appearance was something more modern, seemed willing to enter, yet afraid to ask. He carried in his hand a bundle of essays, of which the coachman was curious enough to enquire the contents. 'These,' replied the gentleman, 'are rhapsodies against the religion of my country.'—'And how can you expect to come into my coach, after thus choosing the wrong side of the question?'—'Ay, but I am right,' replied the other; 'and if you give me leave, I shall, in a few minutes, state the argument.' —'Right or wrong,' said the coachman, 'he who disturbs religion is a blockhead, and he shall never travel in a coach of mine.'—'If, then,' said the gentleman, mustering up all his courage, 'if I am not to have admittance as an essayist, I hope I shall not be repulsed as an historian; the last volume of my history met with applause.'—'Yes,' replied the coachman, 'but I have heard only the first approved at the Temple of Fame; and as I see you have it about you, enter, without further ceremony.' My attention was now diverted to a crowd who were pushing forward a person that seemed more inclined to the Stage-coach of Riches; but by their means he was driven forward to the Fame Machine, which he, however, seemed heartily to despise. Impelled, however, by their solicitations, he steps up, flourishing a voluminous history, and demanding admittance. 'Sir, I have formerly heard your name mentioned,' says the coachman, 'but never as an historian. Is there no other work upon which you may claim a place?'—'None,' replied the other, 'except a romance; but this is a work of too trifling a nature to claim future attention.'—'You mistake,' says the inquisitor, 'a well-written romance is no such easy task as is generally imagined. I remember formerly to have carried Cervantes and Segrais; and if you think fit, you may enter.'

Upon our three literary travellers coming into the same coach, I listened attentively to hear what might be the conversation that passed upon this extraordinary occasion; when, instead of agreeable or entertaining dialogue, I found them grumbling at each other, and each seemed discontented with his companions. Strange! thought I to myself, that they who are thus born to enlighten the world, should still preserve the narrow prejudices of childhood, and, by disagreeing, make even the highest merit ridiculous. Were the learned and the wise to unite against the dunces of society, instead of sometimes siding into opposite parties with them, they might throw a lustre upon each other's reputation, and teach every rank of subordinate merit, if not to admire, at least not to avow dislike.

In the midst of these reflections, I perceived the coachman, unmindful of me, had now mounted the box. Several were approaching to be taken in, whose pretensions, I was sensible, were very just; I therefore desired him to stop, and take in more passengers: but he replied, as he had now mounted the box, it would be improper to come down; but that he should take them all, one after the other, when he should return. So he drove away; and for myself, as I could not get in, I mounted behind, in order to hear the conversation on the way.

A Word or Two on the late Farce called 'High Life Below Stairs'

Just as I had expected, before I saw this farce, I found it formed on too narrow a plan to afford a pleasing variety. The sameness of the humour in every scene could not at last fail of being disagreeable. The poor affecting the manners of the rich might be carried on through one character, or two at the most, with great propriety; but to have almost every personage on the scene almost of the same character, and reflecting the follies of each other, was unartful in the poet to the last degree.

The scene was also almost a continuation of the same absurdity; and my Lord Duke and Sir Harry (two footmen who assume these characters) have nothing else to do but to talk like their masters, and are only introduced to speak, and to show themselves. Thus, as there is a sameness of character, there is a barrenness of incident, which, by a very small share of address, the poet might have easily avoided.

From a conformity to critic rules, which, perhaps, on the whole, have done more harm than good, our author has sacrificed all the vivacity of the dialogue to nature; and though he makes his characters talk like servants, they are seldom absurd enough, or lively enough to make us merry. Though he is always natural, he happens seldom to be humorous.

The satire was well intended, if we regard it as being masters ourselves; but probably a philosopher would rejoice in that liberty which Englishmen give their domestics; and for my own part, I cannot avoid being pleased at the happiness of those poor creatures, who, in some measure, contribute to mine. The Athenians, the politest and best-natured people upon earth, were the kindest to their slaves; and if a person may judge, who has seen the world, our English servants are the best treated, because the generality of our English gentlemen are the politest under the sun.

But, not to lift my feeble voice among the pack of critics, who, probably, have no other occupation but that of cutting up everything new, I must own, there are one or two scenes that are fine satire, and sufficiently humorous; particularly the first interview between the two footmen, which at once ridicules the manners of the great, and the absurdity of their imitators.

Whatever defects there might be in the composition, there were none in the action; in this the performers showed more humour than I had fancied them capable of. Mr. Palmer and Mr. King were entirely what they desired to represent; and Mrs. Clive—(but what need I talk of her, since, without the least exaggeration, she has more true humour than any actor or actress upon the English or any other stage I have seen)—she, I say, did the part all the justice it was capable of. And, upon the whole, a farce, which has only this to recommend it, that the author took his plan from the volume of nature, by the sprightly manner in which it was performed, was, for one night, a tolerable entertainment. This much may be said in its vindication, that people of fashion seemed more pleased in the representation than the subordinate ranks of people.

Upon Unfortunate Merit

Every age seems to have its favourite pursuits, which serve to amuse the idle, and to relieve the attention of the industrious. Happy the man who is born excellent in the pursuit in vogue, and whose genius seems adapted to the times he lives in. How many do we see, who might have excelled in arts or sciences, and who seem furnished with talents equal to the greatest discoveries, had the road not been already beaten by their predecessors, and nothing left for them except trifles to discover, while others of very moderate abilities become famous, because happening to be first in the reigning pursuit.

Thus, at the renewal of letters in Europe, the taste was not to compose new books, but to comment on the old ones. It was not to be expected that new books should be written, when there were so many of the ancient either not known or not understood. It was not reasonable to attempt new conquests, while they had such an extensive region lying waste for want of cultivation. At that period, criticism and erudition were the reigning studies of the times; and he who had only an inventive genius, might have languished in hopeless obscurity. When the writers of antiquity were sufficiently explained and known, the learned set about imitating them: from hence proceeded the number of Latin orators, poets, and historians, in the reigns of Clement the Seventh and Alexander the Sixth. This passion for antiquity lasted for many years, to the utter exclusion of every other pursuit, till some began to find, that those works which were imitated from nature, were more like the writings of antiquity, than even those written in express imitation. It was then modern language began to be cultivated with assiduity, and our poets and orators poured forth their wonders upon the world.

As writers become more numerous, it is natural for readers to become more indolent; from whence must necessarily arise a desire of attaining knowledge with the greatest possible ease. No science or art offers its instruction and amusement in so obvious a manner as statuary and painting. From hence we see, that a desire of cultivating those arts generally attends the decline of science. Thus the finest statues and the most beautiful paintings of antiquity preceded but a little the absolute decay of every other science. The statues of Antoninus, Commodus, and other contemporaries, are the finest productions of the chisel, and appeared but just before learning was destroyed by comment, criticism, and barbarous invasions.

What happened in Rome may probably be the case with us at home. Our nobility are now more solicitous in patronising painters and sculptors than those of any other polite profession; and from the lord, who has his gallery, down to the 'prentice, who has his twopenny copper-plate, all are admirers of this art. The great, by their caresses, seem insensible to all other merit but that of the pencil; and the vulgar buy every book rather from the excellence of the sculptor than the writer.

How happy were it now, if men of real excellence in that profession were to arise! Were the painters of Italy now to appear, who once wandered like beggars from one city to another, and produced their almost breathing figures, what rewards might they not expect! But many of them lived without rewards, and therefore rewards alone will never produce their equals. We have often found the great exert themselves, not only without promotion, but in spite of opposition. We have often found them flourishing, like medicinal plants, in a region of savageness and barbarity, their excellence unknown, and their virtues unheeded.

They who have seen the paintings of Caravaggio, are sensible of the surprising impression they make; bold, swelling, terrible to the last degree,—all seems animated, and speak him among the foremost of his profession; yet this man's fortune and his fame seemed ever in opposition to each other.

Unknowing how to flatter the great, he was driven from city to city in the utmost indigence, and might truly be said to paint for his bread.

Having one day insulted a person of distinction, who refused to pay him all the respect which he thought his due, he was obliged to leave Rome, and travel on foot, his usual method of going his journeys down into the country, without either money or friends to subsist him.

After he had travelled in this manner as long as his strength would permit, faint with famine and fatigue, he at last called at an obscure inn by the wayside. The host knew, by the appearance of his guest, his indifferent circumstances, and refused to furnish him a dinner without previous payment.

As Caravaggio was entirely destitute of money, he took down the innkeeper's sign, and painted it anew for his dinner.

Thus refreshed, he proceeded on his journey, and left the innkeeper not quite satisfied with this method of payment. Some company of distinction, however, coming soon after, and struck with the beauty of the new sign, bought it at an advanced price, and astonished the innkeeper with their generosity; he was resolved, therefore, to get as many signs as possible drawn by the same artist, as he found he could sell them to good advantage; and accordingly set out after Caravaggio, in order to bring him back. It was nightfall before he came up to the place where the unfortunate Caravaggio lay dead by the roadside, overcome by fatigue, resentment, and despair.

No. VI.—SATURDAY, NOVEMBER 10, 1759

ON EDUCATION

To the Author of the Bee

SIR,—As few subjects are more interesting to society, so few have been more frequently written upon, than the education of youth. Yet it is a little surprising, that it has been treated almost by all in a declamatory manner. They have insisted largely on the advantages that result from it, both to individuals and to society; and have expatiated in the praise of what none have ever been so hardy as to call in question.

Instead of giving us fine but empty harangues upon this subject, instead of indulging each his particular and whimsical system, it had been much better if the writers on this subject had treated it in a more scientific manner, repressed all the sallies of imagination, and given us the result of their observations with didactic simplicity. Upon this subject the smallest errors are of the most dangerous consequence; and the author should venture the imputation of stupidity upon a topic where his slightest deviations may tend to injure posterity. However, such are the whimsical and erroneous productions written upon this subject. Their authors have studied to be uncommon, not to be just; and, at present, we want a treatise upon education, not to tell us anything new, but to explode the errors which have been introduced by the admirers of novelty. It is in this manner books become numerous; a desire of novelty produces a book, and other books are required to destroy this production.

The manner in which our youth of London are at present educated is, some in free-schools in the city, but the far greater number in boarding-schools about town. The parent justly consults the health of his child, and finds an education in the country tends to promote this much more than a continuance in town. Thus far he is right: if there were a possibility of having even our free-schools kept a little out of town, it would certainly conduce to the health and vigour of perhaps the mind as well as the body. It may be thought whimsical, but it is truth,—I have found by experience, that they who have spent all their lives in cities, contract not only an effeminacy of habit, but even of thinking.

But when I have said, that the boarding-schools are preferable to free-schools, as being in the country, this is certainly the only advantage I can allow them; otherwise it is impossible to conceive the ignorance of those who take upon them the important trust of education. Is any man unfit for any of the professions, he finds his last resource in setting up a school. Do any become bankrupts in trade, they still set up a boarding-school, and drive a trade this way, when all others fail: nay, I have been told of butchers and barbers, who have turned schoolmasters; and, more surprising still, made fortunes in their new profession.

Could we think ourselves in a country of civilized people—could it be conceived that we have a regard for posterity, when such persons are permitted to take the charge of the morals, genius, and health of those dear little pledges, who may one day be the guardians of the liberties of Europe, and who may serve as the honour and bulwark of their aged parents? The care of our children, is it below the state? is it fit to indulge the caprice of the ignorant with the disposal of their children in this particular? For the state to take the charge of all its children, as in Persia, or Sparta, might at present be inconvenient; but surely, with great ease, it might cast an eye to their instructors. Of all professions in society, I do not know a more useful, or a more honourable one, than a schoolmaster; at the same time that I do not see any more generally despised, or men whose talents are so ill rewarded.

Were the salaries of schoolmasters to be augmented from a diminution of useless sinecures, how might it turn to the advantage of this people—a people whom, without flattery, I may in other respects term the wisest and greatest upon earth. But, while I would reward the deserving, I would dismiss those utterly unqualified for their employment: in short, I would make the business of a schoolmaster every way more respectable by increasing their salaries, and admitting only men of proper abilities.

It is true we have already schoolmasters appointed, and they have small salaries; but where at present there is only one schoolmaster appointed, there should at least be two; and wherever the salary is at present twenty pounds, it should be augmented to an hundred. Do we give immoderate benefices to our own instructors, and shall we deny even subsistence to those who instruct our children? Every member of society should be paid in proportion as he is necessary: and I will be bold enough to say, that schoolmasters in a state are more necessary than clergymen, as children stand in more need of instruction than their parents.

But, instead of this, as I have already observed, we send them to board in the country to the most ignorant set of men that can be imagined; and, lest the ignorance of the master be not sufficient, the child is generally consigned to the usher. This is commonly some poor needy animal, little superior to a footman either in learning or spirit, invited to his place by an advertisement, and kept there merely from his being of a complying disposition, and making the children fond of him. 'You give your child to be educated to a slave,' says a philosopher to a rich man; 'instead of one slave, you will then have two.'

It were well, however, if parents, upon fixing their children in one of these houses, would examine the abilities of the usher as well as the master; for, whatever they are told to the contrary, the usher is generally the person most employed in their education. If, then, a gentleman, upon putting out his son to one of these houses, sees the usher disregarded by the master, he may depend upon it, that he is equally disregarded by the boys: the truth is, in spite of all their endeavours to please, they are generally the laughing-stock of the school. Every trick is played upon the usher; the oddity of his manners, his dress, or his language, is a fund of eternal ridicule; the master himself, now and then, cannot avoid joining in the laugh; and the poor wretch, eternally resenting this ill-usage, seems to live in a state of war with all the family. This is a very proper person, is it not, to give children a relish for learning? They must esteem learning very much, when they see its professors used with such ceremony. If the usher be despised, the father may be assured his child will never be properly instructed.

But let me suppose, that there are some schools without these inconveniences,—where the masters and ushers are men of learning, reputation, and assiduity. If there are to be found such, they cannot be prized in a state sufficiently. A boy will learn more true wisdom in a public school in a year, than by a private education in five. It is not from masters, but from their equals, youth learn a knowledge of the world: the little tricks they play each other, the punishment that frequently attends the commission, is just a picture of the great world; and all the ways of men are practised in a public school in miniature. It is true, a child is early made acquainted with some vices in a school; but it is better to know these when a boy, than be first taught them when a man, for their novelty then may have irresistible charms.

In a public education boys early learn temperance; and if the parents and friends would give them less money upon their usual visits, it would be much to their advantage, since it may justly be said, that a great part of their disorders arise from surfeit,—*plus occidit gula quam gladius*. And now I am come to the article of health, it may not be amiss to observe, that Mr. Locke, and some others, have advised, that children should be inured to cold, to fatigue, and hardship, from their youth; but Mr. Locke was but an indifferent physician. Habit, I grant, has great influence over our constitutions, but we have not precise ideas upon this subject.

We know, that among savages, and even among our peasants, there are found children born with such constitutions, that they cross rivers by swimming, endure cold, thirst, hunger, and want of sleep, to a surprising degree; that when they happen to fall sick, they are cured, without the help of medicine, by nature alone. Such examples are adduced, to persuade us to imitate their manner of education, and accustom ourselves betimes to support the same fatigues. But had these gentlemen considered, first, how many lives are lost in this ascetic discipline; had they considered that these savages and peasants are generally not so long lived as those who have led a more indolent life: that the more laborious the life is, the less populous is the country: had they considered, that what physicians call the *stamina vitæ*, by fatigue and labour become rigid, and thus anticipate old age; that the number who survive those rude trials, bears no proportion to those who die in the experiment. Had these things been properly considered, they would not have thus extolled an education begun in fatigue and hardships. Peter the Great, willing to inure the children of his seamen to a life of hardship, ordered that they should only drink sea water, but they unfortunately all died under the trial.

But while I would exclude all unnecessary labours, yet still I would recommend temperance in the highest degree. No luxurious dishes with high seasoning, nothing given children to force an appetite, as little sugared or salted provisions as possible, though never so pleasing; but milk, morning and night, should be their constant food. This diet would make them more healthy than any of those slops that are usually cooked by the mistress of a boarding-school; besides, it corrects any consumptive habits, not unfrequently found amongst the children of city parents.

As boys should be educated with temperance, so the first greatest lesson that should be taught them is, to admire frugality. It is by the exercise of this virtue alone, they can ever expect to be useful members of society. It is true, lectures continually repeated upon this subject, may make some boys, when they grow up, run into an extreme, and become misers; but it were well had we more misers than we have among us. I know few characters more useful in society; for a man's having a larger or smaller share of money lying useless by him, no way injures the commonwealth; since, should every miser now exhaust his stores, this might make gold more plenty, but it would not increase the commodities or pleasures of life; they would still remain as they are at present: it matters not, therefore, whether men are misers or not, if they be only frugal, laborious, and fill the station they have chosen. If they deny themselves the necessaries of life, society is no way injured by their folly.

Instead, therefore, of romances, which praise young men of spirit, who go through a variety of adventures, and, at last, conclude a life of dissipation, folly, and extravagance, in riches and matrimony, there should be some men of wit employed to compose books that might equally interest the passions of our youth; where such a one might be praised for having resisted allurements when young, and how he, at last, became Lord Mayor—how he was married to a lady of great sense, fortune, and beauty: to be as explicit as possible, the old story of Whittington, were his cat left out, might be more serviceable to the tender mind than either Tom Jones, Joseph Andrews, or a hundred others, where frugality is the only good quality the hero is not possessed of. Were our schoolmasters, if any of them have sense enough to draw up such a work, thus employed, it would be much more serviceable to their pupils, than all the grammars and dictionaries they may publish these ten years.

Children should early be instructed in the arts from which they may afterwards draw the greatest advantages. When the wonders of nature are never exposed to our view, we have no great desire to become acquainted with those parts of learning which pretend to account for the phenomena. One of the ancients complains, that as soon as young men have left school, and are obliged to converse in the world, they fancy themselves transported into a new region: *Ut cum in forum venerint existiment se in aliam terrarum orbem delatos.* We should early, therefore, instruct them in the experiments, if I may so express it, of knowledge, and leave to maturer age the accounting for the causes. But, instead of that, when boys begin natural philosophy in colleges, they have not the least curiosity for those parts of the science which are proposed for their instruction; they have never before seen the phenomena, and consequently have no curiosity to learn the reasons. Might natural philosophy, therefore, be made their pastime in school, by this means it would in college become their amusement.

In several of the machines now in use, there would be ample field both for instruction and amusement: the different sorts of the phosphorus, the artificial pyrites, magnetism, electricity, the experiments upon the rarefaction and weight of the air, and those upon elastic bodies, might employ their idle hours, and none should be called from play to see such experiments but such as thought proper. At first, then, it would be sufficient if the instruments, and the effects of their combination, were only shown; the causes should be deferred to a maturer age, or to those times when natural curiosity prompts us to discover the wonders of nature. Man is placed in this world as a spectator; when he is tired of wondering at all the novelties about him, and not till then, does he desire to be made acquainted with the causes that create those wonders.

What I have observed with regard to natural philosophy, I would extend to every other science whatsoever. We should teach them as many of the facts as possible, and defer the causes until they seemed of themselves desirous of knowing them. A mind thus leaving school, stored with all the simple experiences of science, would be the fittest in the world for the college course; and though such a youth might not appear so bright, or so talkative, as those who had learned the real principles and causes of some of the sciences, yet he would make a wiser man, and would retain a more lasting passion for letters, than he who was early burdened with the disagreeable institution of cause and effect.

In history, such stories alone should be laid before them as might catch the imagination: instead of this, at present, they are too frequently obliged to toil through the four empires, as they are called, where their memories are burdened by a number of disgusting names, that destroy all their future relish for our best historians, who may be termed the truest teachers of wisdom.

Every species of flattery should be carefully avoided; a boy who happens to say a sprightly thing, is generally applauded so much, that he sometimes continues a coxcomb all his life after. He is reputed a wit at fourteen, and becomes a blockhead at twenty. Nurses, footmen, and such, should therefore be driven away as much as possible. I was even going to add, that the mother herself should stifle her pleasure or her vanity, when little master happens to say a good or a smart thing. Those modest, lubberly boys who seem to want spirit, become at length more shining men; and at school generally go through their business with more ease to themselves, and more satisfaction to their instructors.

There has of late a gentleman appeared, who thinks the study of rhetoric essential to a perfect education. That bold male eloquence, which often, without pleasing, convinces, is generally destroyed by such an institution. Convincing eloquence is infinitely more serviceable to its possessor than the most florid harangue, or the most pathetic tones that can be imagined; and the man who is thoroughly convinced himself, who understands his subject, and the language he speaks in, will be more apt to silence opposition, than he who studies the force of his periods, and fills our ears with sounds, while our minds are destitute of conviction.

It was reckoned the fault of the orators at the decline of the Roman empire, when they had been long instructed by rhetoricians, that their periods were so harmonious, that they could be sung as well as spoken. What a ridiculous figure must one of these gentlemen cut, thus measuring syllables, and weighing words, when he should plead the cause of his client! Two architects were once candidates for the building a certain temple at Athens: the first harangued the crowd very learnedly upon the different orders of architecture, and showed them in what manner the temple should be built; the other, who got up after him, only observed, that what his brother had spoken he could do; and thus he at once gained his cause.

To teach men to be orators, is little less than to teach them to be poets; and for my part, I should have too great a regard for my child, to wish him a manor only in a bookseller's shop.

Another passion which the present age is apt to run into, is to make children learn all things,—the languages, the sciences, music, the exercises, and painting. Thus a child soon becomes a *talker* in all, but a *master* in none. He thus acquires a

superficial fondness for everything, and only shows his
ignorance when he attempts to exhibit his skill.

As I deliver my thoughts without method or connection,
so the reader must not be surprised to find me once more
addressing schoolmasters on the present method of teaching the
learned languages, which is commonly by literal translations.
I would ask such, if they were to travel a journey, whether those
parts of the road in which they found the greatest difficulties
would not be most strongly remembered? Boys who, if I may
continue the allusion, gallop through one of the ancients with
the assistance of a translation, can have but a very slight
acquaintance either with the author or his language. It is by
the exercise of the mind alone that a language is learned; but
a literal translation, on the opposite page, leaves no exercise for
the memory at all. The boy will not be at the fatigue of re-
membering, when his doubts are at once satisfied by a glance
of the eye; whereas, were every word to be sought from a
dictionary, the learner would attempt to remember them, to
save himself the trouble of looking out for the future.

To continue in the same pedantic strain, of all the various
grammars now taught in schools about town, I would recommend only the old common one; I have forgot whether Lily's
or an emendation of him. The others may be improvements;
but such improvements seem to me only mere grammatical
niceties, no way influencing the learner, but perhaps loading
him with trifling subtleties, which, at a proper age, he must be
at some pains to forget.

Whatever pains a master may take to make the learning of
the languages agreeable to his pupil, he may depend upon it, it
will be at first extremely unpleasant. The rudiments of every
language, therefore, must be given as a task, not as an amusement. Attempting to deceive children into instruction of this
kind, is only deceiving ourselves; and I know no passion capable
of conquering a child's natural laziness but fear. Solomon has
said it before me; nor is there any more certain, though perhaps
more disagreeable, truth, than the proverb in verse, too well
known to repeat on the present occasion. It is very probable
that parents are told of some masters who never use the rod, and
consequently are thought the properest instructors for their
children; but though tenderness is a requisite quality in an
instructor, yet there is too often the truest tenderness in well-
timed correction.

Some have justly observed, that all passion should be banished

on this terrible occasion; but, I know not how, there is a frailty
attending human nature, that few masters are able to keep
their temper whilst they correct. I knew a good-natured man,
who was sensible of his own weakness in this respect, and
consequently had recourse to the following expedient to prevent
his passions from being engaged, yet at the same time administer
justice with impartiality. Whenever any of his pupils committed a fault, he summoned a jury of his peers,—I mean of the
boys of his own or the next classes to him: his accusers stood
forth; he had liberty of pleading in his own defence; and one or
two more had the liberty of pleading against him: when found
guilty by the panel, he was consigned to the footman who
attended in the house, who had previous orders to punish, but
with lenity. By this means the master took off the odium of
punishment from himself; and the footman, between whom and
the boys there could not be even the slightest intimacy, was
placed in such a light as to be shunned by every boy in the school.

ON THE INSTABILITY OF WORLDLY GRANDEUR

An alehouse keeper near Islington, who had long lived at the
sign of the French King, upon the commencement of the last
war pulled down his old sign, and put up that of the Queen of
Hungary. Under the influence of her red face and golden sceptre,
he continued to sell ale till she was no longer the favourite of
his customers; he changed her, therefore, some time ago, for
the King of Prussia, who may probably be changed, in turn, for
the next great man that shall be set up for vulgar admiration.

In this manner the great are dealt out one after the other,
to the gazing crowd. When we have sufficiently wondered at
one of them, he is taken in, and another exhibited in his room,
who seldom holds his station long; for the mob are ever pleased
with variety.

I must own I have such an indifferent opinion of the vulgar,
that I am ever led to suspect that merit which raises their
shout; at least I am certain to find those great, and sometimes
good men, who find satisfaction in such acclamations, made
worse by it; and history has too frequently taught me, that the
head which has grown this day giddy with the roar of the
million, has the very next been fixed upon a pole.

As Alexander VI was entering a little town in the neighbourhood of Rome, which had been just evacuated by the enemy,
he perceived the townsmen busy in the market-place in pulling

down from a gibbet a figure, which had been designed to represent himself. There were some also knocking down a neighbouring statue of one of the Orsini family, with whom he was at war, in order to put Alexander's effigy in its place. It is possible a man who knew less of the world would have condemned the adulation of those bare-faced flatterers; but Alexander seemed pleased at their zeal, and turning to Borgia his son, said with a smile, *Vides, mi fili, quam leve discrimen patibulum inter et statuam.* 'You see, my son, the small difference between a gibbet and a statue.' If the great could be taught any lesson, this might serve to teach them upon how weak a foundation their glory stands; for, as popular applause is excited by what seems like merit, it as quickly condemns what has only the appearance of guilt.

Popular glory is a perfect coquette: her lovers must toil, feel every inquietude, indulge every caprice; and perhaps at last be jilted for their pains. True glory, on the other hand, resembles a woman of sense: her admirers must play no tricks; they feel no great anxiety, for they are sure, in the end, of being rewarded in proportion to their merit. When Swift used to appear in public, he generally had the mob shouting in his train. 'Pox take these fools!' he would say, 'how much joy might all this bawling give my Lord Mayor!'

We have seen those virtues which have, while living, retired from the public eye, generally transmitted to posterity as the truest objects of admiration and praise. Perhaps the character of the late Duke of Marlborough may one day be set up, even above that of his more talked-of predecessor; since an assemblage of all the mild and amiable virtues is far superior to those vulgarly called the great ones. I must be pardoned for this short tribute to the memory of a man, who, while living, would as much detest to receive anything that wore the appearance of flattery, as I should to offer it.

I know not how to turn so trite a subject out of the beaten road of commonplace, except by illustrating it, rather by the assistance of my memory than judgment, and instead of making reflections, by telling a story.

A Chinese, who had long studied the works of Confucius, who knew the characters of fourteen thousand words, and could read a great part of every book that came in his way, once took it into his head to travel into Europe, and observe the customs of a people which he thought not very much inferior even to his own countrymen. Upon his arrival at Amsterdam, his passion for letters naturally led him to a bookseller's shop: and, as he could speak a little Dutch, he civilly asked the bookseller for the works of the immortal Xixofou. The bookseller assured him he had never heard the book mentioned before. 'Alas!' cries our traveller, 'to what purpose, then, has he fasted to death, to gain a renown which has never travelled beyond the precincts of China!'

There is scarce a village in Europe, and not one university, that is not thus furnished with its little great men. The head of a petty corporation, who opposes the designs of a prince who would tyrannically force his subjects to save their best clothes for Sundays; the puny pedant who finds one undiscovered property in the polype, or describes an unheeded process in the skeleton of a mole; and whose mind, like his microscope, perceives nature only in detail; the rhymer who makes smooth verses, and paints to our imagination when he should only speak to our hearts; all equally fancy themselves walking forward to immortality, and desire the crowd behind them to look on. The crowd takes them at their word. Patriot, philosopher, and poet, are shouted in their train. 'Where was there ever so much merit seen? no times so important as our own! ages yet unborn shall gaze with wonder and applause!' To such music the important pigmy moves forward, bustling and swelling and aptly compared to a puddle in a storm.

I have lived to see generals, who once had crowds hallooing after them wherever they went, who were bepraised by newspapers and magazines, those echoes of the voice of the vulgar, and yet they have long sunk into merited obscurity, with scarce even an epitaph left to flatter. A few years ago, the herring fishery employed all Grub Street; it was the topic in every coffee-house, and the burden of every ballad. We were to drag up oceans of gold from the bottom of the sea; we were to supply all Europe with herrings upon our own terms. At present we hear no more of all this. We have fished up very little gold that I can learn; nor do we furnish the world with herrings as was expected. Let us wait but a few years longer, and we shall find all our expectations a herring fishery.

SOME ACCOUNT OF THE ACADEMIES OF ITALY

There is not, perhaps, a country in Europe, in which learning is so fast upon the decline as in Italy; yet not one in which there are such a number of academies instituted for its support.

There is scarce a considerable town in the whole country, which has not one or two institutions of this nature, where the learned, as they are pleased to call themselves, meet to harangue, to compliment each other, and praise the utility of their institution.

Jarchius has taken the trouble to give us a list of those clubs or academies, which amount to five hundred and fifty, each distinguished by somewhat whimsical in the name. The academies of Bologna, for instance, are divided into the Abbandonati, the Ausiosi, Ociosi, Arcadi, Confusi, Dubbiosi, etc. There are few of these who have not published their transactions, and scarce a member who is not looked upon as the most famous man in the world, at home.

Of all those societies, I know of none whose works are worth being known out of the precincts of the city in which they were written, except the Cicalata Accademica—or, as we might express it, the Tickling Society—of Florence. I have just now before me a manuscript oration, spoken by the late Tomaso Crudeli at that society, which will at once serve to give a better picture of the manner in which men of wit amuse themselves in that country, than anything I could say upon the occasion. The oration is this:

'The younger the nymph, my dear companions, the more happy the lover. From fourteen to seventeen you are sure of finding love for love; from seventeen to twenty-one, there is always a mixture of interest and affection. But when that period is past, no longer expect to receive, but to buy—no longer expect a nymph who gives, but who sells, her favours. At this age, every glance is taught its duty; not a look, not a sigh without design; the lady, like a skilful warrior, aims at the heart of another, while she shields her own from danger.

'On the contrary, at fifteen you may expect nothing but simplicity, innocence, and nature. The passions are then sincere; the soul seems seated in the lips; the dear object feels present happiness, without being anxious for the future; her eyes brighten if her lover approaches; her smiles are borrowed from the Graces, and her very mistakes seem to complete her desires.

'Lucretia was just sixteen. The rose and lily took possession of her face, and her bosom, by its hue and its coldness, seemed covered with snow. So much beauty and so much virtue seldom want admirers. Orlandino, a youth of sense and merit, was among the number. He had long languished for an opportunity of declaring his passion, when Cupid, as if willing to indulge his happiness, brought the charming young couple by mere accident to an arbour, where every prying eye, but that of love, was absent. Orlandino talked of the sincerity of his passion, and mixed flattery with his addresses; but it was all in vain. The nymph was pre-engaged, and had long devoted to heaven those charms for which he sued. "My dear Orlandino,' said she, 'you know I have been long dedicated to St. Catherine, and to her belongs all that lies below my girdle; all that is above, you may freely possess, but farther I cannot, must not, comply. The vow is passed; I wish it were undone, but now it is impossible.' You may conceive, my companions, the embarrassment our young lovers felt upon this occasion. They kneeled to St. Catherine, and though both despaired, both implored her assistance. Their tutelar saint was entreated to show some expedient, by which both might continue to love, and yet both be happy. Their petition was sincere. St. Catherine was touched with compassion; for lo, a miracle! Lucretia's girdle unloosed, as if without hands; and though before bound round her middle, fell spontaneously down to her feet, and gave Orlandino the possession of all those beauties which lay above it.'

No. VII.—SATURDAY, NOVEMBER 17, 1759

OF ELOQUENCE

OF all kinds of success, that of an orator is the most pleasing. Upon other occasions, the applause we deserve is conferred in our absence, and we are insensible of the pleasure we have given; but in eloquence the victory and the triumph are inseparable. We read our own glory in the face of every spectator; the audience is moved; the antagonist is defeated; and the whole circle bursts into unsolicited applause.

The rewards which attend excellence in this way are so pleasing, that numbers have written professed treatises to teach us the art; schools have been established with no other intent; rhetoric has taken place among the institutions; and pedants have ranged under proper heads, and distinguished with long learned names, *some* of the strokes of nature, or of passion, which orators have used. I say only *some*, for a folio volume could not contain all the figures which have been used by the truly eloquent; and scarce a good speaker or writer but makes use of some that are peculiar or new.

Eloquence has preceded the rules of rhetoric, as languages have been formed before grammar. Nature renders men eloquent in great interests, or great passions. He that is sensibly touched, sees things with a very different eye from the rest of mankind. All nature to him becomes an object of comparison and metaphor, without attending to it; he throws life into all, and inspires his audience with a part of his own enthusiasm.

It has been remarked, that the lower parts of mankind generally express themselves most figuratively, and that tropes are found in the most ordinary forms of conversation. Thus, in every language, the heart burns; the courage is roused; the eyes sparkle; the spirits are cast down; passion inflames, pride swells, and pity sinks the soul. Nature everywhere speaks in those strong images, which, from their frequency, pass unnoticed.

Nature it is which inspires those rapturous enthusiasms, those irresistible turns; a strong passion, a pressing danger, calls up all the imagination, and gives the orator irresistible force. Thus, a captain of the first caliphs, seeing his soldiers fly, cried out, 'Whither do you run? the enemy are not there! You have been told that the caliph is dead; but God is still living. He regards the brave, and will reward the courageous. Advance!'

A man, therefore, may be called eloquent, who transfers the passion or sentiment with which he is moved himself, into the breast of another; and this definition appears the more just, as it comprehends the graces of silence and of action. An intimate persuasion of the truth to be proved, is the sentiment and passion to be transferred; and he who effects this, is truly possessed of the talent of eloquence.

I have called eloquence a talent, and not an art, as so many rhetoricians have done, as art is acquired by exercise and study, and eloquence is the gift of nature. Rules will never make either a work or a discourse eloquent; they only serve to prevent faults, but not to introduce beauties; to prevent those passages which are truly eloquent and dictated by nature from being blended with others which might disgust, or at least abate our passion.

What we clearly conceive, says Boileau, we can clearly express. I may add, that what is felt with emotion is expressed also with the same movements; the words arise as readily to paint our emotions as to express our thoughts with perspicuity. The cool care an orator takes to express passions which he does not feel, only prevents his rising into that passion he would seem to feel.

In a word, to feel your subject thoroughly, and to speak without fear, are the only rules of eloquence, properly so called, which I can suffer. Examine a writer of genius on the most beautiful parts of his work, and he will always assure you, that such passages are generally those which have given him the least trouble, for they came as if by inspiration. To pretend that cold and didactic precepts will make a man eloquent is only to prove that he is incapable of eloquence.

But, as in being perspicuous, it is necessary to have a full idea of the subject, so in being eloquent it is not sufficient, if I may so express it, to feel by halves. The orator should be strongly impressed, which is generally the effect of a fine and exquisite sensibility, and not that transient and superficial emotion which he excites in the greatest part of his audience. It is even impossible to affect the hearers in any great degree without being affected ourselves. In vain it will be objected, that many writers have had the art to inspire their readers with a passion for virtue, without being virtuous themselves, since it may be answered, that sentiments of virtue filled their minds at the time they were writing. They felt the inspiration strongly while they praised justice, generosity, or good-nature; but, unhappily for them, these passions might have been discontinued, when they laid down the pen. In vain will it be objected again, that we can move without being moved, as we can convince without being convinced. It is much easier to deceive our reason than ourselves: a trifling defect in reasoning may be overseen, and lead a man astray, for it requires reason and time to detect the falsehood; but our passions are not easily imposed upon,—our eyes, our ears, and every sense, are watchful to detect the imposture.

No discourse can be eloquent that does not elevate the mind. Pathetic eloquence, it is true, has for its only object to affect; but I appeal to men of sensibility, whether their pathetic feelings are not accompanied with some degree of elevation. We may then call eloquence and sublimity the same thing, since it is impossible to be one without feeling the other. From hence it follows, that we may be eloquent in any language, since no language refuses to paint those sentiments with which we are thoroughly impressed. What is usually called sublimity of style, seems to be only an error. Eloquence is not in the words, but in the subject; and in great concerns, the more simply anything is expressed, it is generally the more sublime. True eloquence does not consist, as the rhetoricians assure us, in saying great things in a sublime style, but in a simple style; for there is, properly speaking, no such thing as a sublime style; the sublimity lies only in the things; and when they are not so, the language may be turgid, affected, metaphorical,—but not affecting.

What can be more simply expressed than the following extract from a celebrated preacher, and yet what was ever more sublime? Speaking of the small number of the elect, he breaks out thus among his audience:—'Let me suppose that this was the last hour of us all—that the heavens were opening over our heads—that time was passed, and eternity begun—that Jesus Christ in all His glory, that Man of Sorrows, in all His glory, appeared on the tribunal, and that we were assembled here to receive our final decree of life, or death eternal! Let me ask, impressed with terror like you, and not separating my lot from yours, but putting myself in the same situation in which we must all one day appear before God, our judge,—let me ask, if Jesus Christ should now appear to make that terrible separation of the just from the unjust, do you think the greatest number would be saved? Do you think the number of the elect would even be equal to that of the sinners? Do you think, if all our works were examined with justice, would He find ten just persons in this great assembly? Monsters of ingratitude! would He find one?' Such passages as these are sublime in every language. The expression may be less speaking, or more indistinct, but the greatness of the idea still remains. In a word, we may be eloquent in every language and in every style, since elocution is only an assistant, but not a constitutor of eloquence.

Of what use, then, will it be said, are all the precepts given us upon this head, both by the ancients and moderns? I answer, that they cannot make us eloquent, but they will certainly prevent us from becoming ridiculous. They can seldom procure a single beauty, but they may banish a thousand faults. The true method of an orator is not to attempt always to move, always to affect, to be continually sublime, but at proper intervals to give rest both to his own and the passions of his audience. In these periods of relaxation, or of preparation rather, rules may teach him to avoid anything low, trivial, or disgusting. Thus criticism, properly speaking, is intended not to assist those parts which are sublime, but those which are naturally mean and humble, which are composed with coolness and caution, and where the orator rather endeavours not to offend than attempts to please.

I have hitherto insisted more strenuously on that eloquence which speaks to the passions, as it is a species of oratory almost unknown in England. At the bar it is quite discontinued, and I think with justice. In the senate it is used but sparingly, as the orator speaks to enlightened judges. But in the pulpit, in which the orator should chiefly address the vulgar, it seems strange that it should be entirely laid aside.

The vulgar of England are, without exception, the most barbarous and the most unknowing of any in Europe. A great part of their ignorance may be chiefly ascribed to their teachers, who, with the most pretty gentlemanlike serenity, deliver their cool discourses, and address the reason of men who have never reasoned in all their lives. They are told of cause and effect, of beings self-existent, and the universal scale of beings. They are informed of the excellence of the Bangorian Controversy, and the absurdity of an intermediate state. The spruce preacher reads his lucubration without lifting his nose from the text, and never ventures to earn the shame of an enthusiast.

By this means, though his audience feel not one word of all he says, he earns, however, among his acquaintance, the character of a man of sense; among his acquaintance only, did I say? nay, even with his bishop.

The polite of every country have several motives to induce them to a rectitude of action,—the love of virtue for its own sake, the shame of offending, and the desire of pleasing. The vulgar have one,—the enforcements of religion; and yet those who should push this motive home to their hearts, are basely found to desert their post. They speak to the squire, the philosopher, and the pedant; but the poor, those who really want instruction, are left uninstructed.

I have attended most of our pulpit orators, who, it must be owned, write extremely well upon the text they assume. To give them their due also, they read their sermons with elegance and propriety; but this goes but a very short way in true eloquence. The speaker must be moved. In this, in this alone, our English divines are deficient. Were they to speak to a few calm, dispassionate hearers, they certainly use the properest methods of address; but their audience is chiefly composed of the poor, who must be influenced by motives of reward and punishment, and whose only virtues lie in self-interest or fear.

How, then, are such to be addressed? Not by studied periods, or cold disquisitions; not by the labours of the head, but the

honest spontaneous dictates of the heart. Neither writing a
sermon with regular periods, and all the harmony of elegant
expression—neither reading it with emphasis, propriety, and
deliberation — neither pleasing with metaphor, simile, or
rhetorical fustian—neither arguing coolly, and untying consequences united in *à priori*, nor bundling up inductions *à
posteriori*—neither pedantic jargon, nor academical trifling, can
persuade the poor. Writing a discourse coolly in the closet,
then getting it by memory, and delivering it on Sundays, even
that will not do. What then, is to be done? I know of no
expedient to speak—to speak at once intelligibly and feelingly—
except to understand the language: to be convinced of the truth
of the object—to be perfectly acquainted with the subject in
view—to prepossess yourself with a low opinion of your audience
—and to do the rest extempore. By this means, strong expres-
sions, new thoughts, rising passions, and the true declamatory
style, will naturally ensue.

Fine declamation does not consist in flowery periods, delicate
allusions, or musical cadences, but in a plain, open, loose style,
where the periods are long and obvious; where the same thought
is often exhibited in several points of view: all this, strong sense,
a good memory, and a small share of experience, will furnish
to every orator; and without these, a clergyman may be called
a fine preacher, a judicious preacher, and a man of sound sense;
he may make his hearers admire his understanding, but will
seldom enlighten theirs.

When I think of the Methodist preachers among us, how
seldom they are endued with common sense, and yet how often
and how justly they affect their hearers, I cannot avoid saying
within myself, had these been bred gentlemen, and been endued
with even the meanest share of understanding, what might
they not effect! Did our bishops, who can add dignity to their
expostulations, testify the same fervour, and *entreat* their hearers,
as well as *argue*, what might not be the consequence! The
vulgar, by which I mean the bulk of mankind, would then have
a double motive to love religion; first, from seeing its professors
honoured here, and next, from the consequences hereafter. At
present the enthusiasms of the poor are opposed to law; did law
conspire with their enthusiasms, we should not only be the
happiest nation upon earth, but the wisest also.

Enthusiasm in religion, which prevails only among the
vulgar, should be the chief object of politics. A society of
enthusiasts, governed by reason, among the great, is the most

indissoluble, the most virtuous, and the most efficient of its own decrees that can be imagined. Every country, possessed of any degree of strength, has had its enthusiasms, which ever serve as laws among the people. The Greeks had their *Kalo-kagathia*, the Romans their *Amor Patriæ*, and we the truer and firmer bond of the *Protestant Religion*. The principle is the same in all: how much, then, is it the duty of those whom the law has appointed teachers of this religion, to enforce its obligations, and to raise those enthusiasms among people, by which alone political society can subsist?

From eloquence, therefore, the morals of our people are to expect emendation; but how little can they be improved by men who get into the pulpit rather to show their parts than convince us of the truth of what they deliver; who are painfully correct in their style, musical in their tones; where every sentiment, every expression, seems the result of meditation and deep study.

Tillotson has been commended as the model of pulpit eloquence; thus far he should be imitated, where he generally strives to convince rather than to please; but to adopt his long, dry, and sometimes tedious discussions, which serve to amuse only divines, and are utterly neglected by the generality of mankind—to praise the intricacy of his periods, which are too long to be spoken—to continue his cool phlegmatic manner of enforcing every truth—is certainly erroneous. As I said before, the good preacher should adopt no model, write no sermons, study no periods; let him but understand his subject, the language he speaks, and be convinced of the truths he delivers. It is amazing to what heights eloquence of this kind may reach! This is that eloquence the ancients represented as lightning, bearing down every opposer; this the power which has turned whole assemblies into astonishment, admiration, and awe— that is described by the torrent, the flame, and every other instance of irresistible impetuosity.

But to attempt such noble heights, belongs only to the truly great, or the truly good. To discard the lazy manner of reading sermons, or speaking sermons by rote; to set up singly against the opposition of men who are attached to their own errors, and to endeavour to be great, instead of being prudent, are qualities we seldom see united. A minister of the Church of England, who may be possessed of good sense, and some hopes of preferment, will seldom give up such substantial advantages for the empty pleasure of improving society. By his present method he is liked by his friends, admired by his dependants, not displeasing to his bishop; he lives as well, eats and sleeps as well, as if a real orator, and an eager asserter of his mission: he will hardly, therefore, venture all this, to be called, perhaps, an enthusiast; nor will he depart from customs established by the brotherhood, when, by such a conduct, he only singles himself out for their contempt.

CUSTOM AND LAWS COMPARED

What, say some, can give us a more contemptible idea of a large state, than to find it mostly governed by custom; to have few written laws, and no boundaries to mark the jurisdiction between the senate and people? Among the number who speak in this manner is the great Montesquieu, who asserts that every nation is free in proportion to the number of its written laws, and seems to hint at a despotic and arbitrary conduct in the present King of Prussia, who has abridged the laws of his country into a very short compass.

As Tacitus and Montesquieu happen to differ in sentiment upon a subject of so much importance (for the Roman expressly asserts, that the state is generally vicious in proportion to the number of its laws), it will not be amiss to examine it a little more minutely, and see whether a state, which, like England, is burdened with a multiplicity of written laws, or which, like Switzerland, Geneva, and some other republics, is governed by custom and the determination of the judge, is best.

And to prove the superiority of custom to written law, we shall at least find history conspiring. Custom, or the traditional observance of the practice of their forefathers, was what directed the Romans, as well in their public as private determinations. Custom was appealed to in pronouncing sentence against a criminal, where part of the formulary was *more majorum*. So Sallust, speaking of the expulsion of Tarquin, says, *mutato more*, and not *lege mutata*; and Virgil, *pacisque imponere morem*. So that, in those times of the empire in which the people retained their liberty, they were governed by custom; when they sunk into oppression and tyranny, they were restrained by new laws, and the laws of tradition abolished.

As getting the ancients on our side is half a victory, it will not be amiss to fortify the argument with an observation of Chrysostom's—that 'The enslaved are the fittest to be governed by laws, and free men by custom.' Custom partakes of the nature of parental injunction; it is kept by the people themselves, and observed with a willing obedience. The observance of it must, therefore, be a mark of freedom; and coming originally to a state from the reverenced founders of its liberty, will be an encouragement and assistance to it in the defence of that blessing: but a conquered people, a nation of slaves, must pretend to none of this freedom, or these happy distinctions; having, by degeneracy, lost all right to their brave forefathers' free institutions, their masters will in policy take the forfeiture; and the fixing a conquest must be done by giving laws, which may every moment serve to remind the people enslaved of their conquerors: nothing being more dangerous than to trust a late subdued people with old customs, that presently upbraid their degeneracy, and provoke them to revolt.

The wisdom of the Roman republic in their veneration for custom, and backwardness to introduce a new law, was perhaps the cause of their long continuance, and of the virtues of which they have set the world so many examples. But to show in what that wisdom consists, it may be proper to observe, that the benefits of new-written laws are merely confined to the consequences of their observance; but customary laws, keeping up a veneration for the founders, engage men in the imitation of their virtues as well as policy. To this may be ascribed the religious regard the Romans paid to their forefathers' memory, and their adhering for so many ages to the practice of the same virtues; which nothing contributed more to efface than the introduction of a voluminous body of new laws over the neck of venerable custom.

The simplicity, conciseness, and antiquity of custom, give an air of majesty and immutability that inspires awe and veneration; but new laws are too apt to be voluminous, perplexed, and indeterminate; whence must necessarily arise neglect, contempt, and ignorance.

As every human institution is subject to gross imperfections, so laws must necessarily be liable to the same inconveniences, and their defects soon discovered. Thus, through the weakness of one part, all the rest are liable to be brought into contempt. But such weaknesses in a custom, for very obvious reasons, evade an examination; besides, a friendly prejudice always stands up in their favour.

But, let us suppose a new law to be perfectly equitable and necessary; yet, if the procurers of it have betrayed a conduct that confesses by-ends and private motives, the disgust to the circumstances disposes us, unreasonably indeed, to an irreverence of the law itself: but we are indulgently blind to the most visible imperfections of an old custom. Though we perceive the defects ourselves, yet we remain persuaded that our wise forefathers had good reason for what they did; and though such motives no longer continue, the benefit will still go along with the observance, though we don't know how. It is thus the Roman lawyers speak: 'Non omnium quæ a majoribus constituta sunt, ratio reddi potest, et ideo rationes eorum quæ constituuntur inquiri non oportet, alioquin multa ex his quæ certa sunt subvertuntur.'

Those laws which preserve to themselves the greatest love and observance, must needs be best; but custom, as it executes itself, must be necessarily superior to written laws, in this respect, which are to be executed by another. Thus, nothing can be more certain than that numerous written laws are a sign of a degenerate community, and are frequently not the consequences of vicious morals in a state, but the causes.

From hence we see how much greater benefit it would be to the state rather to abridge than increase its laws. We every day find them increasing; acts and reports, which may be termed the acts of judges, are every day becoming more voluminous, and loading the subject with new penalties.

Laws ever increase in number and severity, until they at length are strained so tight as to break themselves. Such was the case of the latter empire, whose laws were at length become so strict, that the barbarous invaders did not bring servitude but liberty.

Of the Pride and Luxury of the Middling Class of People

Of all the follies and absurdities which this great metropolis labours under, there is not one, I believe, at present appears in a more glaring and ridiculous light than the pride and luxury of the middling class of people. Their eager desire of being seen in a sphere far above their capacities and circumstances, is daily—nay, hourly—instanced, by the prodigious numbers of mechanics who flock to the races, and gaming-tables, brothels, and all public diversions this fashionable town affords.

You shall see a grocer or a tallow-chandler, sneak from behind the compter, clap on a laced coat and a bag, fly to the E. O. table, throw away fifty pieces with some sharping man of quality, while his industrious wife is selling a pennyworth of sugar, or a pound of candles, to support her fashionable spouse in his extravagances.

I was led into this reflection by an odd adventure which happened to me the other day at Epsom races, where I went, not through any desire, I do assure you, of laying bets, or winning thousands, but at the earnest request of a friend, who had long indulged the curiosity of seeing the sport, very natural for an Englishman. When we had arrived at the course, and had taken several turns to observe the different objects that made up this whimsical group, a figure suddenly darted by us, mounted and dressed in all the elegance of those polite gentry who come to show you they have a little money, and rather than pay their just debts at home, generously come abroad to bestow it on gamblers and pickpockets. As I had not an opportunity of viewing his face till his return, I gently walked after him, and met him as he came back; when, to my no small surprise, I beheld in this gay Narcissus the visage of Jack Varnish, an humble vender of prints. Disgusted at the sight, I pulled my friend by the sleeve, pressed him to return home, telling him, all the way, that I was so enraged at the fellow's impudence, I was resolved never to lay out another penny with him.

And now, pray, Sir, let me beg of you to give this a place in your paper, that Mr. Varnish may understand he mistakes the thing quite, if he imagines horse-racing recommendable in a tradesman: and that he who is revelling every night in the arms of a common strumpet (though blessed with an indulgent wife) when he ought to be minding his business, will never thrive in this world. He will find himself soon mistaken, his finances decrease, his friends shun him, customers fall off, and himself thrown into a gaol. I would earnestly recommend this adage to every mechanic in London, 'Keep your shop, and your shop will keep you.' A strict observance of these words will, I am sure, in time gain them estates. Industry is the road to wealth, and honesty to happiness; and he who strenuously endeavours to pursue them both, may never fear the critic's lash, or the sharp cries of penury and want.

SABINUS AND OLINDA

In a fair, rich, and flourishing country, whose cliffs are washed by the German Ocean, lived Sabinus, a youth formed by nature to make a conquest wherever he thought proper; but the constancy of his disposition fixed him only with Olinda.

He was, indeed, superior to her in fortune, but that defect on her side was so amply supplied by her merit, that none was thought more worthy of his regards than she. He loved her, he was beloved by her; and in a short time, by joining hands publicly, they avowed the union of their hearts. But, alas! none, however fortunate, however happy, are exempt from the shafts of envy, and the malignant effects of ungoverned appetite. How unsafe, how detestable are they who have this fury for their guide! How certainly will it lead them from themselves, and plunge them in errors they would have shuddered at, even in apprehension. Ariana, a lady of many amiable qualities, very nearly allied to Sabinus, and highly esteemed by him, imagined herself slighted, and injuriously treated, since his marriage with Olinda. By uncautiously suffering this jealousy to corrode in her breast, she began to give a loose to passion; she forgot those many virtues for which she had been so long and so justly applauded. Causeless suspicion and mistaken resentment betrayed her into all the gloom of discontent; she sighed without ceasing; the happiness of others gave her intolerable pain; she thought of nothing but revenge. How unlike what she was,—the cheerful, the prudent, the compassionate Ariana!

She continually laboured to disturb an union so firmly, so affectionately founded, and planned every scheme which she thought most likely to disturb it.

Fortune seemed willing to promote her unjust intentions: the circumstances of Sabinus had been long embarrassed by a tedious lawsuit, and the court determining the cause unexpectedly in favour of his opponent, it sunk his fortune to the lowest pitch of penury from the highest affluence. From the nearness of relationship, Sabinus expected from Ariana those assistances his present situation required; but she was insensible to all his entreaties, and the justice of every remonstrance, unless he first separated from Olinda, whom she regarded with detestation. Upon a compliance with her desires in this respect she promised her fortune, her interest, and her all, should be at his command. Sabinus was shocked at the proposal; he loved his wife with inexpressible tenderness, and refused those offers, with indignation, which were to be purchased at so high a price. Ariana was no less displeased to find her offers rejected, and gave a loose to all that warmth which she had long endeavoured to suppress. Reproach generally produces recrimination; the quarrel rose to such a height, that Sabinus was marked for destruction, and the very next day, upon the strength of an old family debt, he was sent to gaol, with none but Olinda to comfort him in his miseries. In this mansion of distress they lived together with resignation, and even with comfort. She provided the frugal meal, and he read for her while employed in the little offices of domestic concern. Their fellow-prisoners admired their contentment, and whenever they had a desire of relaxing into mirth, and enjoying those little comforts that a prison affords, Sabinus and Olinda were sure to be of the party. Instead of reproaching each other for their mutual wretchedness, they both lightened it, by bearing each a share of the load imposed by Providence. Whenever Sabinus showed the least concern on his dear partner's account, she conjured him by the love he bore her, by those tender ties which now united them for ever, not to discompose himself; that so long as his affection lasted, she defied all the ills of fortune, and every loss of fame or friendship; that nothing could make her miserable but his seeming to want happiness; nothing pleased but his sympathising with her pleasure. A continuance in prison soon robbed them of the little they had left, and famine began to make its horrid appearance; yet still was neither found to murmur: they both looked upon their little boy, who, insensible of their or his own distress, was playing about the room, with inexpressible yet silent anguish, when a messenger came to inform them that Ariana was dead, and that her will, in favour of a very distant relation, who was now in another country, might easily be procured and burnt, in which case all her large fortune would revert to him, as being the next heir-at-law.

A proposal of so base a nature filled our unhappy couple with horror; they ordered the messenger immediately out of the room, and, falling upon each other's neck, indulged an agony of sorrow, for now even all hopes of relief were banished. The messenger who made the proposal, however, was only a spy sent by Ariana to sound the dispositions of a man she loved at once and persecuted. This lady, though warped by wrong passions, was naturally kind, judicious, and friendly. She found that all her attempts to shake the constancy or the integrity of Sabinus were ineffectual; she had therefore begun to reflect, and to wonder how she could so long and so unprovoked injure such uncommon fortitude and affection.

She had, from the next room, herself heard the reception given to the messenger, and could not avoid feeling all the force of superior virtue: she therefore reassumed her former goodness

of heart; she came into the room with tears in her eyes, and
acknowledged the severity of her former treatment, She
bestowed her first care in providing them all the necessary
supplies, and acknowledged them as the most deserving heirs
of her fortune.   From this moment, Sabinus enjoyed an uninterrupted happiness with Olinda, and both were happy in
the friendship and assistance of Ariana; who, dying soon after,
left them in possession of a large estate, and, in her last moments,
confessed that virtue was the only part of true glory; and that,
however innocence may for a time be depressed, a steady
perseverance will, in time, lead to a certain victory.

No. VIII.—SATURDAY, NOVEMBER 24, 1759

Of the Opera in England

The rise and fall of our amusements pretty much resemble
that of empire.   They this day flourish without any visible
cause for such vigour; the next they decay away without any
reason that can be assigned for their downfall.   Some years
ago, the Italian opera was the only fashionable amusement
among our nobility.   The managers of the playhouses dreaded
it as a mortal enemy, and our very poets listed themselves in
the opposition: at present the house seems deserted, the *castrati*
sing to empty benches; even Prince Vologeso himself, a youth
of great expectations, sings himself out of breath, and rattles
his chain to no purpose.

To say the truth, the opera, as it is conducted among us, is
but a very humdrum amusement; in other countries the decorations are entirely magnificent, the singers all excellent, and
the burlettas, or interludes, quite entertaining; the best poets
compose the words, and the best masters the music.   But with
us it is otherwise: the decorations are but trifling and cheap;
the singers, Matei only excepted, but indifferent.   Instead of
interlude, we have those sorts of skipping dances, which are
calculated for the galleries of the theatre.   Every performer
sings his favourite song, and the music is only a medley of old
Italian airs, or some meagre modern capricio.

When such is the case, it is not much to be wondered if the
opera is pretty much neglected.   The lower orders of people
have neither taste nor fortune to relish such an entertainment;
they would find more satisfaction in the 'Roast Beef of Old

England' than in the finest closes of an eunuch; they sleep amidst all the agony of recitative. On the other hand, people of fortune or taste can hardly be pleased, where there is a visible poverty in the decorations, and an entire want of taste in the composition.

Would it not surprise one, that when Metastasio is so well known in England, and so universally admired, the manager or the composer should have recourse to any other operas than those written by him? I might venture to say, that 'written by Metastasio,' put up in the bills of the day, would alone be sufficient to fill an house, since thus the admirers of sense as well as sound might find entertainment.

The performers also should be entreated to sing only their parts, without clapping in any of their own favourite airs. I must own, that such songs are generally to me the most disagreeable in the world. Every singer generally chooses a favourite air, not from the excellency of the music, but from the difficulty; such songs are generally chosen as surprise rather than please, where the performer may show his compass, his breath, and his volubility.

From hence proceed those unnatural startings, those un-musical closings, and shakes lengthened out to a painful con-tinuance; such, indeed, may show a voice, but it must give a truly delicate ear the utmost uneasiness. Such tricks are not music; neither Corelli nor Pergolesi ever permitted them, and they begin even to be discontinued in Italy, where they first had their rise.

And, now I am upon the subject, our composers also should affect greater simplicity—let their bass cliff have all the variety they can give it,—let the body of the music (if I may so express it) be as various as they please; but let them avoid ornamenting a barren groundwork, let them not attempt, by flourishing, to cheat us of solid harmony.

The works of Mr. Rameau are never heard without a surprising effect. I can attribute it only to this simplicity he everywhere observes, insomuch that some of his finest harmonies are often only octave and unison. This simple manner has greater powers than is generally imagined; and were not such a demonstration misplaced, I think, from the principles of music, it might be proved to be most agreeable.

But to leave general reflection. With the present set of performers, the operas, if the conductor thinks proper, may be carried on with some success, since they have all some merit, if not as actors, at least as singers. Signora Matei is at once both a perfect actress and a very fine singer. She is possessed of a fine sensibility in her manner, and seldom indulges those extravagant and unmusical flights of voice complained of before. Cornacini, on the other hand, is a very indifferent actor—has a most unmeaning face—seems not to feel his part—is infected with a passion of showing his compass; but to recompense all tnese defects, his voice is melodious—he has vast compass, and great volubility—his swell and shake are perfectly fine, unless that he continues the latter too long. In short, whatever the defects of his action may be, they are amply recompensed by his excellency as a singer; nor can I avoid fancying that he might make a much greater figure in an oratorio than upon the stage.

However, upon the whole, I know not whether ever operas can be kept up in England; they seem to be entirely exotic, and require the nicest management and care. Instead of this, the care of them is assigned to men unacquainted with the genius and disposition of the people they would amuse, and whose only motives are immediate gain. Whether a discontinuance of such entertainments would be more to the loss or the advantage of the nation, I will not take upon me to determine, since it is as much our interest to induce foreigners of taste among us on the one hand, as it is to discourage those trifling members of society who generally compose the operatical *dramatis personæ*, on the other.

NOTES

THE CITIZEN OF THE WORLD

The numbers at the beginning of paragraphs refer to the pages.

Text.—The text is based upon that of the third edition of 1774, the last with which Goldsmith can possibly have been concerned. Its title is as follows: The | Citizen of the World; | or | Letters | from a | Chinese Philosopher, | Residing in London, | to his | Friends in the East. | In Two Volumes . . . | London: | Printed for T. Carnan, and F. Newbery, Junior, | at Number 65, in St. Paul's Church Yard. | MDCCLXXIV. The first of the Chinese Letters appeared in John Newbery's *Public Ledger* for 24 January 1760. They came out about twice a week, but until the appearance of No. IV, the series were not numbered. They were continued until 14 August 1761, their forthcoming republication, revised and corrected, 'in two volumes of the usual *Spectator* size,' being announced by a final note. They were eventually issued, 'Price 6s. bound' with a few additional letters, on Saturday, 1 May 1762. The publishers' names differ in different copies, some having John Newbery only. The date of the second edition is not given by Goldsmith's biographers; but an advertisement in *Lloyd's Evening Post*, 5 May 1766, states that a French translation had then 'gone through four Impressions.' An edition appeared at Dublin in 1769. Then came the 'third edition' as above.

Notes.—The notes are chiefly drawn from those prepared for the issue of the *Citizen of the World* in the 'Temple Library' by Mr. Austin Dobson. For this edition various small changes have been made.

3. *Escobar.*—Anthony Escobar y Mendoza, a famous Spanish Jesuit and casuist, 1589–1669. '*Escobar sait un chemin de velours,*' says the burden of the *ballade* which La Fontaine wrote against him.

3. *Caramuel.*—Joh. Caramuel de Lobkowitz, a Spanish controversialist, 1606–82.

3. *the same scale.*—Goldsmith had published a 'poetical scale' on the same plan in the *Literary Magazine* for January 1758.

5. *final quotation.*—From the *Greek Anthology*, i, 80. See also *Notes and Queries*, 16, vii, 98. In the Dublin edition of 1769 is added the following translation:

> 'Fortune and Hope adieu! I see my Port,
> Too long your dupe; be others now your Sport,'

which Percy adopted in his edition of 1801. With a popular Latin version of the original, Señor Gil Blas of Santillane concludes Book IX of his adventures:

> 'Inveni portum. Spes et Fortuna, valete.
> Sat me lusistis; ludite nunc alios.'

7. *Lien Chi Altangi.*—In 1757 Horace Walpole had published anonymously, *A Letter from Xo Ho, a Chinese Philosopher at London, to his friend Lien Chi, at Peking.* Perhaps this suggested Gold-smith's Lien Chi, if not the *Citizen of the World* itself.

7. *a poor philosophic wanderer.*—Johnson suggested *The Philo-sophic Wanderer* as a title for *The Traveller* (Forster's *Life of Gold-smith*, 1871, i, 368).

9. *a paltry piece of painting.*—i.e. the London signs, which practic-ally disappeared when, in 1764, houses began to be systematically numbered.

9. *I have seen . . . three blue boars.*—Cf. *Spectator*, No. 28: 'Our streets are filled with blue Boars, black Swans, and red Lions; not to mention flying Pigs, and Hogs in Armour.'

9. *Fum Hoam.*—In 1725 had been published *Chinese Tales; or, the Wonderful Adventures of the Mandarine, Fum Hoam*, translated from the French, 2 vols., 24mo.

10. *By every remove,* etc.—Cf. *The Traveller,* l. 10:

> 'And drags at each remove a lengthening chain.'

Cibber has a like thought in the *Comical Lovers,* 1707, Act v.

12. *I have seen a lady.*—Cf. Goldsmith's *Double Transformation,* 43–6:

> ''Tis true she dress'd with modern grace,
> Half naked at a ball or race;
> But when at home, at board or bed,
> Five greasy night-caps wrapp'd her head.'

As regards the last line, cf. the College Magnate in *Spectator*, No. 494, who wears 'half-a-dozen Night-Caps upon his Head.'

14. *The sailor,* etc.—This incident is to be found in John Byrom's *Tom the Porter,* where the interlocutors are the same.

16. *I therefore send a specimen.*—There is a certain similarity between what follows and the clever '*Relations Véritables de Différents Endroits d'Europe*' of Anthony Hamilton (see Prof. Saintsbury's *Essays on French Novelists,* 1891, p. 57).

16. *our twelve academies.*—'Jarchius has taken the trouble to give us a list of those clubs or academies [i.e. *the academies of Italy*], which amount to five hundred and fifty, each distinguished by somewhat whimsical in the name. The academies of Bologna, for instance, are divided into the Abbandonati, the Ausiosi, Ociosi, Arcadi, Confusi, Dubbiosi, etc. There are few of these who have not published their transactions, and scarce a member who is not looked upon as the most famous man in the world, at home' (*The Bee*, No. VI, 10 November 1759. See p. 406 *infra*).

16. *father Fudgi.*—This name is obviously coined from Mr. Burchell's immortal monosyllable (*Vicar of Wakefield*, Everyman's Library, pp. 56–8). See also Letter LI, *infra*, p. 141.

18. *We have seventeen flat-bottomed boats.*—During the Seven Years' War (see Letter XVII) invasion from France in this way was constantly expected. Cf. the last stanza of the once popular ballad of 'Captain [of Militia] Sir Dilberry Diddle':

> 'He dreamt, Fame reports, that he cut all the throats
> Of the French as they landed in *flat-bottomed boats*.'

and Letter CVII, p. 284 *infra*.

18. *Damien.*—*i.e.* Robert-François Damiens, a poor half-witted creature who was executed in March 1757, after horrible tortures, for attempting to assassinate Louis XV. An account of his trial was published at Paris in four volumes 12mo. This was summarized in the *Monthly Review* for July 1757, pp. 57–78, during the time of Goldsmith's bondage to Griffiths. Cf. also *The Traveller*, l. 436. Damiens's deed and tragedy form an exceedingly graphic chapter in Augustus Sala's clever *Strange Adventures of Captain Dangerous*, 1863, iii, pp. 154–80.

18. *Wanted an usher to an academy.*—Cf. *The Vicar of Wakefield*, Everyman's Library, p. 116; and *The Bee*, No. VI, 10 November 1759 (p. 397 *infra*), where Goldsmith is eloquent on the ills of Usherdom. He had himself been an usher in Dr. Milner's Academy at Peckham.

18. *Black and All Black.*—A famous racer. 'That famous horse Othello, alias Black and All Black' (*New Foundling Hospital for Wit*, 1784, v. 269).

18. *the Padereen mare.*—Another famous racer. 'There has been more money spent in the encouragement of the Padareen mare there [in Ireland] one season, than given in rewards to learned men since the times of Usher' (Goldsmith to Daniel Hodson in December 1757, Prior's *Life*, i, 248).

18. *born in Carrickfergus.*—Apart from the obvious joke, it might be mentioned that Steele's political opponents falsely accused him of being a native of Carrickfergus.

23. *the laws are cemented with blood.*—Cf. Letter LXXX (*infra*, p. 221); and *The Vicar of Wakefield*, Everyman's Library, p. 175: 'Our possessions are paled up with new edicts every day, and hung round with gibbets to scare every invader.' The severity of the penal laws much exercised Goldsmith. See also *Rambler*, 20 April 1751, and *London*, 1738, ll. 238–44, for Johnson's opinions on the same subject.

30. *When a tradesman dies.*—Cf. *The Good Natur'd Man*, Act I: 'We shall see something that will give us a good deal of pleasure, I promise you; old Ruggins, the curry-comb maker, lying in state; I'm told he makes a very handsome corpse.' Hogarth satirized this fashion in Plate VI of *A Harlot's Progress*.

31. *the employment of his whole life to deserve it !*—Cf. *The Vicar of Wakefield*, Everyman's Library, p. 7: 'I wrote a similar epitaph for my wife, though still living, in which I extolled her prudence, economy, and obedience till death. . . . It admonished my wife of her duty to me, and my fidelity to her; it inspired her with a passion for fame, and constantly put her in mind of her end.'

34. *one Pope, is he there ?*—Pope was buried at Twickenham, by his own desire, near his parents.

34. *they somewhat resemble the eunuchs.*—Cf. M. Alexis Piron's epitaph against the Abbé Des Fontaines:

> 'C'est l'eunuque au milieu du sérail;
> Il n'y fait rien, et nuit à qui veut faire.'

37. *somethingness.*—This version of *je ne sais quoi* is apparently coined by Goldsmith (Prof. Earle's *English Prose*, 1890, p. 221).

37. *that Chinese temple.*—Sir William Chambers's *Designs for Chinese Buildings*, 1757, had made pseudo-Chinese edifices fashionable. Cf. *The Cit's Country Box*, 1757:

> 'The trav'ler with amazement sees
> A temple, Gothic, or Chinese.
> With many a bell, and tawdry rag on,
> And crested with a sprawling dragon,' etc.
>
> (Lloyd's *Poetical Works*, 1774. i, 45.)

40. *the Pope.*—Cf. Prior's *Alma*, canto ii:

> 'Choose then, good Pope, at home to stay;
> Nor westward curious take thy way.
> Thy way unhappy shouldst thou take
> From Tyber's bank to Leman-lake;
> Thou art an aged priest no more,
> But a young flaring painted whore;
> Thy sex is lost: thy town is gone,
> No longer Rome, but Babylon.

43. *a very destructive war.*—The Seven Years' War, 1756–63, between France and England in North America.

46. *one perpetual anastomosis.*—This relic of Goldsmith's medical studies means a junction, or—in Johnsonese—an 'inosculation' of blood vessels.

49. *to find contentment.*—This tale was translated from the Chinese by Père Dentrecolles, a Jesuit missionary. An abstract of the original is given in Davis's *Chinese*, 1845, ii, 194–208. It was rendered fully in 1872 by Dr. Samuel Birch.

52. *Cardanus or Brunus.*—Jerome Cardan, 1501–76, was an Italian physician; Brunus=Giordano Bruno, 1550–1600.

52. *citizens of the world.*—This is the first use by Goldsmith of the title subsequently given to this correspondence. Bacon employs the phrase (Essay XIII): 'If a Man be Gracious and Courteous to Strangers, it shewes he is a *Citizen of the World*'; and Southey refers

in *The Doctor* to a book called *Ripley Revived* by *Eirenæus Philalethes, an Englishman styling himself Citizen of the World*. See also Letter XXIII, *infra*, p. 62.

52. *Freron.*—Élie-Catherine Fréron (1719–76), editor of *L'Année Littéraire*, begun 1754, and one of the principal writers in *Le Journal Étranger*.

57. *I have absolutely forgotten.*—Probably he had partly in mind Home's *Douglas*, which he had reviewed in the *Monthly Review*, May 1757.

58. *essaying an hundred obstacles.*—Experiencing? Perhaps Goldsmith was thinking of the French *essuyer*.

63. *by levelling a pill at the part.*—The reference is doubtless to the famous pill of Dr. Joshua Ward, which, says Fielding, 'flies at once to the particular Part of the Body on which you desire to operate' (*Tom Jones*, Bk. VIII, ch. ix).

67. *whose bulk is only*, etc.—Cf. *The Traveller*, 1764, l. 144:
'Its former strength was but plethoric ill.'

68. *a flourishing empire.*—Cf. *The Deserted Village*, 1770, ll. 265–8.

71. *my history.*—Many Goldsmith family traits are recalled in this narrative. It is like the writer himself to make his 'man in black' say that he generally 'dressed in brown' (p. 72, last par.).

77. *to boast of their former cruelty.*—'I was called the cruel Parthenissa,' says Mrs. Western in *Tom Jones*, Bk. XVII, ch. iv.

81. *he proceeded.*—The first form of the verses that follow is in a letter written by Goldsmith to his brother Henry (Percy, *Memoir*, 1801, pp. 53–9); in their last form they appear in *The Deserted Village*, ll. 227–36.

81. *Calvert's butt, and Parsons' black champaign.*—'British Burgundy,' otherwise 'entire butt beer' or porter.

82. *The royal game of goose.*—See Strutt's *Sports and Pastimes*, Bk. IV, ch. 2 (XXV).

82. *the twelve rules.*—The well-known maxims 'found in the study of King Charles the First, of Blessed Memory,' and common in Goldsmith's day as a broadside.

82. *brave Prince William.*—William Augustus, Duke of Cumberland, 1721–65; probably a silhouette.

82. *a cap by night.*—Cf. *The Deserted Village*, 1770, l. 230:
'A bed by night, a chest of drawers by day.'

92. *'the mountains.'*—This is a parody of the cheap Orientalism of the eighteenth century. Cf. 'Mr. Tibs' in Letter XXIX, who 'throws off an eastern tale to perfection' (*supra*, p. 80).

106. *a man of the first quality.*—Lawrence Shirley, Earl Ferrers, who was hanged at Tyburn, 5 May 1760, for the murder of his steward.

107. *a third time he was pardoned !*—Charles de Bourbon, Comte de Charolais (1700–60), is here referred to. 'Louis XV is reported to have told him when he came to solicit letters of grace for another wanton murder of a fellow-creature, that the pardon of whoever should kill the Count himself would be more readily granted' (Knight's Annotator, 1840).

108. *Ranelagh.*—Opened in May 1742, and by this time more popular than Vauxhall.

108. *a pair-royal of naturals.*—A point in the game of basset.

111. *the race of their poets is extinct.*—Gray, Beattie, and Churchill were the bards of 1760, and Goldsmith loved none of them. Smollett and Johnson had published no verse for years.

112. *Fancy restrained*, etc.—Montaigne has a similar thought (cf. Florio's *Montaigne*, Temple Classics, i, p. 204). Goldsmith had already used the idea in the *Present State of Polite Learning*, 1759, p. 151: 'Fancy, like a fountain, plays highest by diminishing the aperture.'

114. *a brag party.*—Brag was the popular game of cards at this date. Cf. *The Modern Fine Lady* of Soame Jenyns:

> 'Breakfast and auctions wear the morn away,
> Each evening gives an opera or play;
> Then *Brag's* eternal joys all night remain,
> And kindly usher in the morn again.'

118. *Poland* was not divided until 1772.

118. *Voltaire* did *not* die until May 1778. Goldsmith had written his *Memoirs* (*Lady's Magazine*, 1761).

120. *a tragedy.*—*Œdipe*, 'tragédie en cinq actes,' 1718.

120. *of his sister.*—Wilhelmina, Margravine of Baireuth, Voltaire's correspondent and ally. The italics are in the original (see *The Bee*, No. 1, p. 343).

125. *a silken rope.*—See note to p. 106 *supra*. Whether silken or not, the executioners fought for it (Walpole to Mann, 7 May 1760).

126. *between his toes.*—Goldsmith had perhaps in mind Cornelius Ketel of Amsterdam, who, without the excuse of deformity, took to painting with his feet (Walpole's *Anecdotes of Painting in England*, ch. vii). But M. Charles Felu, *Artiste Peintre*, of Antwerp, who died recently (*St. James's Gazette*, 7 February 1900), made many capable copies of the old masters in this way from necessity, as he had no arms. There is an extremely interesting account of him in Paget's *Paradoxes and Puzzles*, 1874, pp. 447–9.

142. *the review of reviews.*—Goldsmith's bookseller, it will be seen, anticipated an enterprise of the present day.

144. *The door must either.*—*Il faut qu'une porte soit ouverte ou fermée.*

147. *How often.*—This letter is aimed at the earlier volumes of *Tristram Shandy*. Goldsmith, the critic of critics (Letter xx), 'has suddenly become his own dreadful example,' as the late Andrew Lang pointed out in a delightful paper 'On an Inconsistency of Dr. Goldsmith's' (*Illustrated London News*, 26 November 1892).

149. *Tom Durfey.*—The 'facetious' and very popular author of *Wit and Mirth; or, Pills to Purge Melancholy*. 'I have . . . learned without book a song of Mr. Thomas D'Urfey's, who is your only poet of tolerable reputation in this country' (Pope to Henry Cromwell, 10 April 1710).

150. *as those first retire.*—A recollection of *Reculer pour mieux sauter*.

151. *Our pursuer.*—According to Forster (*Life of Goldsmith*, 1871, i, 262) the original of this excellent character was supposed to be one Thornton, formerly an officer in the army. He has also a sort of resemblance to Count Tag in Coventry's *Pompey the Little*, 1751; and he is certainly a connection of Goldsmith's own Lofty in the *Good Natur'd Man*.

157. *once more be free.*—'All the symptoms, which I have ever met with in history, previous to great changes and revolutions in government, now exist, and daily increase, in France. I am glad of it; the rest of Europe will be the quieter, and have time to recover' (Chesterfield's *Letters*, II, 332). This particular epistle is dated 25 December 1753, although it was not published until 1774.

159. *A nobleman.*—It was no doubt with a business eye to this prejudice in favour of authors of quality that Goldsmith's subsequent *History of England*, 1764, freely attributed to Lyttelton, Orrery and others, was put forward as 'a Series of Letters from a Nobleman to his Son.'

160. *a* visitation *dinner.*—In connection with the clergy as here depicted, and particularly 'Dr. Marrowfat' (*infra*, p. 162), Forster (*Life of Goldsmith*, 1871, i, 256) recalls the real Dr. Warner, who figures throughout Selwyn's correspondence, and of whose compliant and claret-drinking career a sketch was given in *Temple Bar* for December 1897.

163. *The soul subsides.*—A couplet from Pope's *Second Satire of the Second Book of Horace*, 1737, ll. 79, 80.

166. *I was born.*—The 'Miss S——d' of the footnote still remains unrevealed; but 'Lady W——e' was perhaps Horace Walpole's eccentric sister-in-law, Margaret Rolle, afterwards Countess of Orford, who lived much of an unworshipful life in Italy, and died at Pisa in 1781.

169. *From Lien Chi Altangi to Hingpo.*—This letter was originally headed *From the Same*.

173. *a modern character.*—'H. Spilman, Esq.,' has, apparently, no place in the British Museum Catalogue, so that his manuscript

memoirs (if they ever existed) never attained the dignity of print.
As Knight's Annotator says, Catherine's life is 'rendered somewhat
too romantic.'

177. *a Milo or a Maximin.*—Milo, or Milon, of Crotona, was a
Grecian athlete; Maximinus, a Roman Emperor, of whose strength
extraordinary tales are told.

178. *our Yau, they had their Sesostris.* — The Emperor Yao, to
whom the intercalation of the calendar is attributed, lived about
2300 B.C. Sesostris or Rameses (*circa* 1300 B.C.) was a King of
Egypt.

182. *these migrations.*—Goldsmith was fond of this idea. He
repeats it in another form, p. 209, l. 3; and he had used it in a letter
to his brother-in-law Hodson. In the *Critical Review* for June 1759,
he laughs at those professors whose 'whole lives passed away between
the fireside and the easy-chair,' and in the *Vicar of Wakefield*
(Everyman's Library, p. 2), he says 'all our adventures were by the
fireside, and all our migrations from the blue bed to the brown.'

187. *man wants but little.*—An acknowledged quotation from
Young's *Complaint*, 1743, Night iv, 9. Goldsmith also converted
it into lines 31–2 of *Edwin and Angelina* (*Vicar of Wakefield*, Everyman's Library, p. 39).

189. *some accounts of those personages.*—Rock (familiar to students
of Hogarth), Franks, and Walker, were all well-known characters.
'In the journals of the day,' says Prior, 'Franks advertised in bills
against Rock: "Be not *Rocked* into eternity by that vain and
impudent pretender *Dumpling Dick*, who still lives at the gate of
the inn where he was once porter." To which Rock rejoined: "If
you would avoid destruction, avoid the Old Bailey; for there lives
an old soldier discharged by the *beat of drum*, who has killed his
thousands, but not in battle: his pills are much more fatal than
were his bullets."'

190. *with his breast open.*—Cf. *Tatler*, No. 246: 'There is a fat
Fellow whom I have long remarked wearing his Breast open in the
midst of Winter, out of an Affectation of Youth.'

192. *a flat-bottomed boat.*—Cf. p. 18 *supra.*

192. *the* epidemic terror *which now prevails.*—During the summer
months of 1760 hydrophobia was unusually prevalent; and in August
orders were issued by the Lord Mayor to kill all stray dogs. The
journals of the day abound in references to the subject, and oppor-
tune Mr. John Newbery was promptly in the field with *A Treatise of
Canine Madness*, by Dr. James of the Fever Powder.

192. *with boots and buff gloves.*—'Boots and thick gloves are
thought such a preservative against the bites of mad dogs, that a
person counted not less than forty people that he met so equipped,
between Temple-Bar and St. Paul's.—This may prove no bad
preservative, tho' troublesome in hot weather' (*Lloyd's Evening Post*,
27–29 August 1760).

193. *gone down to be dipt in the salt water.*—This, combined with other treatment, was a popular remedy in the pre-Pasteurian days. 'By accounts from the several bathing places along our coasts, there have been more persons dipped on this account [i.e. bites from mad dogs] this summer, than has been known for any five years preceding' (*Lloyd's Evening Post*, 30 July to 1 August 1760).

194. *smothered between two beds.*—Suffocation and bleeding to death are said to have been resorted to in hopeless cases. Instances of each are reported in *Lloyd's Evening Post* for August 1760.

194. *one of the English poets.*—Otway, *Venice Preserved*, 1682, Act II, sc. ii.

197. *a garden.*—Vauxhall, at this date the chief summer evening attraction of the middle-class London sight-seer. Most people, like the pawnbroker's widow, made a point of visiting it once during the season.

198. *a natural aversion to the water.*—The customary approach to the Gardens from the Middlesex side of the Thames, was by wherry to Vauxhall Stairs. 'The latter I like much the best,' says Lady Jane Coke, in 1751, speaking of Ranelagh and Vauxhall, 'both from the place itself, *and the going by water to it*' (*Letters*, 1899, 83); and Smollett, in 1770, makes the bolder spirits of Mr. Matthew Bramble's party in *Humphrey Clinker* take a wherry from Ranelagh Stairs.

198. *the last night.*—The Vauxhall season lasted from May to August. The present Chinese Letter appeared in the *Public Ledger* for 2 September 1760.

198. *Crooked-lane,*—like the Kent Street of the author's Madame Blaize, must have been especially familiar to him, for he mentions it again in Act I of *The Good Natur'd Man*. It is a turning out of Cannon Street.

199. *the waterworks.*—This was not, as might be supposed, the playing of fountains, but a 'moving picture,' which, for a few minutes, included a genuine cascade. It is described in the *Gentleman's Magazine* for August 1765: 'The exact appearance of water is seen flowing down a declivity; and, turning the wheel of the mill, it rises up in foam at the bottom, and then glides away.'

199. *she once praised the painting.*—Hogarth, rather doubtfully, is credited with some of these. But probably the majority were by his friend, Frank Hayman. There was a picture, 'enlightened to the front with globes,' at the back of each of the old supper-boxes in the Grove.

201. *with the horns.*—The French horns, a special feature of the Vauxhall programme. Cf. Letter LV, p. 155 *supra*.

201. *the little encouragements given to matrimony.*—This paper, which in the 'Contents' is entitled 'The Marriage Act censured,' is aimed at Lord Hardwicke's measure of 26 Geo. II, c. 33 (1753). It

was said to be ill-drawn, and was, perhaps of necessity, unpopular, but it did away, *inter alia*, with the scandalous Fleet marriages.

204. *From Lien Chi to Fum Hoam.*—This was originally inaccurately addressed to Hingpo.

205. *If I should judge.*—Cf. *The Good Natur'd Man*, Act 1, where Honeywood speaks much to this effect.

215. *Those of London.*—See note, p. 9 *supra*.

216. *the birth-night.*—i.e. the evening of the King's birthday, when all the world appeared in new costumes. 'New clothes on the birthday were the fashion for all loyal people. Swift mentions the custom several times. Walpole is constantly speaking of it; laughing at the practice, but having the very finest clothes from Paris, nevertheless.' So says Thackeray, who goes on to quote the following from No. 3 of Henry Fielding's *True Patriot* (1745): 'My little girl entered my bed-chamber, and put an end to my dream by pulling open my eyes, and telling me that the tailor had just brought home my clothes for his Majesty's birthday' (*The Four Georges*, 1866, 96–97). See also *infra*, p. 261, l. 1.

217. *a rigadoon.*—A dance for two persons. 'This so enlivened me, that I led him by the hand into the next room where we danced a *rigadoon* together' (*Guardian*, No. 154).

218. *Upon their roads.*—'On every hillock is a windmill, a crucifix, or a Virgin Mary dressed in flowers, and a sarcenet robe; one sees not many people or carriages on the road; now and then indeed you meet a strolling friar, a countryman with his great muff, or a woman riding astride on a little ass, with short petticoats, and a great head-dress of blue wool' (Gray's *Works*, by Gosse, 1884, ii, 18, 19.) The date is 1739.

218. *riding without a side saddle.*—Cf. extract above from Gray's Correspondence.

219. *her copper tail.*—i.e. her train, probably trimmed by the copper, or 'St. Martin's' lace, for which, in Strype's time, Blow-bladder Street was famous.

219. *Two singing women.*—Mrs. Vincent (Drury Lane) and Miss Brent (Covent Garden), who, at this time, divided the suffrages of the Town as Polly Peachum in the *Beggar's Opera*. (See also Letter LXXXV, p. 234 *infra*.)

220. *One player shines.*—Cf. *The Vicar of Wakefield* (Everyman's Library, p. 103): 'It is not the composition of the piece, but the number of starts and attitudes that may be introduced into it that elicits applause.'

224. *dock their horses.*—Voltaire referred to this when he said that the English cut off with the same scissors the heads of their kings and the tails of their horses. Richardson's 'man of True Honour' declined to fall in with this latter fashion. 'His horses,' said Miss Harriet Byron, 'are not *docked*; their tails are only tied up when they are on the road' (*Grandison*, Letter XXXVI).

228. *Locman.*—An Abyssinian philosopher, mentioned in the Koran.

231. *instruments of debauchery.*—This was true of the literature which at this date constituted the staple material of the then recently established circulating libraries. 'A man,' says the heroine's father in Colman's *Polly Honeycombe*, 1760, 'might as well turn his Daughter loose in Covent garden as trust the cultivation of her mind to A Circulating Library.' Colman, in his Preface, gives a long list of these worthless works. Some editors have thought that the greater part of this letter was Goldsmith's own. But it is all in Du Halde's great folio of 1735.

232. *of fortitude.*—Cf. *The Present State of Polite Learning*, 1759, p. 142.

233. *the great Cervantes died of hunger.*—Neither Mr. H. E. Watts nor Mr. Fitzmaurice Kelly says anything of this, though the author of *Don Quixote* was undoubtedly poor.

233. *Vaugelas.*—Claude Favre, baron de Vaugelas, 1585–1650.

233. *Cassander.*—François Cassandre, d. 1698.

233. *no longer depend on the Great.*—In 1760 'the noble patron' was being supplanted by 'the public'; and the day of subscription editions, such as those of Prior and Gay, was on the wane. Goldsmith himself was never indebted to assistance of this kind. His *Polite Learning* and *Vicar* were issued without dedications; *The Traveller* was inscribed to his brother, one of the 'inferior clergy'; and *The Deserted Village* and *She Stoops to Conquer* were tributes to Reynolds and Johnson, his personal friends.

236. *On seeing Mrs.* * * *.—This is generally included in Goldsmith's poems. But it must be remembered that he gives it as a specimen of the inane panegyrical verses of his time.

249. *to blow the German flute.*—Goldsmith evidently, like Mr. Richard Swiveller, regarded music as a specific for low spirits. In the *Vicar of Wakefield* (Everyman's Library, p. 221), Squire Thornhill, when utterly discredited, devoted himself to 'learning to blow the French horn.'

249. *the Ambusheer.*—Probably the Man in Black means '*embouchure*,' a term applied to the mouthing of wind instruments.

250. *cut paper.*—Cutting paper was a popular eighteenth-century accomplishment. Mrs. Delany was a proficient in it, and Horace Walpole had some specimens of her mosaics at Strawberry Hill. There are others at the British Museum. Lady Burlington was also an adept in this art.

261. *after a reign of many years.*—His Majesty King George the Second died on the morning of 25 October 1760, 'in the 77th year of his age, and the 34th of his reign; beloved, honoured, and regretted by his subjects for his eminent and royal virtues.' So spoke ((in the *London Gazette* for 26 October 1760) the 'full [official] voice which circles round the grave.'

262. *the grey undress frock.*—The undress Court mourning formerly prescribed by the Lord Chamberlain was a 'dark grey frock'; the dress, 'black cloth, without buttons on the sleeves and pockets, plain muslin or long lawn cravats and weepers, shamoy shoes and gloves, crape hat-bands, and black swords and buckles.' The officers of the army were to wear 'red faced with black'; the officers of the fleet 'blue faced with black.'

268. *may I die.*—(See also '*Strike . . .*' on same page.) Such asseverations as these of Mr. Tibbs are happily not essential in our day to the accurate presentment of humorous character. But—to judge by the novelists and essayists—excessive swearing must have been common in all classes of eighteenth-century life, both with men and women.

275. *everything else but her honour.*—Goldsmith may have had in mind Hogarth's *Lady's Last Stake,* painted in 1759 for Lord Charlemont, and exhibited at Spring Gardens in May 1761. But references to this 'last stake' at cards are not uncommon in eighteenth-century literature (see *World,* 11 December 1755).

276. *We long to die in that spot.*—Cf. *The Deserted Village,* 1770, ll. 95–6:

> 'I still had hopes, my long vexations pass'd,
> Here to return—and die at home at last.'

277. *night gown.*—This was the morning or dressing gown referred to *supra,* p. 216, l. 23. 'Mr. *Trulliber,*' says Fielding . . . 'clothed himself in an old *Night-Gown,* being the Dress in which he always saw his Company at home' (*Joseph Andrews,* vol. i, ch. xiv). Cf. also Prior's *Malone,* 1860, p. 410: 'He was sitting in his counting house in his night-gown.'

277. *Father Matthew.*—Matthew Ricci, an Italian Jesuit, went to China in 1583, but did not obtain an introduction to the Emperor until 1601. His mathematical attainments secured him a footing at Court.

279. *the young King's coronation.*—George II was not crowned until September 1761, so that this paper, which appeared in February 1761, is anticipatory.

280. *Pageants, says Bacon, are pretty things.*—What Bacon says is: 'These Things are but Toyes. . . . But yet, since Princes will have such Things, it is better, they should be Graced with Elegancy, than Daubed with Cost' (*Essay* XXXVII, 'Of Masques and Triumphs').

284. *a herring subscription.*—The British White Herring Fishery Company of 1750, from which a mine of wealth was anticipated by speculators. Goldsmith had referred to it before in *The Bee,* No. VI, 10 November 1759 (see p. 405 *infra*): 'A few years ago the herring fishery employed all Grub-street; it was the topic in every coffee-house, and the burden of every ballad. We were to drag up oceans of gold from the bottom of the sea; we were to supply all Europe with herrings upon our own terms.'

286. *an imposture.*—Humboldt did not think so. Gemelli was a Neapolitan whose *Travels round the World* were published in 1699–1700. It was the Jesuit missionaries who cast a doubt on their authenticity.

292. *Among the number.*—Jacob Henriquez was a projector who advertised in the *Public Ledger*; Victor was Treasurer of Drury Lane Theatre; and Lockman, Secretary and Laureate of the Herring Fishery (see note to p. 284, l. 30). In Hogarth's *Beer Street*, 1751, the fishwomen are represented singing one of Lockman's herring ballads, which had created a *furore* at Vauxhall Gardens.

294. *the settlers of the newest pattern.*—Goldsmith, like Anstey, Walpole, Smollett, Hogarth and others, seems to have joined in the popular attacks on the followers of Wesley and Whitefield, the last of which, Foote's *Minor*, with its character of Mother Cole, had recently been produced at the Haymarket. As Knight's Annotator well observes, he 'does not appear to have justly appreciated the moral regeneration which Methodism was producing amongst the poorer classes in England, and which at length stimulated the clergy, and roused them from their slumbering state to renewed zeal and usefulness.'

299. *an author.*—Clearly Charles Churchill of the *Rosciad*. It is doubtful whether the epigrams which follow at pp. 301 and 302 are by Goldsmith. The first had aready appeared in the *Public Ledger*. The 'G. C.' and 'R. L.' are George Colman and Churchill's friend, Robert Lloyd.

310. *Vanini.*—Lucilio Vanini, an Italian priest, was burnt at Toulouse as an atheist in 1619. Voltaire contests the justice of his fate, in a paper which Goldsmith translated in *The Bee*, No. VI, 10 November 1759.

311. *The clock just struck two.*—This letter, which is reprinted, with some omissions, from *The Bee* for 27 October 1759 (No. IV), is there entitled, as in the 'Contents' to this volume, 'A City Night-Piece'—a name no doubt suggested by the 'Night-Piece on Death' of Parnell, whose life Goldsmith afterwards wrote.

311. *Let me no longer waste,* etc.—Cf. Parnell, ll. 1–4:

> 'By the blue taper's trembling light,
> No more I waste the wakeful night,
> Intent with endless view to pore
> The schoolmen and the sages o'er.'

311. *The distant watch-dog.*—Cf. *The Vicar of Wakefield* (Everyman's Library, p. 143). 'No sounds were heard but of the shrilling cock, and the deep-mouthed watch-dog at hollow distance'; and *The Deserted Village*, l. 121:

> 'The watch-dog's voice that bay'd the whispering wind.'

312. *These poor shivering females.*—Cf. *The Deserted Village*, ll. 325–6:

> 'Are these thy serious thoughts!—Ah, turn thine eyes
> Where the poor houseless *shivering female* lies.'

312. *Perhaps, now lying.*—Cf. *The Deserted Village*, ll. 331–2:

> 'Now lost to all; her friends, her virtue fled,
> Near her betrayer's door she lays her head,' etc.

315. *The misfortunes of the great.*—This essay is reprinted, with variations, from *The British Magazine* for June 1760.

323. *My long residence.*—This paper, like Hogarth's *Five Days' Peregrination*, and Fielding's *Letter from a French Gentleman to his friend at Paris*, is an obvious skit upon the trivialities of travellers.

325. *White Conduit House.*—At Pentonville. 'Time was,' says the Rev. Charles Jenner,

> 'When graver citizens, in suits of brown
> Lined every dusty avenue to town,
> Or led the children and the loving spouse
> To spend two shillings at *White Conduit House.*'

Goldsmith was well acquainted with the neighbourhood, and with this particular resort, once the scene of an embarrassing adventure, in which he figures forlornly as an entertainer without funds (see Forster's 'Life,' 1871, i, 264).

THE BEE

The numbers at the beginning of paragraphs refer to the pages.

Text.—*The Bee* originally appeared in threepenny weekly numbers from 6 October to 24 November 1759. It was issued in December as a *duodecimo* volume under the title, *The Bee. Being Essays on the Most Interesting Subjects*. The publisher was J. Wilkie, at the *Bible* in St. Paul's Churchyard. The following is a list of the 'Contents,' those papers which have been omitted on the present occasion being wholly in *italic* type:

[No. 1.] Introduction.

> *Epigram on a beautiful Youth struck blind with Lightning. Imitated from the Spanish.* [See *Poems* (Everyman's Library), p. 54.]

> *Another. In the same Spirit. (Latin, not printed.)*

> Remarks on our Theatres.

> The Story of ALCANDER and SEPTIMIUS. Translated from a Byzantine Historian.

> *A Letter from Mr* VOLTAIRE *to* M. D'ARGET, *of Lausanne. (Not printed.)*

> A Letter from a Traveller.

> A short Account of the late Mr. MAUPERTUIS.

[No. 2.] On Dress.

> Some Particulars relating to CHARLES XII not commonly known.

> *The Gift. To* IRIS, *in Bow Street, Covent Garden.* [See *Poems* (Everyman's Library), p. 54.]

> Happiness in a great Measure dependant upon Constitution.
> On our Theatres.

> *A Letter from Mr* VOLTAIRE *to* M. TIRIOT. *(Not printed.)*

[No. 3.] On the Use of Language.

> The History of HYPASIA.

> On Justice and Generosity.

> *On Wit. By Mr* VOLTAIRE. *(Not printed.)*

> *A Sonnet.* [See *Poems* (Everyman's Library), p. 56.]

> Some Particulars relating to Father FREIJO.

[No. 4.] Miscellaneous.

A Flemish Tradition.

The Sagacity of some Insects.

The Characteristics of Greatness.

A City Night-Piece. [See *Citizen of the World*, p. 311 *supra*.]

An Elegy on that Glory of her Sex, Mrs. MARY BLAIZE. [See *Poems* (Everyman's Library), p. 57.]

[No. 5.] On Political Frugality.

A Reverie.

A Word or two on the late Farce, called *High Life Below Stairs.*

On Unfortunate Merit.

[No. 6.] On Education.

On the Contradictions of the World. From Voltaire. (Not printed.)

On the Instability of Worldly Grandeur.

Some Account of the Academies of Italy.

[No. 7.] Of Eloquence.

Custom and Laws compared.

Of the Pride and Luxury of the Middling Class of People.

SABINUS and OLINDA.

The Sentiments of a Frenchman on the Temper of the English. (Not printed.) Copied with little alteration, from the Abbé Le Blanc's Letters on the English and French Nations, London, 1747, i, pp. 132–6.

[No. 8.] *On Deceit and Falsehood. (Not printed.) Copied, with some variation, from The Humourist, 3rd ed. 1724.*

An Account of the Augustan Age of England. (Not printed— Goldsmith's authorship being somewhat doubtful.)

Of the Opera in England.

The above comprise all the papers included in the original 'Contents' of *The Bee* of 1759. In the case of those papers reprinted in the *Essays* of 1766, the text here given (with the exception of that of the following Introduction) is the later one. (See notes to separate Essays.)

331. *Introduction.*—This was afterwards included in the *Essays*, but while the other papers are printed from the later versions, it has been judged expedient to give this one as it appeared in No. 1 of *The Bee.*

331. *Vastly low.*—'Low,' as opposed to 'genteel,' was a popular form of eighteenth-century criticism, especially with the would-be votaries of 'high life.' Goldsmith had already touched upon the subject in the *Present State of Polite Learning*, 1759, pp. 154–5: 'By the power of one single monosyllable, our critics have almost

got the victory over humour amongst us. Does the poet paint the absurdities of the vulgar; then he is *low*: does he exaggerate the features of folly, to render it more thoroughly ridiculous, he is then very *low*. In short, they have proscribed the comic or satyrical muse from every walk but high life, which, though abounding in fools as well as the humbler station, is by no means so fruitful in absurdity.' 'There's nothing comes out but the most lowest stuff in nature,' says Lady Blarney later in the *Vicar* (Everyman's Library, p. 57); and in 1768, the *London Chronicle* declared Goldsmith's own Bailiff Scene in the *Good Natur'd Man* to be 'uncommonly low.' He was in good company, according to George Borrow. 'Homer himself has never yet entirely recovered from the injury he received by Lord Chesterfield's remark, that the speeches of his heroes were frequently exceedingly low' (*Lavengro*, ch. xli).

332. *a dab at an index.*—i.e. an expert. 'The Great Men themselves, who are (to fetch a Phrase from School, a Place not improperly mentioned on this Occasion) great DABS at this kind of Facetiousness' (Fielding's *Essay on Conversion, Miscellanies*, 1743, i, p. 173).

332. *Colonel Charteris.*—An infamous profligate, satirized alike by Pope's pen and Hogarth's brush. He died in 1732; and Arbuthnot made him the subject of a scathing epitaph.

332. *Like the Bee.*—The motto of *The Bee* was from Lucretius:

'Floriferis ut Apes in saltibus omnia libant,
Omnia Nos itidem.'

332. *a bon-mot.*—This sentence suggests the 'Different longitude, different latitude' of the dramatist T. W. Robertson. See also Shakespeare on 'a jest's prosperity' (*Love's Labour 's Lost*, Act v, sc. ii, l. 871).

333. *four extraordinary pages of letterpress.*—Goldsmith repeats this jibe at the artless seductions of his contemporaries in a later paper (see p. 369): 'All this, together with four extraordinary pages of *letterpress*, a beautiful map of England, and two prints curiously coloured from nature, I fancied might touch their very souls' (*Bee*, No. IV, *Saturday*, 27 October 1759).

333. *sad stuff.*—These were the words which, according to Mrs. Carter, the 'fine folks' applied to Fielding's *Amelia* (*Letters*, 3rd ed. 1819, i, p. 368).

333. *Bayes, in the 'Rehearsal.'*—Goldsmith had probably in mind this passage from Act III, sc. i of Buckingham's play: 'My Play is my Touch-stone. When a man tells me such a one is a person of parts; is he so, say I? What do I do, but bring him presently to see this Play: If he likes it, I know what to think of him; if not, your most humble Servant, Sir, I 'll no more of him upon my word, I thank you' (Arber's reprint, 1869, p. 73).

334. *Our theatres are now opened.*—The Haymarket opened on the 17th September with a Burletta entitled *Galligantus*; Drury Lane on the 22nd with Farquhar's *Recruiting Officer*; and Covent Garden on the 24th with the *Miser* (see note to p. 335).

334. *Grub Street.*—The Grub Street of fact is now Milton Street, Cripplegate. Johnson, who defined it in the *Dictionary* as 'a street . . . much inhabited by writers of small histories, dictionaries, and temporary poems,' according to Miss Burney, had never been there himself (*Diary*, i, p. 415).

334. *as a manager, so avaricious.*—This was a common charge against Garrick (cf. Birkbeck Hill's *Boswell*, 1887, iii, p. 71).

334. *Palmer.*—John Palmer, the Elder, died in May 1768. He was an excellent Plume in Farquhar's *Recruiting Officer*, but a coxcomb on and off the Stage.

> 'PALMER! Oh! PALMER tops the janty part,'

says Churchill (*Poems*, 4th ed. 1769, i, 3).

334. *Holland.*—Charles Holland died of smallpox in December 1769, aged 36. Churchill accuses him in the *Rosciad* of being merely a servile copy of Garrick, some of whose favourite characters he played successfully.

> 'I hate e'en GARRICK thus at second hand.'

(*Poems*, 4th ed. 1769, i, p. 17.)

334. *Shuter.*—Edward, or more familiarly, Ned Shuter (1728–76), who afterwards played Croaker in the *Good Natur'd Man*, and Mr. Hardcastle in *She Stoops to Conquer*. Garrick called him 'the greatest comic genius he had ever seen,' and Dibdin says he was 'one of the best burletta singers in the world.'

335. *Though it would be inexcusable.*—This—technically known as 'gagging'—was Shuter's worst fault:

> 'SHUTER, who never car'd a single pin
> Whether he left out nonsense, or put in.'
>
> (Churchill's *Poems*, 4th ed. 1769, i, p. 31.)

335. *The Miser.*—This was a version by Henry Fielding of Molière's *L'Avare*, first produced in 1733. It entirely superseded the earlier essay of Shadwell (1671); and is recognized by French criticism as practically faithful to the original. On 24 September, shortly before the date of this paper, it had been played at Covent Garden with Shuter as Lovegold, the English Harpagon.

335. *to pick up a pin.*—The pin-picking is not referred to by Molière's editors, but *'le jeu de la bougie'* was a tradition of the French Stage.

336. *The 'Mock Doctor.'*—This again, was Fielding's adaptation (1732) from Molière of the *Médecin malgré lui*. It was played at Drury Lane on 25 September (when Goldsmith probably saw it) and 5 October (the day preceding the date of this number of *The Bee*), with Yates and Mrs. Abington as the principal characters, Gregory and Dorcas.

336. *Riccoboni.*—Riccoboni's book was translated in 1741 under the title of *An Historical and Critical Account of the Theatres of*

Europe, etc. . . . By the famous Lewis Riccoboni of the Italian Theatre at Paris. In his chapter on the English Theatre (pp. 160–181) he says: 'The Architecture of their Play-house is beautiful and commodious. All the Pit is in Form of an Amphitheatre, where both Sexes sit promiscuously, which afford [*sic*] a very agreeable Sight. There is but one Row of Boxes, and above are two Galleries with Benches one above another, where People sit.' As an example 'to what an Exactness the *English* Comedians carry the Imitation of Nature,' he gives an account of an English actor of twenty-six whom he had seen at Lincoln's Inn Fields, and who not only acted but looked the part of an old man to perfection.

336. *our little pages*.—M. Pierre Grosley, who visited London in 1765, was much exercised by the little trainbearers (*caudataires*), who ran about the stage with the trains of the heroines. Addison, fifty-four years before, had commented in the *Spectator* (18 April 1711) upon the same anomaly.

336. *dirty-shirted guards*.—This is apparently a reference to the pair of sentinels whom it was the practice to station upon the stage during the performance of a play. In chap. lix of *The Virginians*, Thackeray makes one of them moved to tears by Mrs. Woffington's acting of Lady Randolph in Home's tragedy of *Douglas*.

337. *the Wapping Landlady*.—This is a character in a farce called *The Humours of Wapping*, 1703, which, according to the *Daily Advertiser*, was still being acted in 1744. A scene with a similar title, and probably from the same play, was painted by Frank Hayman for Vauxhall Gardens, and engraved by L. Truchy.

337. *pining in the character of Jane Shore*.—It is not impossible that his reference is to Mrs. Pritchard, who acted this part as late as 1758 (2 November), although she was forty-seven, and by no means slim. As to this last point, cf. Churchill's *Rosciad* (*Poems*, 4th ed. 1769, i, p. 39):

> 'In Comedy—'Nay, there,' cries Critic, 'hold.
> PRITCHARD's for Comedy too fat and old.
> Who can, with patience, bear the gray coquette,
> Or force a laugh with over-grown Julett?''

337. *Alcander and Septimius*.—Their story is to be found in the *Decameron* of Boccaccio, Tale 8, Day 10. The heroes are there called Titus and Gisippus. The text here given is that of the *Essays* of 1766 (No. II).

340. *A Letter from a Traveller*.—This is thought to be fictitious, in spite of the head-note.

341. *a philosophic vagabond*.—This is the name which, in the 'Contents' of the *Vicar of Wakefield*, Goldsmith gives to George Primrose (ch. xx). Johnson wished to christen *The Traveller* the 'Philosophic Wanderer' (Forster's *Life of Goldsmith*, 1871, i, 368), the name which Lien Chi Altangi gives to himself (*Citizen of the World*, p. 7 *supra*).

342. *Maupertuis.*—Pierre-Louis-Moreau de Maupertuis, 1698–1759 (27 July).

343. *if I remember right.*—'des Astres' should be 'de la terre.'

343. *Micromegas* (the 'little great'), appeared in 1752. It is in the *genre* of Gulliver.

343. *On Dress.*—This is reprinted in the *Essays*, No. XV; and is here reproduced from the edition of 1766.

344. *Sweeping trains.*—Goldsmith devotes a special letter in the *Citizen of the World* to this. See Letter LXXXI, pp. 223–5 *supra*.

344. *trollopees.*—The trollopee, according to Fairholt (*Costume in England*, by Dillon, 1885, ii, p. 400), was 'a loose flowing gown, sometimes gathered up behind and open in front, much worn as a morning dress by ladies about 1750.' Cf. the *Connoisseur* for 19 August 1756 (by William Cowper): 'These were most woefully eclipsed by a burgess's daughter, just come from London, who appeared in a *Trolloppe* or Slammerkin, with treble ruffles to the cuffs, pinked and gymped, and the sides of the petticoat drawn up in festoons.'

344. *her white negligée.*—This also was a loose gown. Cf. the *Early Diary* of Frances Burney, 1889, i, xlviii: '. . . her Ladyship has Bought the silk for a *Negligée* for me, and a slip for Sukey' (1764).

345. *your monstrous muff.*—See Hogarth's *Swearing a Child*, 1735; *Rake's Progress*, 1735, Pt. iv; and *Taste in High Life*, 1742, for examples of men wearing muffs. In November 1766, my Lord of March and Ruglen (the March of *The Virginians*) writes to George Selwyn at Paris: 'The muff you sent me by the Duke of Richmond I like prodigiously; vastly better than if it had been *tigré*, or of any glaring colour: several are now making from it' (Jesse's *Selwyn*, 1843, ii, 71).

346. *the young doctor a big wig.*—Doctors wore tye-wigs. 'A physician,' writes Fielding in 1732, 'can no more prescribe without a full wig, than without a fee' (*The Mock Doctor*, sc. v).

346. *scrubs.*—Mean-looking, or second-rate people. 'There was none at the confession but a set of poor *scrubs* of us, who could sin only in our wills' (*Guardian*, No. 65).

346. *lutestring trollopee.*—For *trollopee*, see p. 344 *supra*. Lutestring, a corruption of *lustring*, was a 'lustrous or bright silk much used in the last [eighteenth] century for ladies' dresses, introduced into this country by the French refugees who fled here after the revocation of the Edict of Nantes' (Draper's *Dictionary*). 'Within my Memory the price of *Lutestring* is raised above two Pence in a Yard' (*Spectator*, No. 21).

346. *bunters.*—Rag-pickers. Cf. *Low Life* (1752), p. 5: '*Bunters* with bits of Candles between their Fingers, and Baskets on their Heads, rummaging the dirty Dunghills . . . for Rags and Bones. . . .' Again, p. 16: 'Great Trafficking among the *Bunters* in *Rotten Row* . . . for the Rags and Bones picked up that Morning.'

346–7. *White Conduit House* (or Tea Gardens) was a popular suburban resort of the eighteenth-century middle classes. It stood until 1849 on the east side of Penton Street, Pentonville. It was a favourite haunt with Goldsmith, who mentions it in the *Citizen of the World* (p. 325 *supra*). From the old advertisements, tea, sugar, and milk was 3d. per head, so that 'sixpennyworth' represents the entire outlay of Mrs. Roundabout's 'marriageable daughters.'

347. *my Lord Bantam's Indian sheep.*—Cf. the 'bell-wether of Bantam' in *Citizen of the World* (p. 224 *supra*). The Syrian and Egyptian sheep have often enormous fleshy tails which sometimes require to be supported.

351. *Happiness*, etc.—This is reprinted in the *Essays*, No. III, and is here reproduced from the edition of 1766.

351. *cross purposes.*—An eighteenth-century game mentioned, but not defined, in *Spectator*, No. 245. Incidentally, it was played before the 18th century (Pepys played it in 1666), and was perpetuated in the 19th century in slightly different guise.

351. *questions and commands.*—This game, of which there is a description in Sydney's *Social Life in England*, 1892, p. 392, is also mentioned in the *Vicar of Wakefield* (Everyman's Library, p. 54). See also *Spectator*, No. 245; and *Lover*, No. 13: 'I might have been a King at *Questions and Commands.*'

351. *Our old dairymaid.*—Peggy Golden: cf. *Vicar of Wakefield* (Everyman's Library, p. 21); and Goldsmith's letter to his brother-in-law, Daniel Hodson, 27 December 1757.

352. *the famous Cardinal de Retz.*—Jean-François-Paul de Gondi, Cardinal de Retz, 1614–79, a prominent instigator of the Fronde. His *Mémoires*, says M. St. Jal (*Dictionnaire Critique*, 1872, 2nd ed., p. 1056), form '*un des livres les plus curieux, les plus piquants, les meilleurs qui se soient produits sur cette époque d'intrigues, de guerre sérieuse et folle, de malheurs publics dus à l'ambition de quelques grands, de haines vigoureuses, de cruels et de gais pamphlets.*' It was very popular in the eighteenth century. Lady Hervey (*Letters*, 1821, 73) says she had 'read it six or seven times over'; and Lord Chesterfield embodies a large number of the Cardinal's political Maxims in Letter CCXXIII to his son. It is included in the *Grands Écrivains de France* series, and there is a translation in Everyman's Library.

354. *Mademoiselle Clairon.*—Claire-Joseph-Hippolyte de Latude, otherwise Mlle. Clairon (1723-1803). Garrick, who saw her in 1752 'in the dawn of her reputation,' and afterwards in 1765, when she retired from the stage, professed the greatest admiration for her talents, while Gibbon (*Autobiographies*, 1896, pp. 204, 262) speaks of her 'consummate art.'

355. *the singing women at Sadler's Wells.*—Sadler's Wells was even then a place of popular entertainment. Its chief 'singing women' at this date (1759), according to the *Public Advertiser*, were Mrs. Dennis and Mrs. Edwards.

355. *never to take notice of the audience.*—Cf. Lloyd's *Actor* (*Works*, 1774, i, p. 18):

> 'Divest yourself of hearers, if you can,
> And strive to speak, and be the very man.
> Why should the well-bred actor wish to know
> Who sits above to-night, or who below?'

355. *Belvidera* is the chief female character in Otway's *Venice Preserved*, 1682.

355. *Mrs. Cibber*, 1710-66, was Thomas Arne's sister, and married Colley Cibber's reprobate son, Theophilus. As an actress, she had more sensibility than beauty:

> 'In Cibber's look commanding sorrows speak,
> And call the tear fast trick'ling down my cheek.'
>
> (Lloyd's *Actor*, *Works*, 1774, i, p. 18.)

355. *his shilling's worth.*—This, at Drury Lane and Covent Garden, was the price of the second or 'upper gallery,' the chosen resort of all 'gentlemen's gentlemen.' The first Gallery was two shillings; the Pit two, or three, shillings.

355. *I remember to have known.*—This anecdote is told of Thomas Sheridan, father of R. B. Sheridan. Goldsmith had already referred to it in a letter to Mrs. Lawder (Jane Contarine), 15 August 1758.

356. *On the Use of Language.*—This is reprinted in the *Essays*, No. V, and is here reproduced from the edition of 1766.

356. *the true use of speech.*—This idea has been employed both before and after Goldsmith—after him, notably, by Voltaire. If it be necessary that he should have borrowed from a predecessor, he may have had in mind Young's *Love of Fame, the Universal Passion*, 6th ed. 1763, Sat. ii, p. 39:

> 'Where nature's end of language is declin'd,
> And men *talk only to conceal the mind*.'

He was certainly familiar with Young, whose poem first appeared in 1725-8.

356. *Seneca himself allows.*—See Seneca *De Beneficiis*, Lib. II, cap. xv, xvi, and xvii.[1]

356. *Ovid finely compares.*—Goldsmith had perhaps in view *Tristia*, Lib. II, 83-6.[1]

359. *just nicked the time.*—i.e. just hit upon the time. 'The just season of doing things must be nick'd and all accidents improved' (L'Estrange in Johnson).

359. *fetches.*—i.e. Artifices, stratagems, subterfuges. Cf. *Hudibras*, Pt. II, canto iii, ll. 1107-10:

> 'But *Sidrophel*, as full of Tricks
> As *Rota-men* of Politicks,
> Streight cast about to over-reach
> Th' unwary Conqu'ror with a *Fetch*.'

---

[1] The editor is indebted for these indications to the kindness of Mr. Sidney I. Irwin, M.A., of Clifton College.

359. *Kent Street*, now Tabard Street, extended in contemporary maps between the present New Kent Road and Blackman Street. According to Strype, it was 'chiefly inhabited by Broom Men and Mumpers [Beggars].' Goldsmith, who mentions it in *An Elegy on Mrs. Mary Blaize* (*Poems*, Everyman's Library, p. 57), was probably familiar with this poor part of Southwark, as he had practised as 'a physician, in a humble way,' in the Bankside.

359. *the Smyrna.*—The Smyrna coffee-house was in Pall Mall, opposite Marlborough House, at the corner of Crown Court. 'Prior and I came away at nine, and sat at the *Smyrna* till eleven, receiving acquaintance' (*Journal to Stella*, 15 October 1710, Aitken's edn. 1901, p. 42). At the Smyrna Thomson invited subscriptions for *The Seasons*.

359. *Dr. Cheyne.*—This was Richardson's friend, Dr. George Cheyne, or Cheney, author of *The English Malady* (i.e. Hypochondria), 1733. He was the eighteenth-century advocate *par excellence* of temperance and a vegetable diet. He died at Bath in April 1743, being then in his seventy-second year.

359. *Samson Gideon* was a noted Jew Broker. He is mentioned in Selwyn's correspondence: 'I received a letter to-day [21 August 1789] in such a hand as you never beheld, from Sir Sampson Gideon, now Sir S. Eardley, a name I never heard of before, to dine with him to-morrow at his house in Kent' (*George Selwyn*, by E. S. Roscoe, 1899, p. 253). Gideon's son became Baron Eardley of Spalding.

360. *The History of Hypatia* is told in Gibbon's *Decline and Fall*, vol. VI, p. 14 (ch. xlvii) of Smith's edn. In 1853 Charles Kingsley based his well-known novel upon it.

363. *'Change Alley.*—In Cornhill. Here stood Jonathan's coffee-house. 'I . . . sometimes pass for a *Jew* in the Assembly of Stock-Jobbers at *Jonathan's*' (*Spectator*, No. 1).

366. *Father Freijo.*—See *Enquiry into the Present State of Polite Learning in Europe*, 1759, p. 65, where Freijo's 'book of vulgar errors,' that 'so finely exposes the monkish stupidity of the times,' is referred to.

367. *Miscellaneous.*—Mr. S. T. Irwin (*Six Dialogues of Lucian*, 1894, xi, n.) finds in this paper an example of the turn of humour of Lucian's *Nigrinus*, where the writer 'permits a friend to ridicule, with sufficient justice, his rhetorical apologies and long-winded preface.'

367. *like Raleigh . . . by burning my manuscript.*—This is a reference to the old, and now discredited story, copied by Aubrey from Winstanley's *English Worthies*, 1660, to the effect that Raleigh burned a second part of his *History of the World* because of the small success of the first instalment.

368. *hearken, O Posterity.*—Goldsmith, unlike many another, did not make this appeal in vain. Cf. his letter to Robert Bryanton, 14 August 1758.

368. *run the gantlope*.—So properly spelled. Cf. *Tom Jones*, Bk. VII, ch. xi: 'Some said . . . that he deserved to run the *gantlope*.'

368. *only approve*.—'For fools admire, but men of sense *approve*' (Pope's *Essay on Criticsm*, 1711, l. 391).

369. *the intended Bridge at Blackfriars*.—Old Blackfriars Bridge was begun in 1760, and opened in 1769.

369. *four extraordinary pages*.—See p. 332 *supra*.

370. *a mistake in the one*.—Here Goldsmith, like Addison (sometimes), makes 'the one' correspond, not with the former, but with 'the latter.' And Johnson would not have permitted him to say 'the one,' which he regarded as 'Scotch' (Fanny Burney's *Diary*, 1892, i, 38).

370. *the court of the King of Prussia*.—The courts of the continental sovereigns seem to have been a favourite wax-work exhibition. In Hogarth's *Southwark Fair* one of the announcements runs: 'The whole court of France is here.'

374. *about four years ago*.—At the date of this paper, 27 October 1759, Goldsmith was living at No. 12, Green-Arbour-Court, which extended from the upper end of the Old Bailey into Sea-coal Lane, on a site now absorbed by the Holborn Viaduct and Railway Station (see frontispiece to *Vicar of Wakefield*, Temple Classics). He had only been there since the end of 1758, so his 'about four years ago' must have been a poetic licence, as was also, in all probability, the maid with her 'fatal broom' (l. 26 same page).

375. *I once put a wasp into the nest*.—Bewick (*Memoir*, ed. 1887, p. 31) records a similar experiment. In Bewick's case, however, the spider attacked the wasp, by whom it was immediately stung, and put to flight.

376. *hunger*.—This paper, which was not reprinted in the *Essays* of 1765, affords a pleasant foretaste of the more fortunate pages of *Animated Nature*. It is necessary, however, to observe that it must be regarded as literature rather than accurate natural history.

377. *most replete*.—Here Goldsmith falls into one of the errors to which he refers.

377. *We shall perhaps never be able to discover the longitude*.—The reward fixed by the Act of 1714 for the discovery of the longitude at sea was gained by John Harrison of Foulby, near Pontefract (1693–1776).

380. *Misers are described*.—See p. 364 *supra*.

382. *We are arrived at a perfect imitation of porcelain*.—The manufacture of porcelain was established at Worcester in 1750. But porcelain had been made at Bow and Chelsea before 1698.

384. *garnishes, freedoms*, etc.—Goldsmith probably refers here, not to the 'garnish' paid by prisoners to the gaol officials, etc., but

to the sums exacted upon entering a trade, e.g. the benvenue (*bienvenue*) or 'footing' fee contributed to the printer's 'chapel' by a workman on taking up a fresh office (*Life of Mr. Thomas Gent, Printer of York*, 1832, p. 15). Goldsmith had himself been a corrector of the press under Samuel Richardson at Salisbury Court.

384. *In the towns and countries.*—This is a useful eighteenth-century testimony to the cause of temperance.

384. *and other pests of society.*—This is rather hard upon attorneys, against whom Goldsmith must have had some grudge. But so apparently had Johnson:

> 'Their ambush here relentless ruffians lay,
> And here *the fell attorney prowls for prey,*'

he sings in ll. 15–16 of *London*.

Goldsmith makes it the 'failing' of Hickey in *Retaliation*, l. 136, that he was a 'special attorney.'

385. *an Economical Journal.*—In the *Citizen of the World*, p. 142 *supra*, the obscure philosopher of Green-Arbour-Court seems to anticipate the *Review of Reviews*. Here he clearly foresees the *Board of Trade Journal*.

386. *Virtus est medium.*—This quotation is from *Epp.* i, 18, l. 9, thus paraphrased by Conington:

> 'Between these faults 'tis virtue's place to stand
> At distance from the extreme on either hand.'

388. *the word 'Inspector'.*—This was Mr. (or Sir) John Hill (1716–75), a voluminous scribbler and quack. He wrote *The Inspector* for the *London Daily Advertiser*.

389. *dressed in lace.*—Hill was remarkable for the splendour of his costume.

389. *carrying nothing but a nosegay.*—This is said to be an allusion to the fact that in 1759 Hill produced four works on botanical subjects.

389. *a rigadoon.*—Presumably a rigadoon *step* (like Damia's in *Tatler* No. 34), for the rigadoon was a dance for two persons. (See note to p. 217 *supra*.)

389. *the person.*—Probably Arthur Murphy, author of the *Orphan of China*, a tragedy based upon Voltaire and produced at Drury Lane, 21 April 1759. Goldsmith reviewed it in the *Critical Review* for May, 1759.

389. *somewhat . . . theatrical.*—Murphy began as an actor at Covent Garden. He quitted the Stage for the Bar.

389. *virtue.*—Goldsmith (in the *Critical Review*) thought Murphy had 'perhaps too frequently mentioned the word *virtue*.'

389. *a very grave personage.*—Samuel Johnson, whose acquaintance Goldsmith had not yet made.

390. *another.*—David Hume, whose *History of the House of Tudor* appeared in 1758.

390. *a person.*—Tobias Smollett, for whose *British Magazine*, perhaps on account of this very paper, Goldsmith presently began to write.

390. *Segrais.*—Jean Regnault de Segrais, 1624–1701.

391. *to hear the conversation on the way.*—This paper, in the original, is marked 'To be continued.' But it was never resumed.

391. *High Life below Stairs.*—This was by the Rev. James Townley of Merchant Taylors' School. It was produced 31 October 1759, three days before the appearance of No. v of *The Bee*.

391. *my Lord Duke and Sir Harry.*—Palmer (see p. 9 *supra*) played the Duke's servant; King, Sir Harry's servant.

392. *Mrs. Clive* took the part of Kitty. Goldsmith seems to have admired her as much as Fielding. 'Mrs. Clive in her Walk on the Stage is the greatest Actress the World ever saw; and if as many really understood true Humour as pretend to understand it, she would have nothing to wish, but that the House [Drury Lane] was six times as large as it is' (*Covent Garden Journal*, 8 February 1752).

392. *the subordinate ranks of people.*—According to Genest's *Account of the English Stage*, iv, 677, the footmen at Edinburgh raised a riot on the second night, and had to be expelled from the theatre.

393. *painters and sculptors.*—By 'sculptors,' Goldsmith here plainly means 'engravers.' Johnson uses 'sculptures' for 'engravings' in his letter to the librarian of Buckingham House (Hill's *Johnson's Letters*, 1892, i, 145).

394. *Caravaggio.*—The painter here referred to was no doubt Michelangelo Merisi, or Amerighi, called from his birthplace near Bergamo, Caravaggio (1569–1609). The accounts of his death do not coincide with that here given.

395. *On Education.*—This is reprinted in the *Essays*, No. vii, and is here reproduced from the edition of 1766, where the following note is prefixed to it: 'N.B. This treatise was published before Rousseau's Emilius; if there be a similitude in any one instance, it is hoped the author of the present essay will not be deemed a plagiarist.' Rousseau's *Émile; ou, de l'Éducation* appeared in 1762.

397. *the usher.*—Cf. chap. xx of the *Vicar of Wakefield* (Everyman's Library), pp. 116–7. Goldsmith himself had been an usher at Dr. Milner's academy at Peckham.

399. *misers.*—Cf. pp. 364 and 380. Goldsmith seems to have had a kindness for misers.

399. *Instead . . . of romances.*—This sentence (down to 'possessed of'), without actually mentioning names, seems to prefer the method of Richardson and Hogarth before that of Fielding.

401. *There has of late a gentleman appeared.*—Thomas Sheridan, father of the dramatist, who was, at this date, delivering a Course of Lectures on Elocution and the English Language.

403. *On the Instability*, etc.—This is reprinted in the *Essays*, No. VIII, and is here reproduced from the edition of 1766.

404. *the late Duke of Marlborough.*—Charles Spencer, third Duke of Marlborough, who died of a fever, 20 October 1758, at Münster in Westphalia.

404. *A Chinese . . . once took it into his head to travel into Europe.*— This shows that the idea which prompted the *Citizen of the World* was already a familiar one with Goldsmith.

405. *an undiscovered property in the polype.*—Perhaps a reference to the paper published by the Royal Society on the Fresh Water Polypus which Fielding ridiculed in vol. I of his *Miscellanies*, 1743, p. 253 (' *The Terrestrial Chrysipus* ').

405. *the herring fishery employed all Grub-Street.*—The British White Herring Fishery Company was instituted in 1750, and under its protection herrings became very plentiful. Its secretary and laureate was one John Lockman, known popularly as the 'Herring Poet.' In Hogarth's *Beer Street*, 1751, the fisherwomen are shown singing one of Lockman's latest ballads on this theme, which had created a *furore* at Vauxhall Gardens. The 'Herring Poet' was an industrious translator from the French; and gained some reputation with that nation for a version of the *Henriade*, a subject afterwards essayed by Goldsmith's friend, Ned Purdon. For vol. I of another of Lockman's translations, the Abbé de St. Fontaine's *Travels of Mr. John Gulliver*, 1731, Hogarth, who seems to have been intimate with the translator, executed a frontispiece. (See also *Citizen of the World*, pp. 284 and 292 *supra*.)

406. *Cicalata Accademica.*—'Cicalata' means 'chatter.' Goldsmith may have mistaken the meaning, though in a sense 'tickling' could be quite justly applied to the indiscriminate and rather superficial treatment that is accorded to a host of varied subjects in certain literary societies.

408. *What we clearly conceive.*—See Boileau, *L'Art Poétique*, Chant I:

> 'Ce que l'on conçoit bien s'énonce clairement,
> Et les mots pour le dire arrivent aisément.'

410. *a celebrated preacher.*—Jean-Baptiste Massillon, Bishop of Clermont, 1663-1742. Much of what follows on preaching was more or less advocated in No. XVII of the *Essays* of 1765 and 1766.

411. *the Bangorian Controversy.*—Arose out of a sermon preached before George I (31 March 1717) by Dr. Benjamin Hoadly, Bishop of Bangor, upon John xviii 36: 'My kingdom is not of this world'; in which he argued that Christ had not delegated his powers to any ecclesiastical authorities. It was printed by royal command, and gave rise to a storm of clerical pamphlets.

414. *the present King of Prussia.*—In the so-called *Code Frédérique*. Napoleon did the same in the *Code Napoléon*.

416. *the E. O. table.*—'E. O.' was another name for roulette, E and O being the letters on the bands or rings. There is an early and well-known caricature by Rowlandson entitled '*E. O.; or, the Fashionable Vowels*' (28 October 1781).

420. *Prince Vologeso.*—This was the character taken by Cornacini at the Haymarket in the opera of *Vologeso*.

421. *Mr. Rameau.*—Jean-Philippe Rameau, 1683–1764.

421. *Matei.*—The famous Italian songstress, Colomba Mattei. 'The Mattei (I assure you) is much improved by his [Elisi's] example, and by her great success this winter' (Gray to Mason, 22 January 1761). See also p. 420.

422. *Cornacini.* See note to page 420.

MADE AT THE
TEMPLE PRESS LETCHWORTH
IN GREAT BRITAIN

EVERYMAN'S LIBRARY

A LIST OF THE 905 VOLUMES
ARRANGED UNDER AUTHORS

Anonymous works are given under titles.
Anthologies, Dictionaries, etc. are arranged at the end of the list.

NOTE—The following numbers are at present out of print: 89, 110, 111, 146, 227, 228, 244, 275, 390, 418, 565, 597, 664

LONDON: J. M. DENT & SONS LTD.
NEW YORK: E. P. DUTTON & CO. INC.

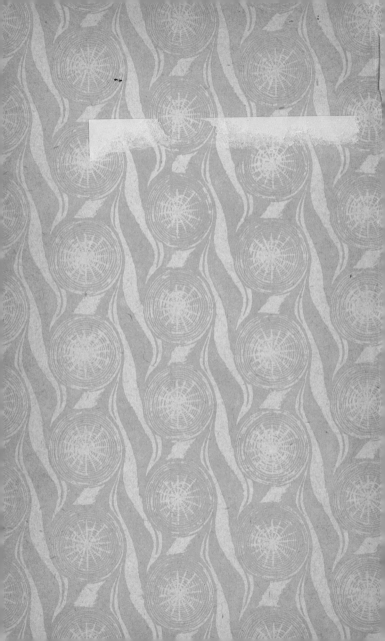